Conceptions of Modern Psychiatry

By HARRY STACK SULLIVAN, M.D.

Conceptions of Modern Psychiatry
The Interpersonal Theory of Psychiatry
The Psychiatric Interview
Clinical Studies in Psychiatry
Schizophrenia as a Human Process
The Fusion of Psychiatry and Social Science

Prepared under the auspices of
THE WILLIAM ALANSON WHITE PSYCHIATRIC FOUNDATION
COMMITTEE ON PUBLICATION OF SULLIVAN'S WRITINGS
Mabel Blake Cohen, M.D.   Dexter M. Bullard, M.D.
David McK. Rioch, M.D.   Otto Allen Will, M.D.

Conceptions of
Modern Psychiatry

The First William Alanson White Memorial Lectures

With a Foreword by the Author
and a Critical Appraisal of the
Theory by PATRICK MULLAHY

W · W · NORTON & COMPANY · INC · *New York*

PRINTED IN THE UNITED STATES OF AMERICA
FOR THE PUBLISHERS BY THE VAIL-BALLOU PRESS
6 7 8 9

Contents

Preface to the
Second Edition

This new edition of Sullivan's 1939 lectures on *Conceptions of Modern Psychiatry* marks the fifth time that these lectures have been reprinted, but the first time that they have ever appeared on a book publisher's list. The story of how these lectures came to be written down, printed in a journal, reprinted as a sort of makeshift book, and reprinted again and again—all simply because people had heard of them by word-of-mouth and wanted them—is a tribute to the contagion of the ideas themselves.

In 1939, the William Alanson White Memorial Lectures were inaugurated by the White Psychiatric Foundation, and Sullivan was asked to give the first series of lectures. The series consisted of the five lectures in this book, which were given to a small audience in the U. S. Interior Department auditorium in Washington. Immediately there was an influx of requests for copies of the lectures, and Sullivan hastily prepared the transcriptions of the lectures for inclusion in the February 1940 issue of Psychiatry, the Journal which he edited for 12 years. In the following months and years, requests for this issue of the Journal kept coming in, and finally the stock was exhausted. In 1947, the Board of Trustees of the Foundation authorized a small reprinting of the lectures for the use of students. Sullivan himself was somewhat reluctant. He felt that the first three lectures were "grossly inadequate," as he put it; but he gave his permission, since by then he was deep in a heavy teaching and training program, and did not know when he would have time to revise them. The reprints were yellow, because the Journal is printed on yellow paper, and the printer had a supply of it on hand. At the last minute, someone had the idea that the reprint should have a hard cover to make it more durable.

The subsequent story of this yellow reprint in the hard cover which was intended for students is remarkable even in the commercial publishing world. For in five years, it had sold over 13,000 copies. It had gone to countries all over the world. It was being used as a textbook in social science departments in several universities. The first indication of what to expect came when, in the summer of 1947, several months after its publication, Lloyd Frankenberg published a review of it in the *New York Times Book Review*. It was given modest space, and Frankenberg pointed out that it was a difficult book to read. But the review had about it the magic of the book— the excitement of Sullivan's ideas and personality. And that summer, the entire administrative staff of the Foundation wrapped and mailed books, hundreds of them, carrying sacks of them out to the mail box every night. Thus the reprint for students had turned into a book.

At the time that the reprints were made, the Foundation decided to include a critique of Sullivan's theories by Patrick Mullahy, which had been published as an article in PSYCHIATRY in May 1945. This article, which appears in the back of this book with a few changes, was one of the very first comprehensive evaluations of Sullivan's work, and was in great demand by students. Mr. Mullahy has since written extensively and brilliantly on Sullivan's ideas, but this 1945 article remains a classic explanation of these lectures.

As the only book of Sullivan's writings published during his lifetime, this book has a certain historical significance. But it is by no means a fossil. The challenge of its ideas, as evidenced by the feeling of excitement with which each new reader "discovers" it, makes it indeed a new book for an ever-growing audience.

DEXTER M. BULLARD, *President*,
The William Alanson White Psychiatric Foundation

Foreword

THIS SERIES OF five lectures, of which only the last two were expanded to reasonable proportions before publication, has had to serve as the available statement of my theoretical position while a four-year collaboration with the faculty of the Washington School of Psychiatry was testing and refining the theory and developing some technical innovations in intensive psychotherapy which are implicit in it.

This collaboration has included a series of 248 lecture-discussions at Chestnut Lodge, 66 seminars on clinical research, 57 teaching seminars, and almost 2,000 supervising conferences concerned with treatment or the training of candidates for a career in intensive psychotherapy, in addition to eight courses of lectures given in the regular curriculum of instruction.

Continuing close contact with the practical problem and theoretical preoccupations of twenty colleagues has done much to clarify and make communicable the views derived from 15 years of research with schizoid and obsessional people in a quarter century of practice.

The here reprinted lectures fail of close correspondence with my current views in the following more significant respects.

The theory of *anxiety*, its bearing on personality development, and its crucial importance in observing and influencing interpersonal relations, is not adequately stated. The developmental history of the *self-dynamism* is, therefore, left relatively unclear, its functional activity in *selective inattention* and in other peculiarities of interpersonal relations is not set forth, and the concept of *dissociation* comes to have undue importance as an explanatory principle. Mr. Mullahy's analysis will help to correct this inadequacy.

These lectures are nowhere else as open to criticism as in their sketch of the *developmental history of interpersonal relations*. Here certainly one of Mr. Philip Sapir's many valuable criticisms of these lectures—"nothing can justify condensing two paragraphs into one sentence"—applies with peculiar force. Five lectures averaging two hours in length here 'cover' all psychiatry. In the current series of 34 School lectures, *infancy* as a phase in the human animal's becoming a person is not finished by the twelfth hour.

It is in the structure of inferences about the first few years of life that one finds the key to formulating the otherwise baffling complexities of later stages of interpersonal relations which are brought into being by the combination of serially matured potentialities, experience, and the function of *recall* and *foresight* in the sundry interpersonal situations through which we live. In this connection, also, Mr. Mullahy's analysis adds something, but could scarcely communicate views which are but now at last becoming systematic.

Psychiatry as it is—the preoccupation of extant psychiatric specialists—is not science nor art but confusion. In defining it as the study of interpersonal relations, I sought to segregate from everything else a disciplinary field in which operational methods could be applied with great practical benefits. This made psychiatry the probable locus of another evolving discipline, one of the social sciences, namely, *social psychology*. Both seek an adequate statement of living, including every instance of relative success or failure that is open to participant observation. The scientific psychiatrist would know wherein and wherefore his patient fails and whither his remedial efforts could reasonably be expected to lead an improved facility for living.

This psychiatry was scarcely to be learned by administering the affairs of patients in custodial hospitals for the mentally disordered, nor by effecting a consensus of uninformed prejudice with patients in private practice. Needless to say, it would scarcely evolve from "treating" people with metrazol, electro-shock or ablative brain surgery. It required great technical refinement of the psychiatrist as a participant observer inter-acting with his patients in the context of life as it has to be lived. From this, the psychiatrist must inevitably gain informa-tion about living; his patient, in some instances, all that he needs for continuing favorable change.

Because the psychiatrist is always dealing with living—partly adequate, partly unfortunate, but always simply human—the terms of his scientific language might well be refined from the common speech by chief virtue of which he and his patient have acquired some skill at communicating. The terms of scientific psychiatry would then be misunderstood by the uninitiate, as what terms are not? The absurdity of much meaningless discourse might be more easily discovered, with great saving of something other than "face."

Gordon Allport and H. S. Odbert some years ago listed 17,953 words used to indicate alleged qualities of human *indi-viduality*. Mr. Mullahy has some pithy comment on my disaf-fection for people's "individuality" as an interest of the psy-chiatrist. That his discussion is germane is attested by a great variety of misunderstandings in this connection. I have in-veighed against "the delusion of unique individuality" and re-ferred to personality as the hypothetical entity which we posit to account for interpersonal relations. I do not believe that this denies anyone "a personality"; it serves its purpose if it warns anyone that I never expect to *know* all about his personality—and am as certain as can be that he too will always share my ignorance in that regard.

Personality, I now define in the particularist sense as *the relatively enduring pattern of recurrent interpersonal situations which characterize a human life*. The term, *pattern*, in this statement is to be taken to mean *the envelope of all insignifi-cant differences*. *Significant* differences in to-be-recurrent in-terpersonal relations occur, at times, when personality changes.

Some of these changes are relatively invariant, marking important phases in the progress from birth towards maturity. Some of them are by no means universal and may represent peculiarly fortunate incidents, incidents of so-called serious mental disorder, or of recovery therefrom.

That there are particular human lives, each with a unique career line, I no more deny than do I the fact that I am a particular person who has a particular dog. I can say with Bridgman that "I act in two modes—my public mode . . . and in the private mode [in which] I feel my inviolable isolation from my fellows. . . ." So doubtless does my dog; the transformations of energy which he manifests in living his canine life often transcend being-my-dog in the culturally patterned world of dogs and people which is his life space. He doubtless acts much more frequently in the private mode than could I think that I do, and I doubtless act much less frequently in the private mode than it is easy to think that I do. The immutably private in my dog and in me escapes and will always escape the methods of science, however absorbing I may once have found the latter.

Without digressing on the value of the comparative approach in formulating noncultural and especially nonlanguage aspects of living, I seek here to stress the central fact that the true or absolute individuality of a person is always beyond scientific grasp and invariably much less significant in the person's living than he has been taught to believe.

Individual differences, especially those which are principally matters of language and customs in people from widely separate parts of the world, may be extremely impressive and may present great handicap to discovering the significant differences in relative adequacy and appropriateness of action in interpersonal relations, which constitute extraordinary success, average living, or mental disorder.

The therapist or the research psychiatrist, however, participates intelligently in interpersonal relations with his confrere only to the extent that these handicaps are successfully overcome or evaded and finds opportunity to gain skill in this particular in his dealings with any stranger.

HARRY STACK SULLIVAN

31 December 1946

Conceptions of Modern Psychiatry

LECTURE
I

Basic Conceptions

In the preface to his autobiography,[1] Dr. White remarked "when we look about us and see the confusion that the world is in at the present moment, see the antagonisms that are loosed by national rivalries and realize the possibilities of war, of disaster, of death, which they conceivably may entail, then realize that all of these results hang upon the way in which mental factors are evaluated and the powers of mind are utilized, we must come to the conclusion that we cannot overemphasize the importance of this field of interest."

Rather than attempt some expression of the honor which this occasion brings to me, let me take these words of one of the pioneers of modern psychiatry as my text and proceed with what is bound to prove too great a task for adequate performance. A definitive expression of the conceptions inhering in modern psychiatry would be a task indeed. I shall attempt in this series of lectures little more than an outline of the field of thought within which there are insights that seem destined to illuminate some age-old and many future problems of living, of the relations of man to man, perhaps even of peoples to peoples.

For those of you who are not too familiar with the thinking

[1] *William Alanson White: The Autobiography of a Purpose;* Garden City, N. Y.; Doubleday, Doran and Co., 1938 (xix and 293 pp.). The next paragraph in the preface expresses the author's qualified belief "that the average medical man is, by and large, about as thoroughly lacking in information as to the significance of mental factors in relation to disease as is the average layman."

of psychiatrists, I might suggest something of the diversity of their views by mentioning three sorts of psychiatrists: those to whom all mental processes are but epiphenomena; those to whom mental disorders signify biological—or spiritual—inferiority; and, happily, those who accept the mental as a scientifically valid, if largely unexplored, field.

Quite beyond diversity of views, however, our discipline has two chief bodies of meaning. One reaches back clearly to the Hippocratic school of medicine, among the writings of which there are excellent psychiatric contributions. This part of psychiatry—this definition of the psychiatric field, if you please—I have elsewhere described as the art of observing and perhaps influencing the course of mental disorders.[2] It was overwhelmed in the recession from the Classic Period and had its renaissance with Pinel—1745 to 1826—as physician to the Bicêtre in 1793. In those days, people who were the victims of serious mental disorders were treated in rather barbarous fashion, only occasionally being as fortunate in this regard as were those imprisoned for crime. He eliminated the chains and shackles, the brutal handling, exsanguination, and drugging. As Director of the Salpetriere, from 1795, he evolved a remarkably modern system of psychiatric institutional care, which was fortunately perpetuated by his most distinguished student, and successor, Esquirol—1772 to 1840.[3]

[2] Psychiatry. *Encyclopædia of the Social Sciences;* New York, Macmillan (1934) 12:578–580.

[3] A history of culture would have as its most significant part a history of ideas and information about man's constitution, functional activity, and communal existence with his natural, biological and personal environment. This would be the history of "human nature." These and the following remarks are no more than a laying of the pen-point on paper for writing such a history. The appended references are but an iota in the alphabet of psychiatric history. Given opportunity, one should certainly read Semelaigne, René, *Aliénistes et Philanthropes;* Paris, Steinheil, 1912 (4 and 548 pp.).

See Pinel, Phillippe, *Traité médico-philosophique sur l'aliénation mentale ou la manie* [2 ed.]; Paris, Brosson, 1809 (xxxii and 496 pp.), and *Nosographie philosophique* [6 ed.]; Paris, Brosson, 1818 (3 volumes). See also Esquirol, Jean-Etienne Dominique, *Des maladies mentales considérées sous les rapports médical, hygiénique et médico-légal;* Paris, Baillière, 1838 (2 volumes)—

The second body of meaning of psychiatry—the alternative definition of the psychiatric field—is coeval with man as a social being. In the shadows before prehistory, as man began to take on the social habit of life, the germs of this discipline must have sprouted. As man appears clearly in history, it showed itself in the performances of his medicine men and magicians, his seers and prophets and sages. They observed their fellows with unusual clarity and elaborated wisdom from experience to the end of leadership, guidance, and the cure of disorders of living.

This broader aspect of psychiatry would include the narrower medical aspect and, if I mistake not, in time to come the medical aspect must expand to the full breadth of human psychiatry. However, of this, more anon.

The medical man of the Hippocratic era was a skillful observer, and, since Paracelsus, this tradition has been renewed in the Western world. The course of development of modern medicine ran through anatomical and then pathological studies, with increasing concentration on the cellular structure of living tissues—and recently on the biochemical and biophysical aspects of the tissue and cell function. While there arose a class of medical practitioners who tended to exemplify the finest sort of physician, the vast increase of medical information led presently to increasing specialization of interest, and diagnostic

Esquirol, Jules-Etienne Dominique, *Mental Maladies. A Treatise on Insanity* [tr. from the French, with additions, by E. K. Hunt, M.D.]; Philadelphia, Lea and Blanchard, 1845 (xviii and 496 pp.).

Esquirol may be called the father of modern psychiatry, for Pinel, while spurning materialistic philosophy, looked chiefly to physiological formulations and taught that mental disorders were the results of heredity and stresses and excesses in living. Esquirol's observations directed his thinking much more towards explanations in psychological or psychobiological terms.

It is to be noted that Johannes Weyer, a sixteenth century psychiatrist—author of *De Præstigiis Dæmonum* published in 1566—is considered by Gregory Zilboorg to be the father of scientific psychiatry. He refers its moral awakening to Weyer; its humanistic, to Pinel. See his *The Medical Man and the Witch During the Renaissance* [The Hideyo Noguchi Lectures]; Baltimore, The Johns Hopkins Press, 1935 (x and 215 pp.); also Binz, Carl, *Doktor Johann Weyer;* Bonn, Mareus, 1885, to which Zilboorg refers.

and therapeutic practice. The physician to the ailing patient tended to fade out and give way to the medical expert dealing with the disease which interested him.

Again in retrospect, in the days of Pinel, there lived Pierre Jean George Cabanis—1774 to 1838—a medical scientist who came to hold that all mental functions were functions of the brain.[4] Franz Joseph Gall—1758 to 1828—meanwhile having devoted some years to the study of the brain, came to understand something of cerebral localizations of motor functions, and reported on his work to the Institute of France. The great comparative anatomist, Georges Cuvier—1769 to 1832—and Pinel were members of the Institute's committee. The phrenological buncombe which was mixed with Gall's scientific work led to an unfavorable reception.

Pierre Flourens—1794 to 1867—about the same time was experimenting on localized damages to the brain with observations of the animal's subsequent loss of functions. This pioneer neurophysiologist is entitled to high honor, for he perceived clearly the total-function aspect of the central nervous system in contradistinction to those more localized phenomena which were soon—prefaced by Marshall Hall, 1790 to 1857, who evolved in 1833 the conception of reflex action—to influence the psychological formulations throughout the era of the mechanistic philosophies, and to underwrite the mésalliance of medical psychiatry with neurology which persists in many quarters to this day. A great figure in this was Hughlings Jackson—1834 to 1911—who progressed from the study of epileptic phenomena to the formulation of rather simple cerebro-mechanical explanations of many of our most complex performances in relations with others. Henry Head—b. 1861 —may be said to have reopened the field,[5] although the neuro-

---

[4] The remark is attributed to Cabanis that the brain secretes thought as the liver secretes bile. See his *Rapports du physique et du moral de l'homme;* Paris, Bureau de la Bibliothèque choisie, 1830 (2 vols. 405 and 430 pp.).

[5] Head, Henry, *Aphasia and Kindred Disorders of Speech;* Cambridge, The University Press, 1926 (Vol. 1:xiv and 549 pp.).

physiologists had already destroyed the neat structure of reflexology.[6] We may rest secure in the knowledge that much is yet to be learned concerning the central nervous system.

The mésalliance of neurology and psychiatry has by no means been dissolved. The emergency of the World War brought us *neuropsychiatrists*, and a cultural factor, the aversion to mental disorder which is the linear descendant of belief in demoniacal possession and witchcraft, still makes it more certainly respectable to be treated by a neurologist for a "nervous breakdown" than to consult a psychiatrist about one's difficulties in living. The euphemism covers superstition and protects conceit: both are powerful checks on the progress not alone of psychiatry, but of civilization as a whole.

Processes in the central nervous system, in the other nervous systems, and in the autacoid dynamism, have importance in explaining *some* of the conditions of behavior, human or infrahuman. We have to look to the broader aspects of psychiatry for light on some other indispensable conditions of human behavior.[7] And we have a great deal to learn in both fields.

In the enlightenment, the broader field of psychiatric interest evolved in directions which took many of its students far from medical preoccupations. It became the conviction of many that the study of man in the group would be productive of information valuable in government and in promoting the

[6] See, in particular, among many relevant contributions: Bard, Philip, On Emotional Expression after Decortication with Some Remarks on Certain Theoretical Views. *Psychol. Rev.* (1934) 41:309–329 and 424–449. Rioch, David McK. and Brenner, Charles, Experiments on the Corpus Striatum and Rhinencephalon. *J. Comp. Neurol.* (1938) 68:491–507. Rioch, David McK., Certain Aspects of the Behavior of Decorticated Cats. PSYCHIATRY (1938) 1:339–345. Rioch, David McK., Neurophysiology of the Corpus Striatum and Globus Pallidus. PSYCHIATRY (1940) 3:119–139. See, also, Bard, Philip, Central Nervous Mechanisms for Emotional Behavior Patterns in Animals. *Research Publications of the Association for Research in Nervous and Mental Diseases,* 19:190–218.

[7] My own interest in those types of explanations which Adolf Meyer has so aptly termed "neurologizing tautology," I owe to a conversation with Gilbert Horrax, the neurosurgeon, shortly after the World War. His comments on the sequelæ, and the lack of sequelæ, of serious cerebral wounds was most illuminating.

common weal. The social sciences thus developed techniques for studying, and allegedly studying, group behavior, factors making for mass performances, and specialized aspects of man's social life. Only recently have there appeared social scientists who are interested in the data of medical psychiatry, and still more recently psychiatrists who are interested in such fields as cultural anthropology and sociology. While I had something to do with starting the latter rapprochement, the appearance of this trend towards a complete psychiatry depended primarily on three great figures who appeared in the later years of the Nineteenth Century—Sigmund Freud, Adolf Meyer, and William Alanson White.[8]

Freud—1856 to 1939—and Josef Breuer—1842 to 1925— published in 1895, *Studien über Hysterie* in which they indicated that hysterical symptoms arose from extra-conscious mental processes, the energy of which was diverted or converted into a personally meaningless disorder of function. Freud presently invented the free-associational technique for reintegrating *repressed* material, evolved the psychoanalytic instinct-theory, and drew attention to what he called the *transference*. His *Traumdeutung* was published in 1900, and by 1905, he had formulated the *libido* theory and the doctrine of the *Œdipus complex*, as the most important conflict in the growth of the child, and the problem, failure to solve which leads to "neurosis." There followed the evolution of psychoanalysis as *depth-psychology* with dynamic, economic, and topographical points of view; and the postulation of a *Todestrieb*, or death-instinct.

It is with the first fruits of Freud's genius that we shall con-

----

[8] Listings of recent significant persons must express personal convictions as to the probable appraisal of their work by scholars yet to come. Compare for example, Stanley Cobb's statement ". . . . of the six major contributors to psychiatry in the last twenty-five years (Kraepelin, Freud, Sherrington, Pavlov, Wagner von Jauregg, and Cannon), three are physiologists"; a footnote to his "Problems in Cerebral Anatomy and Physiology" in *The Problem of Mental Disorder*; N. Y. and London, McGraw-Hill, 1934 (x and 388 pp.). Dr. Cobb is of the opinion that "no sound psychologist doubts that the brain is the organ of the mind."

cern ourselves. The phenomena appearing in prolonged free-associational interviews, with the study of the transference-distortions that accompany—or precede—the verbal material, together provide a bridge across those discontinuities which had hitherto prevented the formulation of a comprehensive psychology of mental content. Freud revealed the experiential origin of specific limitations of personal awareness. By this achievement, he cleared the way for the scientific study of people, in contradistinction to mind, or society, or brain, or glands.[9]

"It is manifestly impossible to formulate all the difficulties of human adaptation in biological terms, in psychological terms, or in sociological terms; or, for that matter, in a meaningful blend of any or all of these. The psychobiology of Adolf Meyer—b. 1866—is the most distinguished recent effort to find a new locus for problems, a new level of reality and knowledge, and new conceptual tools. Meyer recognizes the hierarchies of organization and proceeds from a consideration of organismic integrating factors . . . . to bridge the gap between biology and psychiatry by the concept of *mentation*, a peculiarly effective integrating activity by the use of symbols and meanings." Meyer finally emancipated psychology from its medieval heritage. Himself a most competent neurologist and neuropathologist, he denied the usefulness of preoccupation with neural analogies. He indicated that it is by a superordination of physiology by means of the integrating functions and particularly by means of the use of symbols as tools that man was able to develop, on the one hand, his grasp on reality, and on the other, his remarkable problems in dealing with his personal reality and the reality of others around him.[10]

The genius of William Alanson White—1870 to 1937—

[9] See Intuition, Reason, and Faith: An Editorial. PSYCHIATRY (1939) 2:129-132 from which the quotation that follows is taken.

[10] The bibliography of Meyer is published in a special number of *Archives of Neurology and Psychiatry* (1937) 37:725-751. For an exposition closely related to his views and often in his own language, see Muncie, Wendell, *Psychobiology and Psychiatry;* St. Louis, Mosby, 1939 (739 pp.).

was of amazing scope. The particular contribution which I would stress here is his perception that this psychiatry, now principally centered on mentation and the utilization of symbols, very convenient and effective devices for dealing with very complex entities and relations in the world—that this science, which had begun to grasp the realities of the troubles of living, was a science not only qualified to deal with the mentally ill, but a science having vast relevance in human affairs, touching I know not how many fields of human endeavor and human problems; in fact, a fundamental discipline for all those fields that deal with the performance of man, whether in health or in illness or in those vast congeries of twilight states which the individual regards as health but society might well regard as illness.

There was effected in Dr. White's vision the first synthesis of the two great trends of psychiatric meaning—the medical discipline concerned with human ills, and the other great body of observational techniques, formulations, hypotheses and experiments which are included in all those efforts to understand social situations and to deal with social problems as they have appeared in the history of man.

This synthesis is not yet complete. The next, I trust, great step in its emergence came with the realization that the field of psychiatry is neither the mentally sick individual, nor the successful and unsuccessful processes that may be observed in groups and that can be studied in detached objectivity. Psychiatry, instead, is the study of processes that involve or go on between people. The field of psychiatry is the field of interpersonal relations, under any and all circumstances in which these relations exist. It was seen that a personality can never be isolated from the complex of interpersonal relations in which the person lives and has his being.[11]

[11] Sullivan, Harry Stack, Socio-Psychiatric Research: Its Implications for the Schizophrenia Problem and for Mental Hygiene. *Amer. J. Psychiatry* (1931) 10[o.s. 87]:977–991.

Let me suggest to you a few of the problems that we encounter by mentioning that our ordinary relation between an object and a percept has as a generally overlooked but none the less necessary link the act of perceiving. There is the object: emanations from it in the form of light waves, odors, sounds and so on impinge on our sense organs. They send certain specific impulses to a more central organ in which this group of impulses is connected with more or less related impulses which we experienced in our historic past. And out of this blend, this instantaneous comparison in the central nervous system and related tissue, there arises in our mind a conviction that we are observing, say, an orange, or something of that kind; on the one hand, the object, eternally separated from us by the act of perceiving it, and, on the other, the percept in our mind.

Now, when it comes to the matter of perceiving another person, not only is there the object, this other person, and the perception of the emanations from that person—appearances transmitted by light rays, indices transmitted by sound waves, meanings transmitted by statements, implications transmitted in the whole act of communicating—but also the distorting and confusing and complicating factor of our past experience with other people who looked like this, who sounded like this, who made those statements, who had certain implications that happen to be irrelevant here, and so on. In other words, the central synthesis of acquaintance, the percept in our mind, concerning another person is fabulously more complicated than is the case with non-personal reality.

So complex is this synthesis that it is practically impossible to elaborate techniques by which we can make our objective contact with another individual reasonably good. His performances in a situation, what he says and does; and, with increased uncertainty, what he says as to what is going on *in* him: these we can observe scientifically. We can improve our techniques for participant observation in an interpersonal situation in which we are integrated with our subject-person. This is evidently *the* procedure of psychiatry. I urge it as implying the root-premise of psychiatric methodology.

The unique individuality of the other fellow need never concern us as scientists. It is a great thing in our wives and our children. They have, however, æsthetic and other values that are outside of science; when it comes to science, let us confine ourselves to something at which we have some chance of success. We can study the phenomena that go on between the observer and the observed in the situation created by the observer participating with the observed. I hold that this is the subject matter of psychiatry; some rather remarkable results have already come from its definition.

It must be understood that the performances of a person in interpersonal relations include not only acts, including speech, but also the subject matter of certain remarks. If I say to you, "This is a beautiful room," while it may not possess quite the validity of *your* opinion that it is a beautiful room, still it may be accepted as highly probably my opinion of the room. It is the type of indirect communication of a subjective phenomenon which gives the, if you please, lunatic fringe to psychiatry even in its much more refined state.

Human performances, the subject of our study, including revery processes and thought, are susceptible of a two-part classification which is based on the end states, the end conditions toward which these processes are obviously moving, or which our prevision has reached. In other words, now and then you set out to start for somewhere. You preview the steps which will be necessary to get there and we can foresee the whole process on the basis of your reaching that place.

The most general basis on which interpersonal phenomena, interpersonal acts, may be classified, is one which separates the sought end states into the group which we call satisfactions and those which we call security or the maintenance of security. Satisfactions in this specialized sense are all those end states which are rather closely connected with the bodily organization of man. Thus the desire for food and drink leads to certain performances which are in this category. The desire for sleep leads to such performances. The state of being which is marked by the presence of lust is in this group; and finally, as the most middling example, the state of being which we call loneliness. All these states lead to activity which is the pursuit of satisfaction.

On the other hand, the pursuit of security pertains rather more closely to man's cultural equipment than to his bodily organization. By "cultural" I mean what the anthropologist means—all that which is man-made, which survives as monument to preexistent man, that is the cultural. And as I say, all those movements, actions, speech, thoughts, reveries and so on which pertain more to the culture which has been imbedded in a particular individual than to the organization of his tissues and glands, is apt to belong in this classification of the pursuit of security.

The thing which many people if they were quite honest with themselves would say that they were after when they are showing a process of this type is prestige, and one of my long-acquainted colleagues, Harold D. Lasswell, a political scientist, worked out a statement for this field in three terms: security, income, and deference. All these pertain to the culture, to the social institutions, traditions, customs, and the like, under which we live, to our social order rather than to the peculiar properties of our bodily or somatic organizations.

This second class, the pursuit of security, may be regarded as consisting of ubiquitous artifacts—again in the anthropological sense, man-made—evolved by the cultural conditioning or training; that is, education of the impulses or drives which underlie the first class. In other words, given our biological equipment—we are bound to need food and water and so on—certain conditioning influences can be brought to bear on the needs for satisfaction. And the cultural conditioning gives rise to the second group, the second great class of inter-personal phenomena, the pursuit of security.

To follow this line of thought profitably, however, one must look closely at this conception of conditioning, and one must consider especially the states characterized by the feeling of ability or power. This is ordinarily much more important in the human being than are the impulses resulting from a feeling of hunger, or thirst, and the fully developed feeling of lust comes so very late in biological maturation that it is scarcely a good source for conditioning.

We seem to be born, however, with something of this power motive in us. An oft-told story beautifully illustrates the early appearance of what I am discussing as the motive toward the manifestation of power or ability. The infant seeing for the first time the full moon, reaches for it. Nothing transpires. He utters a few goos and nothing transpires; then he starts to cry in rage, and the whole household is upset. But he does not get the moon, and the moon becomes 'marked' unattainable.

This is an instance of the frustration of the manifestation of power; one has failed at something which you might say one expects oneself to be able to achieve—not that the infant does much thinking, but the course of events indicates the applica-tion of increasingly complex techniques in the effort to achieve the object.

The full development of personality along the lines of se-curity is chiefly founded on the infant's discovery of his power-lessness to achieve certain desired end states with the tools, the instrumentalities, which are at his disposal. From the disap-pointments in the very early stages of life outside the womb—in which all things were given—comes the beginning of this vast development of actions, thoughts, foresights, and so on, which are calculated to protect one from a feeling of insecurity and helplessness in the situation which confronts one. This ac-cultural evolution begins thus, and when it succeeds, when one evolves successfully along this line, then one respects oneself, and as one respects oneself so one can respect others. That is one of the peculiarities of human personality that can always be depended on. If there is a valid and real attitude toward the self, that attitude will manifest as valid and real toward others. It is not that as ye judge so shall ye be judged, but as you judge yourself so shall you judge others; strange but true so far as I know, and with no exception.

The infant has as perhaps his mightiest tool the cry. The cry is a performance of the oral apparatus, the lips, mouth, throat, cheeks, vocal cords, intercostal muscles, and diaphragm. From this cry is evolved a great collection of most powerful tools which man uses in the development of his security with his fellow man. I refer to language behavior, operations including words.

Originally the infant's magical tool for all sorts of purposes, all too many of us still use vocal behavior as our principal adaptive device; and while none of you, of course, would do this, you must all know some people who can do in words practically anything and who have a curious faith that having said the right thing, all else is forgiven them. In other words, they are a little more like the infant than we are; they figure that a series of articulate noises turns any trick. We have, of course, learned that many other acts, performances, and foresights are necessary for success in living. None the less, denied our language behavior and the implicit revery processes that reach their final formulations in words, we would be terribly reduced in our competence and materially diminished in our security in dealing with other people.

At this point, I wish to say that if this series of lectures is to be reasonably successful, it will finally have demonstrated that there is nothing unique in the phenomena of the gravest functional illness. The most peculiar behavior of the acutely schizophrenic patient, I hope to demonstrate, is made up of interpersonal processes with which each one of us is or historically has been familiar. Far the greater part of the performances, the interpersonal processes, of the psychotic patient are exactly of a piece with processes which we manifest some time every twenty-four hours. Some of the psychotic performances seem very peculiar indeed, and, as I surmised in 1924,[12] for the explanation and familiarization of these performances, we have to look to the interpersonal relations of the infant, to the first eighteen months or so of life after birth. In most general terms, we are all much more simply human than otherwise, be we happy and successful, contented and detached, miserable and mentally disordered, or whatever.

To return to the epoch of infancy, first let me state that this is the period of maturation, of experimentation, of empathic 'observation,' and of autistic invention in the realm of power. Two of these terms may need some explanation.

From birth it is demonstrable that the infant shows a curious relationship or connection with the significant adult, ordinarily the mother. If the mother, for example, hated the pregnancy and deplores the child, it is a pediatric commonplace that there are feeding difficulties, unending feeding difficulties, with the child. If a mother, otherwise deeply attached to the infant, is seriously disturbed by some intercurrent event around nursing time, is frightened by something or worried about something around the time of nursing, then on that occasion there will be feeding difficulty or the infant has indigestion. All in all we know that there is an emotional linkage between the infant and the significant adult.

[12] See discussion of "Primitive Mentality and the Racial Unconscious," *Amer. J. Psychiatry* (1925) 4:671. The matter in point is illustrated, for example, by Ribble, Margarethe A., Clinical Studies of Instinctive Reactions in New Born Babies. *Amer. J. Psychiatry* (1938) 95:149–158. Note the stupor reaction following defeat of the infant's efforts at sucking—pp. 154–157. See, then, Sullivan, Harry Stack, The Oral Complex. *Psychoanalytic Rev.* (1925) 12:31–38 and, the same, Erogenous Maturation. *Psychoanalytic Rev.* (1926) 13:1–15. Note also Hadley, Ernest E., The Psychoanalytic Clarification of Personality Types. *Amer. J. Psychiatry* (1938) 94:1417–1430; in particular, pp. 1424–1425. Some observations in this connection were reported at the 1938 meeting of the Association for Research in Nervous and Mental Diseases; McGraw, Myrtle B., *Research Publications* 19:244–246.

Empathy is the term that we use to refer to the peculiar emotional linkage that subtends the relationship of the infant with other significant people—the mother or the nurse. Long before there are signs of any understanding of emotional expression, there is evidence of this emotional contagion or communion. This feature of the infant-mother configuration is of great importance for an understanding of the acculturation or cultural conditioning to which I have referred.

We do not know much about the fate of empathy in the developmental history of people in general. There are indications that it endures throughout life, at least in some people. There are few unmistakable instances of its function in most of us, however, in our later years; I find it convenient to assume that the time of its great importance is later infancy and early childhood—perhaps age six to twenty-seven months. So much for empathy.

The other strange term in our statement about the epoch of infancy is *autistic*, an adjective by which we indicate a primary, unsocialized, unacculturated state of symbol activity, and later states pertaining more to this primary condition than to the conspicuously effective consensually validated symbol activities of more mature personality. The meaning of the autistic will become clearer in my discussion of language.

We see our infant, then, expanding as a personality through the exercise of ability or power. We see him using the magic tool of the cry. We now see him acquiring another tool, which in turn also becomes magical. I refer here to his expression of satisfaction. It is biological for the infant when nourished to show certain expressive movements which we call the satisfaction-response, and it is probably biological for the parent concerned to be delighted to see these things. Due to the empathic linkage, this, the reaction of the parent to the satisfaction-response of the infant, communicates good feeling to the infant and thus he learns that this response has power. Actually, this may be taken to be the primitive root of human generosity, the satisfaction in giving satisfaction and pleasure: another thing learned by some people in infancy.

I shall pass infancy now, to return presently to one aspect of it. As soon as the infant has picked up a vocal trick, saying perhaps "ma" and getting a tremendous response from the significant adult, without any idea of precisely what has happened but catching on the second time it happens, as soon as the rudiments of language habits have appeared, we say that infancy as a state of personality development has ceased and that the young one has become a child.

Childhood includes a rapid acculturation, but not alone in the basic acquisition of language, which is itself an enormous cultural entity. By this I mean that in childhood the peculiar mindlessness of the infant which seems to be assumed by most parents passes off and they begin to regard the little one as in need of training, as being justifiably an object of education; and what they train the child in consists of select excerpts from the cultural heritage, from that surviving of past people, incorporated in the personality of the parent. This includes such things as habits of cleanliness—which are of extremely good repute in the Western culture—and a great many other things. And along with all this acculturation, toilet habits, eating habits, and so on and so forth, there proceeds the learning of the language as a tool for communication.

The ability to make articulate noises and the ability to pick phonemal stations in vocal sound—that is, the peculiar ones of a continuum of sounds which are used in the forming of words, which varies, incidentally, from language to language —the ability, as I say, to learn phonemes,[13] to connect them

---

[13] The *phoneme* is a particular zone or station in the continuum of audible vibrations around which the use of a particular language has established meaning for the identification of verbal intention. A phoneme is more than a particular number of cycles per second of vibration; it is a family of such particular c.p.s. plus overtones, etc. The K sounds in *can, cool, keep, come* are of one phoneme. The phoneme is the linguistic unit of the person's speech; the *diaphone* is the corresponding term for the approximate phonemal coin-

into syllables and words, is inborn. That is given in the human organism. The original usage of these phonemal stations, syllables, words, however, is magical, as witness the "ma" and as witness, for example, any of you who have a child who has been promised on a certain birthday a pony. As you listen to the child talk about the pony you realize perhaps sadly that twenty-five years from now when he talks about ponies, pony will not have a thousandth of the richness of personal meaning that pony has for him now. The word of the child is autistic, it has a highly individual meaning, and the process of learning language habits consists to a great extent, once one has got a vocabulary, in getting a meaning to each particular term which is useful in communication. None of us succeeds completely in this; some of us do not succeed noticeably.

Along with learning of language, the child is experiencing many restraints on the freedom which it had enjoyed up till now. Restraints have to be used in the teaching of some of the personal habits that the culture requires everyone should show, and from these restraints there comes the evolution of the self system—an extremely important part of the personality—with a brand-new tool, a tool so important that I must give you its technical name, which unhappily coincides with a word of common speech which may mean to you anything. I refer to *anxiety*.

With the appearance of the self system or the self dynamism, the child picks up a new piece of equipment which we technically call anxiety. Of the very unpleasant experiences which the infant can have we may say that there are generically two, pain and fear. Now comes the third.

cidences that make up intelligible speech. See Sapir, Edward, *Language, An Introduction to the Study of Speech;* New York, Harcourt, Brace, 1921, reprinted 1929 (vii and 258 pp.); Sound Patterns in Language. *Language* (1925) 1:37–51; Dialect. *Encyclopædia of the Social Sciences;* New York, Macmillan (1931) 5:123–126; Language. *The same* (1933) 9:155–169; La Réalité Psychologiques des Phonèmes. *Journal de Psychologie* (1933) 30:247–265. A selected bibliography of this great linguist and cultural anthropologist appears in PSYCHIATRY (1938) 1:154–157.

It is necessary in the modification of activity in the interest of power in interpersonal relations, including revery and elementary constructive revery—that is, thought—that one focus, as it were, one's interest into certain fields that work. It is in learning this process that the self is evolved and the instrumentality of anxiety comes into being.

As one proceeds into childhood, disapproval, dissatisfaction with one's performances becomes more and more the tool of the significant adult in educating the infant in the folk ways, the tradition, the culture in which he is expected to live. This disapproval is felt by the child through the same empathic linkage which has been so conspicuous in infancy. Gradually he comes to perceive disapproving expressions of the mother, let us say; gradually he comes to understand disapproving statements; but before this perception and understanding he has felt the disapproval which he was not able to comprehend through the ordinary sensory channels.

This process, coupled with the prohibitions and the privations that he must suffer in his education, sets off the experiences that he has in this education and gives them a peculiar coloring of discomfort, neither pain nor fear but discomfort of another kind. Along with these experiences there go in all well regulated homes and schools a group of rewards and approbations for successes. These, needless to say, are not accompanied by this particular type of discomfort, and when that discomfort is present and something is done which leads to approbation, then this peculiar discomfort is assuaged and disappears. The peculiar discomfort is the basis of what we ultimately refer to as anxiety.

The self dynamism is built up out of this experience of approbation and disapproval, of reward and punishment. The peculiarity of the self dynamism is that as it grows it functions, in accordance with its state of development, right from the start. As it develops, it becomes more and more related to a microscope in its function. Since the approbation of the important person is very valuable, since disapprobation denies satisfaction and gives anxiety, the self becomes extremely important. It permits a minute focus on those performances of the child which are the cause of approbation and disapprobation, but, very much like a microscope, it interferes with noticing the rest of the world. When you are staring through your microscope, you don't see much except what comes through that channel. So with the self dynamism. It has a tendency to focus attention on performances with the significant other person which get approbation or disfavor. And that peculiarity, closely connected with anxiety, persists thenceforth through life. It comes about that the self, that to which we refer when we say "I," is the only thing which has alertness, which notices what goes on, and, needless to say, notices what goes on in its own field. The rest of the personality gets along outside of awareness. Its impulses, its performances, are not noted.

Not only does the self become the custodian of awareness, but when anything spectacular happens that is not welcome to the self, not sympathetic to the self dynamism, anxiety appears, almost as if anxiety finally became the instrument by which the self maintained its isolation within the personality.

Needless to say, the self is extremely important in psychiatry and in everyday life. Not only does anxiety function to discipline attention, but it gradually restricts personal awareness. The facilitations and deprivations by the parents and significant others are the source of the material which is built into the self dynamism. Out of all that happens to the infant and child, only this 'marked' experience is incorporated into the self, because through the control of personal awareness the self itself from the beginning facilitates and restricts its further growth. In other words, it is self-perpetuating, if you please, tends very strongly to maintain the direction and characteristics which it was given in infancy and childhood.

For the expression of all things in the personality other than those which were approved and disapproved by the parent and other significant persons, the self refuses awareness, so to speak. It does not accord awareness, it does not notice; and these impulses, desires, and needs come to exist disassociated from the self, or *dissociated*. When they are expressed, their expression is not noticed by the person.

Our awareness of our performances, and our awareness of the performances of others are permanently restricted to a part of all that goes on and the structure and character of that part is determined by our early training; its limitation is maintained year after year by our experiencing anxiety whenever we tend to overstep the margin.

Needless to say, limitations and peculiarities of the self may interfere with the pursuit of biologically necessary satisfactions. When this happens, the person is to that extent mentally ill. Similarly, they may interfere with security, and to that extent also the person is mentally ill.

The self may be said to be made up of reflected appraisals. If these were chiefly derogatory, as in the case of an unwanted child who was never loved, of a child who has fallen into the hands of foster parents who have no real interest in him as a child; as I say, if the self dynamism is made up of experience which is chiefly derogatory, then the self dynamism will itself be chiefly derogatory. It will facilitate hostile, disparaging appraisals of other people and it will entertain disparaging and hostile appraisals of itself.

As I have said, the peculiarity exists that one can find in others only that which is in the self. And so the unhappy child who grows up without love will have a self dynamism which shows great capacity for finding fault with others and, by the same token, with himself. That low opinions of oneself are seldom expressed with simple frankness can also be explained.

So difficult is the maintenance of a feeling of security among his fellows for anyone who has come to have a hostile-derogatory self, that the low self-appreciation must be excluded from direct communication. A person who shrewdly attacks the prestige of sundry other people can scarcely add to each such performance a statement to the effect that he knows, because he has the same fault or defect. At the same time, we know that that which is in the self is not dissociated from the self; in other words, if it shows in the witting performances towards others, it is within the limits of personal awareness and not outside, resisted, so to say, by anxiety.

The relative silence about the low self-appraisal is achieved in part by the clamor of derogating others, in part by preoccupation with implicit revery processes that dramatize the opposite of one's defects, or protest one's rights, or otherwise manifest indirectly one's feeling of unworthiness and inferiority.

Let us rest this matter here for the time being, and review what has been said. We have seen something of the origin and organization of the self and of its marked tendency to stabilize the course of its development. We have seen that if, for example, it is a self which arose through derogatory experience, hostility toward the child, disapproval, dissatisfaction with the child, then this self more or less like a microscope tends to preclude one's learning anything better, to cause one's continuing to feel a sort of limitation in oneself, and while this can not be expressed clearly, while the child or the adult that came from the child does not express openly self-depreciatory trends, he does have a depreciatory attitude toward everyone else, and this really represents a depreciatory attitude toward the self.

The stabilizing influence of past experience is due to the fact that when it is incorporated in the organization of the self, the structure of the self dynamism, it precludes the experience of anything corrective, anything that would be strikingly different. The direction of growth in the self is maintained by the control exercised over personal awareness and by the circumscribing of experience by anxiety when anything quite different from one's prevailing attitude tends to be noticed.

We have seen how the self can be a derogatory and a hateful system, in which case the self will inhibit any experience of friendliness, of positive attitude toward other persons, and thus continue to go on derogatory, hostile, negative, in its attitude toward others.

This selective exclusion of experience which leads to one's being occupied with or noticing only the hostile unfriendly aspect of living not only is manifested in one's attitude toward others, but also is represented in the attitude toward the self. No matter how well the outward manifestations of self-contempt may be disguised, we may be assured that they are there. We see here the explanation of one of the greatest mysteries of human life, how some unfortunate people carry on in the face of apparently overwhelming difficulties, whereas other people are crushed by comparatively insignificant events, contemplate suicide, perhaps actually attempt it.

This is to be understood on the basis not of the particular 'objective' events which bring about the circumstance of success under great hardship or self-destruction; it is to be understood on the basis of the experience which is the foundation of the self system, the organization of experience reflected to one from the significant people around one—which determines the personal characteristics of those events. In no other fashion can we explain the enormous discrepancy between people's reactions to comparable life situations.

Every one of you knows of circumstances in which people encounter things which you would regard as too much to be borne, yet they go on with a certain measure of cheerfulness and optimism; whereas other people who, so far as you can see, have every advantage, have much to look forward to, meet some, to you, rather trifling rebuff, become depressed, and may actually destroy themselves.

The practice of suicide is a strange ingredient of culture. So far as we know, there is nothing remotely approaching it in the infrahuman primates or any of the lower animals. It is distinctly a human performance, and to some a very mystifying one. It is to be understood in many cases, if not in all, by realizing the force of the dictum which I have offered to the effect that the attitude manifested toward others reflects faithfully the attitude which must be manifested toward oneself. It is merely a question, then, of when a derogatory and hostile attitude, ordinarily directed toward the outer world, is directed with full force toward the self.

I do not need to tell you in this connection how hatefully conceived and executed many suicides really are, if you have taken the trouble to study any instance of this event. This, of course, does not get into the newspaper accounts, but if you know a family situation in which such an event has occurred you will be impressed with the fact that the self-destruction had an evil effect, and may well have been calculated to have a prolonged evil effect on some other people. This is literally a miracle of the dissociation which education gives us, by which our impulse to live—our grasp on the always numerous and largely unpredictable future possibilities—by which the optimism that makes us look toward the unpredictable with hope shall, in these people, be vanquished entirely by a hateful combination of impulses which leads to destroying oneself in order to strike at some other person.

The act of suicide at the moment is again becoming fashionable. When I say that it is becoming fashionable, I do not refer to some index, some statistical sign, which means that out of 100,000 such and such number have this year destroyed themselves. I refer to the fact which has been seen repeatedly during so brief a compass as my own lifetime, that, regardless of economic factors and other indices of the gross movements in the population and in the affairs of the people, the frequency of suicide periodically—or aperiodically—mounts rapidly and then declines. It is common human experience that suicide is much more often contemplated than it is attempted. It appears that to think of destroying oneself, to follow a train of revery

in which one's death is a feature, is not at all unusual; certainly
in many people it is not at all unusual, although, parenthetically,
in some people it would be very strange indeed.

The revery in which self-destruction is, for our purpose, the
theme, does not stop with the contemplation of self-destruction.
It goes on. Self-destruction, therefore, is not the goal of this
revery process, of this daydream, this private symbolic operation, if you please. Something else is the goal. A quite frank
report of some of these reveries shows that while one may
start out meditating on how worthless life is, how gladly one
would be rid of it and all, one drifts from there to contempla-
tions of what the situation in regard to other people would be
after the act.

This is the sort of revery which is not uncommon. It very
often discharges the suicidal impulse. One thinks about it to
oneself, which we call having a revery, and then one drops it.
One drops it because the revery process, after the fashion of
revery processes, is a constructive movement, calculated to discover the probable effects of an event or the probably successful ways of achieving an end. From that standpoint the rumina-
tion on self-destruction, thought through, is seen not to be a
means of obtaining any desire.

The revery studies danger, personal probabilities, with, as
an unwitting goal, a goal that is not noticed by the person who
is entertaining the suicidal fantasy, the prevention of this very
act of self-destruction. The prevention of the hostile-destructive act is the unwitting goal, the unnoticed goal, of the revery
process. Suicidal reveries are not as a rule fantasies with, as an
end, the destruction of oneself; they are reveries in which one
actually considers consequences and reaches the decision, if
you please, that self-destruction would not achieve the object
concerned. It would follow that that object is the exterioriza-
tion of an hostile, derogatory attitude which one has acquired
in infancy and childhood, particularly childhood, which one

has continued to entertain because of the focussing effect of the self system, and to manifest toward other people.

Almost incidentally the having of this suicidal revery resolves the situation which provokes the impulse to self-destruction. Then one drifts into reverie processes that lead to constructive, or at least much less destructive, ends.

More illuminating in the same connection is the unsuccessful attempt at suicide. To call your attention to a group of processes that are concerned in many of these attempts, I shall tell a story from my own experience which has, so far as I know, nothing to do with suicide.

Once upon a time I was able to enjoy my pleasure in horse-back riding, and on a certain occasion, under certain unamusing circumstances which I must suppress because their recital would reduce the solemnity of this occasion, I fell from a horse. Of course, as I could tell it, the horse threw me; but in any case I ceased to be on the back of the horse and contacted the earth with considerable violence, such that I fractured a jaw.

Prior to this accident I had been somewhat given to jumping horses. Subsequent to the accident, for over a year and a half, I made no successful jumps. I invariably pulled the horse off as we approached the hurdle, to my great embarrassment and very considerable loss of prestige. It none the less happened inevitably, and it was only after about a year and a half that I succeeded in so 'controlling' my motor apparatus that I and the horse could get over a hurdle again.

The story is told to illustrate the vanquishing of my desire for prestige and my satisfaction in such things well done by something which was quite exterior to my control. In all it was me, but when I say it was me I mean that it most emphatically was not my self. My self was all set to resume jumping horses with the pleasure that comes from it and that special expansive satisfaction that attends doing something about which many people are somewhat hesitant and which not too many people do quite well. Not any need of security on my part in the sense that I have expressed here, nor any lack of need for the satisfaction that comes from this particular type of sport; neither of these groups of impulses had anything to do with my pulling the horse away from the jump. Something else had to do with that, something of which I had no vivid awareness and over which I certainly had nothing of what is ordinarily meant by control. My will, to drop into the archaic language, was too weak to control some base impulse in me that thwarted the horse and me.

We have here an instance of a part of personality working in dissociation, but working very powerfully, more powerfully than all the motives that are channelled through the self.

Many of the attempted suicides which prove such dramatic failures that we are inclined to suspect the honesty and reality of the attempt are of much the same order as my failure to jump the horse. The act has been contemplated carefully and the motivation is there. So far as the person is aware there is no room for doubt but that he will now destroy himself. But something 'stupid' is done so that the act fails and he does not die.

This is not by any means as often a fraudulent dramatic attempt to do something which one doesn't intend to do for the purpose of coercing someone else as it is the intervention of the dissociated part of personality, the part of the personality that has been growing up under great handicap in contradistinction to the experience to which the self is receptive. In the particular instance which I have stressed so much, where the individual experience as incorporated in the self has been almost entirely derogatory and hateful, you will realize that the dissociated part consists of the experience of human warmth and friendliness. It is this part of personality, this group of processes, which intervenes to prevent a fatal issue of the impulse.

It is almost cavalier to rest with such fleeting reference to the extra-self—at that, almost as an addendum to a consideration of suicide. If, however, you have finally seen the dichotomous character of these hypothetical personalities of ours—how that which is excluded from awareness by virtue of the directing influence of the self dynamism, must be quite different in some essential aspects from that which is incorporated in and manifests as the self—you can see why we seem so individuated, and yet can be, to quote myself, much more simply human than otherwise.

LECTURE
II

The Human Organism and Its Necessary Environment

It has been suggested that a consideration of the meaning of psychiatry could carry us from the dimmest past through the work of innumerable people, with almost as many contradictory views—sometimes self-contradictory views—as there were workers. So also would a survey of the history of the meaning of man spread before us an ineffably wearisome account of circuitous progress in the face of stupendous obstacles created by man. As in the first case, so here we would come finally to a present view which is anything but universally accepted.

In the dreary progression, if our wits are not bemused, we would observe many views that represent what we now know that man is *not*. Man is not a creature of instinct—the view of Aristotle and of William McDougall; of transcendental powers between or among which he may choose his allegiance—the medieval view rather sympathetic to Otto Rank; of logic and its categorical opposite—Bacon and in a way Alfred Adler and Alfred Korzybski; of the evolution of social intellect—Compte and some mental hygienists; of racial fitness—de Gobineau and Fuhrer Hitler; of a conflict of society and one's instincts—Freud; or of a racial unconscious—Jung.

As we survey the present, we can see four significant conceptions. For the general biologist, man is the most complexly integrated organism thus far evolved. For the psychobiologist, man is an individual organism the total-function of which is mentally integrated life. For the social psychologist, man is the human animal transformed by social experience into a human being. For the psychiatrist as a student of interpersonal relations, man is the tangible substrate of human life.

These definitions grow progressively more complex in scope. Let us consider the beginning of anyone, the fecundated ovum in the uterus. This cell manifests the basic categories of biological process. The cell carries almost stupifying potentialities. It exists as a demonstrable entity. It lives, however, and starts the realization of its potentialities, not as a unit organism surrounded by a suitable environment. It lives communally *with* the environment. Physico-chemical factors, substances, plentiful in the uterine environment flow into the cell. They undergo changes while they are within the describable cell-area. They return presently as other physico-chemical factors, to the environment. The cell dies if the continuous exchange is interrupted. Progressive changes depend utterly on the communion; retrogressive changes appear swiftly on its restriction.

From a relative position in time and space, the environment flows through the living cell, becoming of its very life in the process; and the cell flows and grows through the environment, establishing in this process its particular career-line as an organism. It is artificial, an abstraction, to say that the cell is one thing and the environment another. The two entities thus postulated refer to some unitary thing in which organism and environment are indissolubly bound—so long as life continues.

In the cell-medium complex one can observe much that is marvelous. There are factors of organization, including polarity and dynamic gradients, which establish an oral and an aboral end in the expanding cell mass, which gradually evolves the fœtus, ready for birth.

Before there are any elaborate differentiations of tissue, however; before in fact there has been a single division of the fertile cell, there is organization in the cell-medium complex such that a vital balance is maintained in the more purely organismic part of the complex. True, a change in the maternal blood may prove too great for the successful maintenance of this balance, and the complex disintegrates, the ovum dies. Quite marked changes in the medium, however, do not disturb the optimum conditions in the cell-medium complex, due to functional activity of the region to which we refer as the cell wall. This region performs the function for which the fœtus will ultimately be provided with elaborate organizations of tissues; in fact, duplicate organizations of whole systems.

Biologically, then, an organism is a self-perpetuating organization of the physico-chemical world which manifests life by functional activity in the complex. It is easy to think that the organism is an entity that can be removed from the complex, and some color is given this erroneous view by virtue of the storage capacity that is part of the vital organization.

The process of birth would seem to a naive observer to cut off the infant from the maternal—placental—medium and project him into the medium of the outer world. The communion with the physico-chemical environment has in fact to be maintained with but a short-term interruption—during which the oxygen and other necessary substances stored in the fœtus are all that prevent death. Breathing must begin promptly. It is essential also that coverings be supplied to prevent loss of heat. Nursing cannot long be delayed.

The infant is born in far too immature a state to live by its own functional activity, unaided by interventions from others. This is quite different from the guinea pig, which has been described as born in its old age.[14] It reflects a fundamental fac-

[14] Tilney, Frederick, and Casamajor, Louis, Myelinology as Applied to the Study of Behavior. *Arch. Neurol. and Psychiat.* (1924) 12:1–66. Note, also, Hooker, Davenport, Fetal Behavior. *Publications of the Association for Research in Nervous and Mental Diseases* 19:237–243; and the relevant part of Conel, J. Leroy, The Brain Structure of the Newborn Infant. . . . *The same*, 19:247–255.

tor that makes civilization possible—the long stretch of post-natal life required by the human young for the attainment of independent competence to live. As growth and maturation proceed acculturation is inevitable, because in the earliest stages, the infant is cared for by people, and modified by this personal element in the environment. The course of existence from fecundation of the ovum may be said to be: parasitic, new born (animal), then infantile (human). The change from new born to infantile is less dramatic than its predecessor, but it is a very great change indeed; and also entails a change of medium implying a change of functional activity in a complex of changing organization.

Almost from birth, the infant begins to attend to movements and objects about him.[15] Several of Peterson's infants looked at him and followed his movements with their eyes as early as the seventh day after birth. There is no room for doubt as to the significance attached to the object which satisfies the hunger and thirst of the infant, and we may safely infer that the *mothering one* is the first vivid perception of a person relatively independent of the infant's own vague entity.

I surmise that a part of her, the nipple, provides the first of all vividly meaningful symbols—a vaguely demarcated "complex-image" or protoconcept with very wide reference. The clarification of the nipple as borne by another person instead of its being a relatively unmanageable part of one's own cosmic entity is the first step in shrinking to life size. Outer objects of a more neutral sort—that do not satisfy physico-chemical needs directly—come gradually to mark off the limits of one's private world, and so to establish the reality of the relatively manageable as against the wholly independent.

[15] See Peterson, Frederick, The Beginnings of Mind in the New Born. *Bulletin of the Lying-in Hospital of the City of New York* (1910) 7:99–122. In this paper, the work of Adolf Kussmaul (1859), Alfred Genzmer (1873), and Traugott Kroner (1882) on infants in maternity hospitals is summarized, and new observations on 1060 babies—some premature—are reported. Special sense responsivenesses were determined in from 31 to 78 infants within the first six hours after delivery.

We learn in infancy that objects which our distance receptors, our eyes and ears for example, encounter, are of a quite different order of relationship from things which our tactile or our gustatory receptors encounter. That which one has in one's mouth so that one can taste it, while it may be regurgitated to the distress of everyone, is still in a very different relationship than is the full moon which one encounters through one's eye but can in no sense manage.

This difference of relationship to objects is an important category for organizing one's knowledge about the world. We organize our acquaintance with the world in order to maintain necessary or pleasant functional activity within the world with which, whether the objects be manageable or unmanageable, remote or immediate, one has to maintain communal existence —however unwittingly.

I have spoken of the functional interaction, in infancy and childhood, of the significant other person, the mother, as a source of satisfaction, as an agency of acculturation, and finally as a source of anxiety and insecurity in the development of social habits which is the basis of development of the self system. Let us now attend, particularly, to the mediate channels of acculturation, in particular the products of the printer's art.

In this culture all children fairly early encounter pictures. Many of them have picture books, as they are called. Picture books often have a little printed matter in them, and gradually the child learns to read. Remembering what was said before as to the autistic, the highly personal meaning of everything to the young child, we can best illustrate the process of consensual validation by referring to what goes on when, for example, the young child learns that a certain colored or black and white pattern in a book is "kitty," although, of course, there is also "kitty" who runs around and occasionally scratches one.

I am sure no child who can learn has not noticed an enormous discrepancy between this immobile representation in the book which, perhaps, resembles one of the momentary states that kitty has been in on some occasion. I am certain that every child knows that there is something very strange in this printed representation being so closely connected with the same word that seems to cover adequately the troublesome, amusing, and very active pet. Yet, because of unnumbered, sometimes subtle, sometimes crude experiences with the carrier of culture, the parent, the child finally comes to accept as valid and useful a reference to the picture as "kitty" and to the creature as "kitty."

The child thus learns some of the more complicated implications of a symbol in contradistinction to the actuality to which the symbol refers, which is its referent; in other words, the distinction between the symbol and that which is symbolized. This occurs, however, before verbal formulation is possible.

From the picture book and the spoken word in this culture one progresses to the printed word and finally discovers that the combination of signs, c-a-t, includes "kitty" in some miraculous fashion, and that it always works. There is nothing like consistent experience to impress one with the validity of an idea. So one comes to a point where printed words, with or without consensually valid meaning, come to be very important in one's growth of acquaintance with the world.

There was first the visually and otherwise impressive pet, which was called "kitty" (an associated vocalization); then came the picture of the kitten; now comes the generic *c a t* which includes kitty, picture of kitten, a kitten doll, and alley cats seen from the windows. And all this is learnt so easily that —since no one troubles to point it out—there is no lucid understanding of the sundry types of reality and reference that are being experienced. Familiarity breeds indifference, in this case. The possibilities for confusion in handling the various kinds of symbols, naturally, remain quite considerable.

Let me now suggest something of the wide spread of significance in speech as speech, rather than as spoken words and

sentences. Some of you may recall from childhood the experience of first encountering a person whose dialect was not the
accustomed one. Or, perhaps, you may recall the first hearing
of a conversation in a foreign tongue.

If some such experience is recaptured, let us compare it
with the general experience of children with strangers. When
the stranger speaks in the accustomed dialect—quite aside from
the extensive significance of other non-verbal factors in everyone's speech—the insecurity felt by the child is diminished.
The familiar diaphonic progressions convey some reassurance
as to the *naturalness* of the stranger. He is not some awesome
creature from the autistic world blended out of dreams and
longings and tales of wonder that one has been told.

This unity in one's dialect-group, which presently spreads
to include one's language-group, is by no means restricted to
the era of childhood. Many Americans who go to Europe and
move among peoples in the use of whose tongue they are not
competent, show the same factor in the attitudes that they
manifest. The people whom they encounter are not invested
with as complete a set of human traits as are even the more
obnoxious of our acquaintances at home. These foreigners are
not quite human. One feels emancipated correspondingly from
some or many of the restraints that govern one in life at home.
One does odd things—sometimes durably regrettable things—
that have never occurred to one before. There is an attenuation
of our conventional inhibition because we do not recognize
these strangers as fully human and do not accord them the same
critical attitudes towards us that we have accustomed ourselves
to live with.

The solidarity creating power of a common tongue is most
important. This factor comes gradually to manifest itself, also,
in the matter of the printed word.

That which is printed is ordinarily directed to a larger and
less specific audience than is the spoken word.[16] It almost neces-

---

[16] The written expression of any language must be recognized to be more

sarily conveys some feeling of impersonality, of larger than tete-a-tete situations. Correspondingly, it usually tends to expand one's feeling of acquaintance with the world—the world of behavior, of opinion, of geographical facts. This function of the printed page is what I meant by mediate acculturation: the accession of cultural factors not directly from a significant person who manifests them, but through the instrumentality of narrative and reading.[17]

We come now to the juvenile era, in which the use of this mediate channel is very important. Childhood, for our purpose, is marked off from the juvenile era by the appearance of an urgent need for compeers with whom to have one's existence. By "compeers" I mean people who are on our level, and have generically similar attitudes toward authoritative figures,

---

or less *a different* language than is the same tongue, used in vocal speech. The "inner speech" of more elaborated revery processes is still a different language. The degrees of difference of these three categories of verbal symbol operations vary from person to person. See: Sapir's Language; *Encyclopædia of the Social Sciences* (1933) 9:155–169, already cited; also Newman, Stanley S., Personal Symbolism in Language Patterns. PSYCHIATRY (1939) 2:177–184 and Vigotsky, L. S., Thought and Speech [translation of Chapter VII of his 1934 monograph on Language and Thought, by Drs. Helen Kogan, Eugenia Hanfmann, and Jacob Kasanin]. PSYCHIATRY (1939) 2:29–52.

[17] The processes of acculturation are rich, largely unexplored, fields for research. In the last few years, a new *mediate* channel has appeared in the shape of the radio. The person who speaks over the wireless is addressing a presumptively great number of people. His speech—all the more because of existing rules as to submitting "script" in advance—tends to approximate the written rather than the spoken version of the language. If he is at all expert, however, his voice communicates the impression *not* of someone reading something aloud *but of a rounded personality talking to one.* In this fact, there lies a field of investigation of very great importance. The study of the personalizations of the radio speaker, as they appear in persons who habitually listen to him, is a certainly fruitful approach to an understanding of the nonverbal communicative aspects of the voice.

American radio research seems quite indifferent to this problem. See, however, Pear, T. H., *Voice and Personality;* London, Chapman and Hall, 1931 (ix and 247 pp.) and Allport, Gordon W. and Cantril, Hadley, Judging Personality from the Voice. *J. Soc. Psychology* (1934) 5:37–55. The accuracy of judging personality from the voice is not, of course, the point of my discussion. By discovering what sort of personalizations the voice may evoke, by seeking out the factors in voice and in hearer that are concerned in this, we may finally come to some understanding of the voice as a uniquely important factor in interpersonal relations.

activities, and the like. This marks the beginning of the juvenile era, the great developments in which are the talents for co-operation, competition and compromise.

But before we have done with the developmental epoch of childhood, let me recall to you the biological fact of communal existence. If one scrutinizes the performances of any child, it will be evident that the child as a creature is existing in communal existence in or with an environment now importantly cultural in its composition. The cultural entities, so to speak, are part of the necessary environment. The human being requires the world of culture, cannot live *and be human* except in communal existence with it. The world of culture is, however, clearly manifest only in human behavior and thought. Other people are, therefore, an indispensable part of the environment of the human organism. This is absolutely true in the earlier phases of personality development. The factor of fantasy may cloud this issue in later stages, as in fact, it may be observed to do at the end of the epoch of childhood in the case of isolated children.

The era of childhood ends with the maturation of a need for compeers. The child manifests a shift from contentment in an environment of authoritarian adults and the more or less personalized pets, toys and other objects, towards an environment of persons significantly *like* him. If playmates are available, his integrations with them show new meaningfulness. If there are no playmates, the child's revery processes create imaginary playmates. In brief, the child proceeds into the *juvenile era* of personality development by virtue of a new tendency towards cooperation, to doing things in accommodation to the personality of others. Along with this budding ability to play with other children, there goes a learning of those performances which we call competition and compromise.

In the juvenile era, in this culture, school is the great new arena for experience. If one's parents have been reasonably wise, one is somewhat prepared for what one encounters. If that was not the case, one is apt to have a very hard time, for one's compeers are not yet come to possess sympathy and forbearance. Quite the contrary, they are having enough problems of their own, enough new thwartings and humiliations, to be very unpleasant to the luckless juvenile who has recourse to inappropriate magic from childhood—tears, tantrums, telling mamma, or the like.

School brings new experience in adjusting oneself to authority. We may assume that one has evolved techniques for handling one's parents with only a modicum of pain. Now come other adults who have to be managed. One discovers quite suddenly that parents are by no means the worst people in the world; that parents, whatever their faults, take one rather more seriously than do teachers and older boys and girls. One finds that tried and trusted symbol operations—speech, gesture, excuses, promises—are no longer effective. Autistic fringes begin to stand out as barriers to communication. Mediate and immediate acculturation proceed apace. The world begins to spread, the horizons move off. One begins to see that there is a great deal which one had not previously suspected.

The interpersonal factors between teacher and the pupil in this school situation may work good or may work evil effects on the growth of personality. Where, for example, there has been an eccentric parent, let us say for example a person of extreme puritanical rigidity, a teacher may give the first clue to the child that this is not the ubiquitous attitude of people, of important people, to life. The child, at first—because novel experience is very difficult to get within the focus of the self—may feel that the teacher is some queer kind of dangerous inferior creature, the sort of person with whom one's parents would not associate. Still gradually, gradually, because other children who are now important put up with this, take it for granted, seem to think that it is perfectly natural; because of this powerful support or validation of the novelty, the self may expand somewhat. This is always a difficult achievement; but the self may come as it were to doubt certain of the harsh puritanical restrictions which have been incorporated in it, and while perhaps they do not disappear and in times of stress throughout life may manifest themselves clearly, still the experience of the school may head the self dynamism in another direction which will make for much greater opportunity for contented living, for mental health.

On the other hand, harsh, cruel teachers—and there are certain people teaching school who enjoy the discomfiture of their charges—may affect the child from a happy home who has been taught to expect friendliness and a receptive and inquiring attitude, may teach him gradually by reiterated pain and humiliation, that the world into which he has moved is an unfriendly and cruel world, and may start revery processes in him the goal of which is to return to the home from which he has unhappily been expelled, apparently for no reason other than that he had gotten older. In this, a very considerable evil has been done because the character of these reveries is regressive. They seek to go back, and this child may indicate this regressive, retreating-into-the-past tendency by regretting that he has grown older, by wishing that he was younger again.

This regressive tendency is a great evil because development still has a very long way to go. If at the very beginning of the more specialized socialization of personality which the juvenile era, according to its limits, initiates, there is this strong reverse, this powerful rebuff, this cutting off of satisfactions or undermining of security, in the mind's eye the child turns backward, he seeks to avoid the future, to escape experience which would . teach how to live with one's fellows. This example may suffice to emphasize the effect on the growth of personality of the interpersonal factors which exist between teacher and pupil. Even as this is true, it is also true that barring extraordinary situations—all too frequent before school entry—the effect is neither very bad nor very good. By and large it is useful.

Besides contacts with the school personnel there is the playground situation with other children, the bully, and so on, perhaps with a supervisor of playgrounds, a useful addition in many situations. Also, there is another side of the school situation; namely, the reaction of the home to the rumors of what goes on in school. This, too, can work good and evil. And then there is the attitude of the home toward the compeers, these others who have now become so significant in the development of personality.

With this briefest of indications I shall leave this prolonged and tremendously important era and go on to the next era of personality development.

Around the age of eight and one-half, nine and one-half to twelve, in this culture, there comes what I once called the quiet miracle of preadolescence. Quiet because there is nothing dramatic or exciting about its appearance; there is no sudden change by which one has ceased to be a juvenile and has become a preadolescent. In fact, everything is rather gradual, flows out of the past through the present into the future in personality performance, however dramatic somebody else's story of it may sound. I say "miracle" of preadolescence because now for the first time from birth, we might say even from conception, there is a movement from what we might, after traditional usage, call egocentricity, toward a fully social state.

Up to this time there have been *no* instances in which some other person approximated to the subject person, the child, the juvenile, the affectional significance which the child or juvenile had for himself. Those of you who have children know your children love you, know how thoughtful they are of you, how very foresightful they are for your comfort and happiness. The student of personality who has nothing at stake but observed phenomena is, however, unable to listen with complete conviction to your accounts. He will, instead, wonder as to what particular devices, training or conditioning you have used to bring about this to you so satisfactory state. If he can get near enough to the child or the juvenile to hear what the child or juvenile can say of the situation with you, it will sound much less sentimentally perfect. It will suggest a realistic appreciation of a necessity and a human development of devices to meet the necessity. There will not be this sentimental glow of love, consideration, and so on, but rather that marvelous human thing, great adaptive possibilities applied successfully to a situation.

I suggest thus the egocentric character of personality up to the epoch of preadolescence. Adjustments made? Yes. Very subtle adjustments made? Yes. Great satisfactions to people who are interested in the child as a human? Yes. Great successes in school, great respect from the teacher, adoration of the teacher—all sorts of things which, on careful study, seem, however, to leave the child or the juvenile as the center of his processes, the thing that matters above everything to him.

This is exceedingly fortunate. The human race would have expired long centuries ago were it not so. A most thoughtful, considerate parent who would change this and who would bring about the miracle to which I am about to refer before its time would cripple his offspring, at least to the second generation. There are the most excellent reasons why true social orientation takes a long time coming. But it comes in preadolescence. The capacity to love in its initial form makes appearance as the mark that one has ceased to be juvenile and has become preadolescent. What this means in the outline of situations which it brings about is this: at this point the satisfactions and the security which are being experienced by someone else, some particular other person, begin to be as significant to the person as are his own satisfactions and security.

You have just heard a definition of the end state of love which, if you are not accustomed to this type of thinking, may seem to you a strange one. Let me repeat it, because it has certain objective validity which many other definitions might be found to lack. When the satisfaction or the security of another person becomes as significant to one as is one's own satisfaction or security, then the state of love exists. So far as I know, under no other circumstances is a state of love present, regardless of the popular usage of the word.

This state of affectional rapport—generically love—ordinarily occurs under restricted circumstances. In the beginning many factors must be present. Some of these may be called obvious likeness, parallel impulse, parallel physical development. These make for situations in which boys feel at ease with boys rather than with girls. This feeling of species identity or identification influences the feeling involved in the preadolescent change. The appearance of the capacity to love ordinarily first involves a member of one's own sex. The boy finds a chum who is a boy, the girl finds a chum who is a girl. When this has happened, there follows in its wake a great increase in the consensual validation of symbols, of symbol operations, and of information, data about life and the world.

This comes about as a fairly obvious consequence of the fact that the other fellow has now become highly significant to one. Whereas previously, one may have learned to say the right thing to one's companions, to do the right things, now these sayings and doings take on a very special significance. One's security is not imperilled by one's love object. One's satisfactions are facilitated by the love object. Therefore, naturally, for the first time one can begin to express oneself freely. If another person matters as much to you as do you yourself, it is quite possible to talk to this person as you have never talked to anyone before. The freedom which comes from this expanding of one's world of satisfaction and security to include two people, linked together by love, permits exchanges of nuances of meaning, permits investigations without fear of rebuff or humiliation, which greatly augments the consensual validation of all sorts of things, all in the end symbols that stand for—refer to, represent—states of being in the world.

In this period there begins the illumination of a real world community. As soon as one finds that all this vast autistic and somewhat validated structure to which one refers as one's mind, one's thoughts, one's personality, is really open to some comparing of notes, to some checking and counter-checking, one begins to feel human in a sense in which one has not previously felt human. One becomes more fully human in that one begins to appreciate the common humanity of people— there comes a new sympathy for the other fellow, whether he be present to the senses or mediated by rumors in the geography, or the like. In other words, the feeling of humanity is one of the aspects of the expansion of personality which comes in preadolescence. Learning at this stage begins to assume its true aspect of implementing the person in securing satisfactions and maintaining his security in interpersonal relations through the rest of life.

Previous to this time many people have learned for fun. Those were the bright pupils who very often satisfy the teacher perfectly, and the year after haven't the ghost of an idea of what the deuce it was all about. Or learning has been difficult, for rewards and punishments. It is only when the world expands as a tissue of persons and interpersonal relations which are meaningful that knowledge becomes truly significant, and learning becomes a serious attempt to implement oneself for one's future life.

It is true that some people arrive at preadolescence so crippled by 'educational' experience that this particular phenomenon in regard to learning may appear erratically, rather than uniformly. There are instances in our educational system in which the utility of the knowledge, of the learning, is so distorted that a field of information is permanently barred to any ordinary development of the personality. You will find, for example, a good many people who tell you that they are no good at mathematics. Now, it is true that mathematical genius seems to have something to do with germinal constitution. It appears in some imbeciles as well as in some people who are definitely geniuses. It runs in certain stocks, certain families, perhaps; that is, it is more abundant in them than in the population, generally. Germinal constitution is not, however, what is involved when a person tells you, "Oh, I am no good at mathematics." If you can establish a condition of sufficient confidence with this person and work back to the time when he encountered mathematics, usually in the teaching of arithmetic, you will learn that his security was grossly undermined in this process, that in some fashion or other he suffered so much pain, so much threat of anxiety, so much anxiety itself, that the whole field of intrinsically mathematical symbol operations has taken on a vague mark of anxiety. When he is confronted with a mathematical problem he experiences anxiety. He ordinarily avoids becoming involved in such problems, for this excellent reason.

When there is anxiety, it tends to exclude the situation that provoked it from awareness, and so the person made anxious by the mathematical problem tends to overlook certain commonplace, obvious aspects of the problem that are well within his grasp. The tendency is to move away from, rather than simply to grasp, the factors making up the situation presented to him.

The juvenile era often includes experience which dams certain fields of learning; the preadolescent expansion of consciousness and sympathy for a larger world of many relationships, many complexities and many people then tends to be blocked off from particular fields of knowledge. Otherwise one now begins to learn because knowledge is demonstrating its usefulness to oneself and one's friend.

One thus comes to an expansion of the necessary human environment that—with but one great interruption—goes on to the fullest development of the human organism. The interruption is the coming of genital sexuality. It may be well to review the path that we have been following, before we take up the era of adolescence, itself.

We have seen how the self comes into being as a dynamism to preserve the feeling of security. We have observed that it is built largely of personal symbolic elements learned in contact with other significant people. We have noted that the self comes to control awareness, to restrict one's consciousness of what is going on in one's situation very largely by the instrumentality of anxiety with, as a result, a dissociation from personal awareness of those tendencies of the personality which are not included or incorporated in the approved structure of the self.

The point is that the self is approved by significant others, that any tendencies of the personality that are not so approved, that are in fact strongly disapproved, are dissociated from personal awareness.

We saw that these dissociated tendencies, which do not cease to exist merely because they are excluded from the self, manifest themselves in actions, activities, of which the person himself remains quite unaware. The actions are unnoticed and the goals of the activities are things of which the person has no conscious knowledge.

This dissociation of components of the personality is not restricted to the pursuit of satisfaction. Some of the power processes which the infant and the child, perhaps even the juvenile, found effective also come under such stern disapproval at a later stage of personality that they, too, are dissociated, and from then on manifest outside of the awareness of the person himself.

They were tolerated by the significant personal environment for a time, as shown, for example, for the attitude that the infant has no particular mind, and, therefore, is justified in being wholly irresponsible about certain things; but when he gets to be a child these activities are no longer satisfactory, and under certain circumstances at least he must dissociate some of the power operations, magic performances, of infancy from his consciousness of performance as a child.

It may be that anything which is useful at one stage of personality development will be dissociated in the next stage unless the culture-carrying adults encourage its continued elaboration within the self. The elaboration of some drives, like these drives to maintain security and to manifest personal power, personal capacity, capability, importance, have reasonable chance of being elaborated, at least in the case of people who grow up in rather hygienic homes. Certain other tendencies are not so fortunate and are quite certain to suffer dissociation from the personal consciousness.

We may say, however, as a generality, that healthy development of personality is inversely proportionate to the amount, to the number, of tendencies which have come to exist in dissociation. Put in another way, if there is nothing dissociated, then whether one be a genius or an imbecile, it is quite certain that he will be mentally healthy. The precise meaning of this term "mentally healthy" will gradually appear.

If, on the other hand, a person be very talented but be required by his experience, by the significant people who bear on him at various stages in his development, to dissociate from his awareness a considerable number of powerful and durable motivational systems, then that person will be markedly exposed to mental disorder. He will inevitably be maladjusted in some of the situations through which his life must develop, and that maladjustment, due to the partition in his activity, will come about quite certainly, the partition being between those activities of which he is aware versus those which he does with no awareness.

Inverting the entire proposition, one might say that the larger the proportion of energy systems in a personality which act exterior to the awareness of the person, the greater the chances that he will meet some crisis in interpersonal relations in which he cannot act in the fashion which we call mental health.

The likelihood of an acute disturbance in some interpersonal relation is greatly increased by the presence of an important motivational system in dissociation.

We have considered the growing complexity of the human environment, which we pointed out was made up of not only the physico-chemical universe, which may be assumed to be present to all the living things, and the biological universe, plants and animals that are of some interest to us, but the personal and the cultural, the cultural manifesting itself through persons, but none the less being susceptible of abstract study, as is done by the cultural anthropologists. Culture in this sense we hold to include institutions like the government, the Department of the Interior, the church, the school, and so on; the forceful convictions as to right and wrong ways of living, the mores, as sociologists are wont to call them, the traditions of the family group, of the community, and the like, and the fashions which are in force at the particular time concerned.

These are the cultural entities which are highly significant in the human environment, and all of them have their being and their manifestation so far as any particular person is concerned in other people who are significant for one reason or another to him, originally the mother as the provider of all sorts of necessary protection and satisfaction; in childhood the parents and the home society, people who are frequently in the home and related by bonds of intimacy or hostility to the parent; in the juvenile era, the school, the school teacher and all that machinery, and to a certain extent one's play companions; and in preadolescence the chum and the people in whom the chum is interested.

We have seen how this personal environment is expanded by the mediate channels of communication, the telephone, the radio, and particularly the printed word.[18]

---

[18] We might illustrate the power of the press by commenting on its unintended effect of determining the fashions of suicide from time to time. Fashion is used advisedly. As I recall, I have lived through three periods in which self-destruction by way of bichloride poisoning enjoyed typical vogue. Bichloride poisoning is a horrible way of terminating life. The newspapers, without

We have considered the stage of personality development in which the other fellow, the chum, someone of the same sex and approximately the same age, becomes highly significant, and by this very fact acts as the final binding agency to connect the growing individual with the full force and control action of the cultural environment. One can follow certain autistic courses, certain individualized highly personal courses of development, giving lip service to the requirements of one social environment so long as nobody in that environment has more than instrumental meaning to one. One can for instance do homage to people who are afflicted with a sense of greatness without feeling any sympathy with what they regard as important. It pays; it gives something that is repaid with what one wants—satisfactions or security. But when somebody else begins to matter as much as I do, then what this other person values must receive some careful consideration from me. So it is in the preadolescent change that the great controlling power of the cultural, social, forces is finally inescapably written into the human personality.

We will presently discuss the phase of personal evolution which is the last step toward fully human estate, with respect for others as for oneself, with the dignity befitting the high achievement and with the freedom of personal initiative which

------

mentioning this, report, some time or other, that some more or less notable person has died of bichloride of mercury poisoning, self-administered. Shortly afterwards there are little squibs here and there in the newspapers to the effect that this and that person has died by bichloride. The fashion is spreading.

The most dreadfully satirical element of this particular fashion in poisoning lies in the peculiar deviltry of the drug. One is horribly ill. If one survives the first days of hellish agony, there comes a period of relative convalescence—during which all the patients I have seen were most repentant and strongly desirous of living. Then comes the third phase, during which one suffers unimaginable agonies, again for days. Then with awful inevitability, one finally dies.

The ephemeral printed word of the news sheet influences the style of suicide after the pattern of fashion change, and the growth and the decay of a fashion of destroying oneself, the grossest of misdirections of living, literally can be traced to the accounts of a, for the moment, new method, and to the gradual ennui that comes from multitudinous reports of the same thing.

is comfortably adapted to the circumstances which characterize the particular social order of which one is a part.

Before I can discuss the phase of adolescence it is necessary that I say something more about the impulses which underlie the pursuit of satisfaction and the protection or pursuit of the feeling of security. Many of you have doubtless noticed that thus far in a presentation which started with the statement that the study of individual personality did not seem to be within the field of science, the only thing that seems amenable to scientific approach being the actions in interpersonal situations; that which someone does with me, that can be observed, both by me and by some objective third person—what goes on in that person, the unique peculiarity of his personality, seems to escape any method of science—yet I have proceeded after this preamble for over two hours with such terms as tendency, impulse, goal, and so on, as if I had departed my own dogma and were discussing individual human personality as the subject of study.

We have finally come to the point where this convenient, this false unitary individualistic language becomes highly confusing instead of definitely indicative. By that I mean this, that while I have tried thus far to indicate by the use of the conventional individualistic language some of the considerations relevant to psychiatry, I can no longer continue in that course without apology and without reemphasizing my original position, because one cannot even seem to make sense, from here on, in the individualistic language of common speech and of the traditional psychology.

We have to realize that when we talk about an impulse that underlies the pursuit of satisfaction we are using a figure of speech that comes very naturally to us, by which we must be referring to something quite different. Let me try to express the more valid content of this instance of individualistic speech more lucidly and more accurately.

When we speak of impulse to such and such action, of

tendency to such and such behavior, of striving toward such and such goal, or use any of these words which sound as if you, a unit, have these things in you and as if they can be studied by and for themselves, we are talking, according to the structure of our language and the habits of common speech, about something which is observably manifested as action in a situation. The situation is not any old thing, it is you and someone else integrated in a particular fashion which can be converted in the alembic of speech into a statement that "A is striving toward so and so from B."

As soon as I say this, you realize that B is a very highly significant element in the situation. Many situations are integrated in which A wants deference from B, and B, mirabile dictu, wants deference from A. It looks as if there were something in A and something in B that happened to collide. But when one studies the situation in which A and B pursue, respectively, the aim of getting from the other person what he himself needs and what the other person needs, we find that it is not as simple as it looks. The *situation* is still the valid object of study, or rather that which we can observe; namely, the action which indicates the situation and the character of its integration.

The situation is integrated in such manner as to resolve itself after a change that is satisfactory or satisfaction giving, or tributary to security. This is the general statement of all interpersonal situations. They are integrated in such fashion that as processes—and you remember the living are always manifesting processes and you do not have static situations, nor static people—the situation is so integrated that what action there is in it can move to the discharge or resolution of some dynamic component in each of the people.

When that has happened, the situation is at least temporarily adjourned. It has ceased to be more than a memory and a potentiality for similar situations to occur. Following, however, what we have said about the impulses that are accompanied by awareness and those that are dissociated from the awareness of the person, you will see that many situations may be integrated among or between people such that both a witting impulse, a known impulse, an understood and recognized impulse, and a dissociated impulse, are involved.

I should illustrate this, for example, by having a person integrate a situation with another person in order to get a promotion. Let us say that he is subjected to a rigid interrogatory, not only to determine his qualifications and the justification for his promotion, but also to humiliate him very cruelly.

What have we here? In the old language of common speech you would say, "Well, he has to deal with a cruel or a sadistic superior." The "has to" is open to question. Whence the compulsion which requires at this time that he should take steps to get a promotion? That might be anything. It *may* be that he has to.

Yet, let us study the superior instead of this person whom we have just discussed. Let us observe that someone else in his organization wishes to be promoted. He is interrogated, but he is interrogated carefully, so that his self-respect will not be wounded, so that he will not be humiliated or hurt.

Let us say that neither gets the promotion. There is nothing in either situation as I have described them, which implies favorable or unfavorable action. But there is a difference in these two situations which have in common an administrative person. How do we understand this? We may understand this by saying that the first person, the one who was hurt and humiliated, manifested toward his superior certain actions which called out the superior's hostility and destructiveness, that the second person in the integration with the administrator prohibited, in some fashion, the manifestation of these durable traits of the administrator.

In the first case we may safely assume that the underling did not wittingly, did not to his knowledge or with his conscious awareness, provoke the cruel impulses in the administrator. In the second case we may say that the underling did not consciously prohibit those impulses in the superior. But both situations were multiply determined. There was the acknowledged, the known, the consciously evidenced desire for progress, for improvement in one's life situation in both the applicants. There was in the first case a willingness to undergo pain, humiliation, and so on; in the second case there was some dangerous hostility which it was well to let sleep. This is a crude, perhaps not too convincing, illustration of a situation integrated by the consciously accepted motives within awareness and other impulses more or less incongruent to them.[19]

You will realize that it is very difficult for a person to feel secure and self-respecting if he knows that he carries in himself impulses which cause him to be humiliated or otherwise made to suffer by anybody in authority. And you will also, such of you as have any trace of this not too rare impulse, know that one seldom is clearly and unblushingly aware of the fact that he is rather dangerous when he is hurt. These things have been dissociated from the self in the process of development to the state, in our example, of our underlings before they apply to the superior.

Now let us consider preadolescence in connection with that type of self organization in which the predominating attitude toward others is hate. Such a state does not necessarily preclude a development to preadolescence. It may be a great handicap. It often leads to experience which does prevent development

---

[19] Even in so sketchy an imaginary situation as that described, multiple possibilities as to the dissociated impulses appear. In the first case, for example, the administrator may have used the applicant as a convenient foil for expressing attitudes called out by some third person, in the immediate past. In the second case, the administrator's cruel-sadistic impulse may have been inhibited from any expression by some feature of the applicant's personality which attracted him powerfully. If we have applicant Number One follow Number Two, under these circumstances, the inhibiting of the cruel-sadistic impulse towards Number Two will provide a reinforcement for its (invited) expression towards Number One. There are several other possibilities; the actual dynamics of any real situation depend on a large but finite group of factors and can be discovered by investigating the actual historic courses of patterning that have resulted in the manifest behavior of persons concerned.

to preadolescence. But it does not always do so, and quite often people whose attitude toward others is almost uniformly derogatory, whose attitude toward the self is hostile, do get on to preadolescence, and in preadolescence undergo what I have called the quiet miracle of developing the capacity of love. Someone else begins to be as significant as oneself.

What do we see in these situations? What do we see of the no longer acceptable hateful attitude in so far as it pertains to the love object? We see the evidences of a recent dissociation; in the midst of rather effective *toward* performances there will come some untoward acts of hostility to the person newly elevated to an equality of importance with oneself.

These acts are ordinary mysteries. They mystify the person who manifests them, despite the fact that such acts were about all that he manifested until, say, two months ago. Now it comes to him as shocking, he cannot understand why he does it. It has been dropped out of the realm of awareness, but it has been dropped so recently and after such a great body of experience that dissociation is not complete. It is in the anteroom, you might say, on the way out. One can remember that it is not as novel as it seems, and, therefore, one may well develop a plausible perplexity about it.[20]

We touch here on a situation that is clearly in the realm of personal problems, of mental disorder in contradistinction to the progression which we call mental health. Preadolescence to a considerable degree and adolescence to a high degree, are the epochs in which warp of development in earlier stages manifests itself as severe handicap. I shall, for this reason, postpone the discussion of adolescence to the next lecture, con-

---

[20] *Rationalizing* is the technical word for this misuse of reasoning which, in some people, amounts to their major nuisance value in society. All the things they do that don't happen to receive just the right response from the other fellow are "explained," and they are always explained plausibly, although few indeed of us know why we make particular social mistakes. If I were asked at a moment of weariness, "What is the outstanding characteristic of the human being?", I believe I would say, "His plausibility."

cluding tonight with a reconsideration of the communal environment of the preadolescent era.

Preadolescence is usually spent in school and at home. Parents are still people of significance, but their merits and demerits have been fairly well appraised. This does not mean that from henceforth they are to be accorded a simple, realistic status. Quite the contrary; the adolescent upheaval which is impending will bring with it a revaluation of everyone, parents included. The preadolescent frames of reference are, at least in our culture, about the clearest and most workable ones that we have. They do not include lust as a complicating and distorting factor—generally, a confusing and misleading element. Love is new and uncomplicated. The parental complex is viewed from this new angle and, while there may still be aspects which do not make sense, the appraisal is often more valid than is the view which will be adopted some five or six years hence.

The relatively uncomplicated experience of love is entirely ennobling. Sympathy flows from it. Tolerance as a respect for people—not as an intellectual detachment from prejudice —follows it like a bright shadow. Authoritarian figures in the home and elsewhere are recast as of good intention, however stupid and uninformed.

A remedy has at last been found for many thwartings and humiliations, for sundry prohibitions. One looks about one at one's compeers, without sentimentality but with a feeling that they have come naturally by their assets and deficiencies.

A new form of participation develops, in part from sympathy and understanding, in part from awe at the newly expanded world. The preadolescent evolves the practice of *collaboration*, a valid functional activity as a person in a personal situation. This is a great step forward from cooperation—*I* play according to the rules of the game, to preserve *my* prestige and feeling of superiority and merit. When we collaborate, it is a matter of *we*. The achievement is no longer a personal success; it is a group performance—no more the leader's than the led.

In this brief phase of preadolescence, the world as known gains depth of meaning from the new appraisal of the people who compose it. The world as rumored is a wonderful place; the quest of Sir Lancelot rises from the mists of faëry to all but a pattern of life to be lived. Experiences reported from excursions away from home carry a coloring of friendly wonder. The future is constructed in relatively noble terms by the reveries that prepare for tomorrow and that assuage disappointment, take the humdrum out of monotonous tasks.

The imaginary people of preadolescent fantasy may seem to us insubstantial; the imaginary play of the preadolescent may seem but old, romantic folklore crudely adjusted to the spirit of the times. The illusions that transmute his companions —if they be illusions—may seem to us but certain of an early end, a disillusionment. But whatever his people, real, illusory or frankly imagined, may be, they are not mean. Whatever his daydreams with his chum, whatever his private fantasies, they are not base. And as to his valuations of others, here we may take pause and reflect that it may be we who see "as through a glass, darkly."

These young folk are grossly inexperienced. They are often grossly misinformed as to the motives that are prominent in adult life around them. But I surmise that after the measure of their experience, they see remarkably clearly. Also, I believe that for a great majority of our people, preadolescence is the nearest that they come to untroubled human life—that from then on the stresses of life distort them to inferior caricatures of what they might have been.

Developmental Syndromes

WE SHALL now consider the phase of personality development which is the last stage on the road to the fully human estate. Once successfully negotiated, the person comes forth with self-respect adequate to almost any situation, with the respect for others that this competent self-respect entails, with the dignity that befits the high achievement of competent personality, and with the freedom of personal initiative that represents a comfortable adaptation of one's personal situation to the circumstances that characterize the social order of which one is a part.

The epochs that lead up to adolescence are closely if obscurely related to somatic maturation. Adolescence begins with the most spectacular maturation of all, the puberty change, with its swift alteration of physiological processes to the completion of bodily development. I still find virtue in dividing the epoch of adolescence into three eras: [21] early adolescence, from the first evidences of puberty to the completion of voice change; mid-adolescence, to the patterning of genital behavior; and late adolescence, to the establishment of durable situations

[21] This conception reaches back certainly as far as the *Sheppard Farewell Lectures* [to the staff of the Sheppard and Enoch Pratt Hospital] 12 Oct. to 9 Nov. 1929 (Privately circulated in mimeograph). The clarification of the stages had to await my emancipation from the residues of faculty-psychology, etc. I have not yet solved the problem of communicating in writing the special implications of the interpersonal view. If, on first reading, these lectures seem difficult *but* probably significant, may I bespeak a review—perhaps section by section—after the rough outlines of the whole have been apprehended.

of intimacy such that all the major integrating tendencies are freely manifested within awareness in the series of one's interpersonal relations.

The farther one moves from birth, the less relevant an absolute physiological chronology becomes. The epoch of adolescence is thus the least fixed by mere somatic duration. It varies from culture to culture, and its actual time of appearance in young people among us is very widely varied. Over the world, the puberty change would seem to occur from as early an age as eight to as late as the twenties. Among some 250 people whom I have studied more or less intensively, I have seen quite a few in whom the inception of adolescence was deferred to around the eighteenth year.

It is from the data of these patients that I have come to feel that environmental influences, cultural influences emanating from significant people, are the predominant factor in bringing about delays—and accelerations—in the later stages of personality development.

The data of these patients, in so far as they have been of American and Western European stock, certainly emphasize the significance of experience—remote and recent—connected with genital (sexual) behavior and the emotion of lust. I have to add a word of caution, here, for there are those among us psychiatrists who make of sex a nuclear explanatory concept of personality, or at least of personality disorder. This is an error from insufficiency of the data. The highly civilized Chinese of the pre-Christian era were not bowled over by sex. A number of the primitive peoples who have been studied by anthropologists are found to take sex rather in their stride. Even the American Negro crashes through adolescence with relative impunity—if he is of the lower classes.

The lurid twilight which invests sex in our culture is primarily a function of two factors. We still try to discourage pre-marital sexual performances; hold that abstinence is the moral course before marriage. And we discourage early marriage; in fact progressively widen the gap between the adolescent awakening of lust and the proper circumstances for marriage. These two factors work through many cultural conventions to make us the most sex-ridden people of whom I have any knowledge.

I think that it might be well at this point to indicate something of what this means by discussing an instance of maladjustment in adolescence. To do this, I must go a long way back from the problem as it presents itself, say, at age 15. To formulate any personal situation, one must almost certainly know a great deal about how it came into being. I shall then take a few minutes to sketch the picture of a boy to whom adolescence will be quite disastrous.

We will take him in the cradle, and here we will see him, after the fashion of all his predecessors, actively and pleasantly engaged in the exercise of such ability as he has discovered. He will perhaps not have kicked a slat out of the cradle, but he certainly will have poked all the slats of the cradle, he will have felt of nearly everything, including a great deal of himself, he may have put a good deal of himself in his mouth, or tried to, but in this business of exercising newly elaborated motor systems and gradually clarifying sensory feel, he will almost inevitably, since we make it a "him," have fallen upon a small protuberance in the groin, and in doing this he will have found it handy. It is suited to manipulation. It is astonishingly well located geometrically. A slight curve in the elbow puts it well within reach of the already nimble fingers.

So far nothing of any moment has occurred. But we will now have, let us say, the mother—fathers usually keep fairly far from the nursery—we will have the mother encounter this discovery of the infant, and we will make her a person who has been forced to organize the self on the basis of our more rigid puritanic tradition.

Under these circumstances, although in ordinary consciousness she is not wholly unaware of this anatomical peculiarity of the male, in her own infant she will feel that Satan is in the very near vicinity, that here is a manifestation of the bestial nature of man in the very act of erupting in her infant, and she will want to do something about it. She will wish to save this infant; Lord knows what awful visions unroll before her eyes as she witnesses this; but anyway the infant is badly upset by empathy, undergoes various somatic disturbances, and experiences what amounts to an acute and severe discomfort.

Infants are not afflicted by long, carefully formulated memories. To the infant whose discrimination of such things is nil, this discomfort does not attach to the manipulation of the little protuberance. Almost anything in the situation may be related to this feeling of discomfort so far as the infant is concerned. He has not learned.

This course of events is discovered again, perhaps the same day. The stress in the mother is terrific. The doctor is consulted, and we will say that the doctor is either very anxious to build up a good practice and surmises that this mother will bring him patients, or that he, too, knows no better; so he puts medical 'intelligence' or rumor that has come to him, to work. And so the infant has a mitten put on the hand and tied around the wrist.

Thus begins the emphasis in the infant's mind that something about this hand is connected with the recurrent feelings of acute and severe discomfort—the *anlage* of insecurity and later of anxiety.

Well, infants, like people, are ingenious. And the immobilization of, let us say, the right hand, does not effect the immobilization of the left. As the genital is handy, and as it has a slightly different sensation from the thumb, the nose, and so on, the event recurs. Again there is the great discomfort in the presence of the mother. Presently both hands may be tied at the side, and by that time even an infant begins to realize that it has something to do with the genital.

All animals tend to react with rage to immobilization, or to any thwarting or restraint which amounts generically to immobilization. To leap over months of struggle between the mother, aided by her medical adviser, and the infant's natural impulse to explore all his abilities and the limits of himself and the rest of the world; after months of struggle there has been impressed upon this infant a type of interest, a mark, if you please—an emotional mark—about the groin area which is so significant that when I was younger and more reckless about language, I called that state "primary genital phobia," which, being translated, is primary fear, irrational fear, of the genitals.

One does not fear something of no interest to one. Anything invested with fear must by definition, by the inherent character of our contact with the universe, be of interest to us. And, therefore, because of this taboo the child has interest, unusual interest, an utterly useless interest so far as the development of personality is concerned, attached to the penis.

As a child and as a juvenile he continues to have this interest. Why? Because this thing was precipitated in personality very early, very firmly. All the red flags of anxiety came to attach to it. Moreover, mamma is always watching. Where the devil has shown up once, you may confidently expect him to return —quite unlike lightning.

And so here we have a person who, long before the puberty changes, has come to have a considerable conflict of impulse pertaining to genital manipulation, a thing fully meaningful only years later; and a conscious center of interest in the genitals, but a negative one, in that they are to be left alone at any cost.

Of course, one is always waking up to discover that one has violated this regulation in one's sleep. Interest has some way or other gotten one to violate this taboo. One is horrified. One has the feeling, "Oh, the devil that is in me. Here I am, doing this worst of possible things in my sleep."

Such a person, having stumbled through preadolescence, let us say, carefully avoiding any physical intimacies with anybody, comes to adolescence. At adolescence the genital dynamism awakens. Experience begins to be colored by a new emotion, and one of singular emphasis, to which we apply the term, lust.[22] As hunger is generically a state of dissatisfaction which orients awareness towards the integration of nutritive— and related—situations chiefly affecting the oral zone of interaction, so lust is a state of dissatisfaction which orients awareness towards the tendency to integrate situations chiefly affecting the genital zone.

Even in our particular boy with the puritanical mother, lust swings his attention towards his penis as an instrument in social situations. Along with the coming of this impulse there appears a curiosity as to the stories about it which the social environment produces, and it gets to be frightfully troublesome. Being compelled to enter into interpersonal situations, and being subjected to powerful social pressure which makes it proper, right, respectable and decent for him to go with a girl, he now goes with a girl.

What, then, occurs? He comes presently to realize quite clearly that he is not acting as was expected. He may know what should be done, but cannot do it. He may have to inquire to discover what is the matter. The knowledge does not help him. Nor does his inability in any way relieve him of the driving lust. It does not resolve the activity of the genital dynamism. But it does put very serious kinks in his relations with a member of the other sex. He is doubly unsatisfied, and, in all likelihood more or less chronically anxious. The failure reflected to him from the companion also strikes at self-esteem

---

[22] I can picture the commotion to which this statement may provoke the more conforming of the psychoanalysts by recollecting a conversation had some ten years ago with Ives Hendrick—*Facts and Theories of Psychoanalysis* [2 ed.]; New York, Knopf, 1939 (xiv and 369 pp.)—in the course of which I remarked that I could not accept the *phallic* phase of development, as formulated by Freud.

and the feeling of personal competence and security. It is small wonder that things go from bad to worse with him.

Let us say that this boy about whom we are talking has had anxiety a number of times when he awoke to discover that he was violating the taboo that had been written into his personality. We have said that the instrumentality of anxiety is ordinarily sufficient to maintain in dissociation impulses which are entirely contradictory to the self dynamism, impulses which are entirely unsuited to the type of life for which the self-system has been organized.

What happens when the sexual impulses, the impulses to genital behavior, collide with the self system, as in our particular example? Under certain circumstances, the self is able to dissociate lust and the impulses to genital behavior. This can be achieved only by the development of new and elaborate "apparatus" in living. I make here but a crude and hurried touching on something which I will develop at greater length, presently. The point which I wish to emphasize now is that, late as it is in maturing, the genital lust dynamism is something that can be dissociated only at grave risk to effective living, and that in most people it cannot be dissociated at all. It will again and again, at whatever great expense to security, whatever suffering from anxiety, manifest itself.

When the genital drive is dissociated, what precisely do we observe? I shall use this rather uncommon situation to give new emphasis to the meaning of our interpersonal viewpoint. When we speak of drives, impulses, tendencies, we mean always tendencies to integrate situations that will be resolved in a particular significant fashion—often by activity chiefly pertaining to one of our zones of interaction with the environment, and activity chiefly that of one of our several dynamisms.

Without hoping to make clear in a small part of one lecture the greater than somatic character of these dynamisms, let me make a rather necessary digression to discuss the physiological substrate of the zones of interaction of the personality.

We say that the principal zones of interaction are as follows: the *oral*, the retinal, the auditory, the general tactile, the vestibulo-kinæsthetic, the *genital*, and the *anal*, or aboral.[23]

The zones of interaction are developed, elaborated, equipped for dealing with particular phases of the physico-chemical, biological, and interpersonal environment.

The oral zone is made up of a great deal of apparatus. It includes for practical purposes the respiratory apparatus and the food-taking apparatus, from which is evolved the speaking apparatus; so that this zone is very important indeed, and is utilized from the first moment of life to the last. It has special tactile equipment in the lips, in the mouth, and in the nasopharynx. It includes our two most purely chemical receptors, the gustatory sense, and the olfactory.

As I say, this oral zone may be considered as a unit, and while it is always reckless to speak of any part of a person as a unit, still the oral zone is at least a describable part of the person, and the function of the oral zone, in common with all of these zones of interaction, is probably awarded a certain amount of the vital energy, whether it is needed there or not. Given, let us say, twenty units of vital energy from the chemical changes going on in us, two units, perhaps, will be partitioned to this oral zone and will tend very strongly to be used in oral activity, which as you can conceive may be very highly variegated in later life, but in the beginning consists largely of breathing, sucking, and crying.

The retinal area of interaction brings us our most incredibly expanded integration with things not immediately within reach —the retinal receptor is the distance receptor par excellence, and with the aid of optical apparatus permits us to see over distances of a great many light years. Besides this, it is peculiarly related to things *within* reach, for its evolution is closely con-

---

[23] By the italics, I wish to set off the three zones the dynamisms of which are greatly varied from person to person because of the special cultural influences that are included in their organization and functional activity.

nected with dexterity, with our prehensile and manipulative skills shown primarily in the functional activity of the hands.

The auditory apparatus dealing with air vibrations, vibrations in fluid media, is also a distance receptor, but one of very slight ability compared with the retinal. Regardless of this comparative weakness in overcoming distance, it is the exceedingly important channel for word-learning, and is closely connected with speech—thus being involved with the oral dynamism, of which it might be considered a part. This fusion is not helpful, however, excepting that it shows the interdependence of the parts in the whole.

The general tactile receptors, on the other hand, are for immediate contact.

The kinæsthetic apparatus is involved with the activities of the muscles and joints, and locating ourselves in regard to the relevant geometry of space. It includes the equilibrium equipment.

The genital zone combines highly specialized tactile receptors and apparatus which could be put in the kinæsthetic class except that it pertains to involuntary muscles rather than to striated muscles, equipment connected with corpus spongiosum, the prostatic urethra, the motor elements in the seminal vesicles, and the prostate itself.

At the other end of the alimentary tract again around a muco-cutaneous juncture there is a highly specialized tactile apparatus, similar to that around the lips—conceivably necessary for the maintenance of safety of these delicate areas, there being special nutritional problems wherever the mucous membrane joins the skin.[24]

The oral, genital, and anal zones of interaction with the en-

---

[24] They are quite different types of tissue, the skin and mucous membrane, with different biochemical processes; the blood supply of the two is specifically different, and the junctures are unusually vulnerable because all this differentiated tissue is combined more or less along a line. Injuries of the muco-cutaneous junctures are troublesome, as all of you who have had cold sores or anal fissures must know.

vironment are greatly affected in the educational acculturation procedure. Many people have their olfactory abilities seriously reduced as a result of the distaste with which culture-carriers in authority treat interest in smells and acts of smelling on the part of the child.

The special tactile activity of the mouth is conditioned by peculiarities and restrictions about taking nourishment, sucking, and the like. The gustatory part is conditioned by prejudices about what is food and what is clean and proper to take into the mouth, and so on and so forth. We shall have more to say about this, presently.

The genital is so conditioned by the prejudices and beliefs of the parents that it is apt to be permanently impaired for its biological function, if not for all forms of interpersonal activity, and similarly, the anal zone is strongly conditioned by culture, in the teaching of our rather elaborate toilet habits.

The result of this strong invasion of culture into the physiology of the organism is very apt to be attended with phenomena of symbolic segregation of various parts of the body. If you are taught that you are a good boy when you do not put your thumb in your mouth, *not doing* so as a virtue begins to be mixed up with being a good boy; and when you are impressed with the cataclysmic character of manipulating your genital, the genital is apt to get invested with marks of danger to be avoided, and also mixed up in yourself, in the self dynamism; and tinkering around the lower end of one's alimentary tract is quite distracting to many parents, and one is apt to get to understand that that particular part of one's anatomy is to be treated only indirectly. You must have your hand wrapped in paper before you approach this part of the body, and that is apt to get itself invested with considerable interest in itself.

The oral zone is involved in such varied functions that it is perhaps the central trunk, the main stem for evolutions of the self. It is fortunate that the excrementary orifice does not get so much significance. Now and then, however, it gets rather remarkable significance. What with the parents' interest in cleanliness and the general American conviction that regularity of bowel action is vital—and the delicate organization of the infant, anyway, so that one can't ignore its bowel action completely—quite often this zone is used in interaction with the parents to express hostility and resentment which usually takes the form of extraordinary interferences with the excrementary function. Biologically things are so keyed that when the rectum is pretty well engorged, its emptying is automatic. That does not do at all among civilized people who wear clothes, and late in infancy or early in childhood quite often the parents have to cudgel their brains, and sometimes the child, a great deal to overcome his *excessive* control of the sphincters. In other words, he refuses to accommodate. Having had his excrementary function thoroughly acculturated, he simply improves on example, you might say, and outdoes this highly desirable learning, and that causes consternation in the environment—thus proving that it is an instrument of power.

The cry was originally the powerful tool of the infant. All too frequently the constipation becomes the powerful tool of the child. The parents have gotten used to listening to him talk and he does not get very much that way, but clamping down on the sphincters at the lower end of the alimentary tract gets action—lots of action, lots of attention, and, thereby, begins to take on significance in this important matter of power, which is so woven into the self dynamism as to be in one way the explanation of the self's existence. One of the great elements in the feeling of security is the conviction that one has power enough in an interpersonal situation: One can feel 'in control' of the situation.

Let us now return to the question, What do we observe in our young man. He is free from awareness of lust, he does not wittingly enter any situation with the purpose of having something genital happen. What do we perceive? We perceive that this man is hounded by the accidents by which he finds himself involved with the wrong type of person. What does this mean? It means that the power of this integrating tendency is such that even though it works entirely outside of his awareness, it works, and works conspicuously, and while he believes that he has become interested in a young lady, has sought her company and has finally got himself noticed so that he can discuss calculus with her, the facts which determine that situation are very much more on the side of the genital lust motive than they are on the intellectual pursuit of calculus. But it is only of the latter that he can be aware, and so he is constantly having difficulties in his interpersonal relations.

The girl has regarded his 'approach' as quite subtle—but he never arrives. She may give him a helping hand, but he somehow overlooks or misinterprets it. If she makes the best of a bad job and they actually discuss calculus problems; even then— as under any other circumstance—he leaves unsatisfied, with a feeling that things have not worked well. That night, he awakens wet with perspiration, from a dream in which he has been kissing and fondling this girl's breasts—and has just bitten one and swallowed the nipple!

And here we must digress again from our young man, and consider the psychiatrist's views of sleep and dreams. I have asserted that psychiatry is the study of interpersonal relations. What are the interpersonal relations of one who is asleep? It is true that most people have a relatively short period each night of what we call *deep* sleep, in which there are no evidences of anything personal at work. Most of the time that one is asleep, however, one is engaged in a peculiar kind of interpersonal activity. Now and then the sleeper is awakened by a dream. If you were to ask why he awoke, he might say that he had been frightened by the dream. He may have had a dream attended by terror, or horror, or a danger that grew so threatening that, almost as if by force, he suspended sleep. He woke up, he says, to reassure himself. Perhaps this was not too successful; when wide awake—according to his judgment—the shadows of the dream hung on. The familiar furnishings of the bedroom did not appear. The bureau persisted in being a menacing object. Perhaps he had to rise from bed and walk around before he was again quite at home in his bedroom, quite free from the threat of a resumption of the dream did he but fall asleep again.

Now these are phenomena of dreams, you say. And what are dreams? Dreams are interpersonal phenomena in which the other fellow is wholly illusory, wholly fantastic, a projection, if you please, of certain constructive impulses, or of certain destructiveness, or of certain genital motivations, or something of that kind.

Dreams, we have to assume, are for the purpose of maintaining sleep, and the fact that they fail now and then is not any reflection on the utility and efficacy of dreams, but is an index to the gravity of the situation with which the person is confronted. If one awakes from a terror dream, it is quite certain that one's life situation is treacherous. If one awakes with inexplicable anxiety, it is quite certain that one's life situation includes plenty of cause for anxiety. The fact that he knows nothing about what he dreamed is a suggestion, not an inevitable index, but a strong suggestion that the problem is in the field of something dissociated from the self system, or by the self system, as you will.

This tells us something about dreams. It is quite possible that minor integrating tendencies dissociated from the awareness often discharge themselves predominantly during sleep, and, therefore, the dream-work not only protects the incident of sleep but also helps to maintain adjustment and mental health despite dissociation.

Our boy, in whom the genital lust dynamism is involved in conflict—and some components of which are dissociated—has horrible disturbances of sleep. Either he commits sins in his sleep and awakens feeling ruined, all tired out, or he commits these sins and wakens feeling fine, which again is a sin. More often than that, however, he has no clear sexual dreams.

He has dreams in which he commits atrocious crimes, like his dream of cannibalistic incorporation of the girl's nipple.

How does this come about? Clearly in sleep, in dreams, impulses which in waking life are dissociated make their appearance and play out dramas of interpersonal relations with more or less purely fictitious people. This suggests that in sleep the force which maintains the dissociation in waking life is enfeebled. We say that as the self system was evolved primarily for the maintenance of interpersonal security, since sleep is impossible unless some distinct measure of security exists, it is only natural that the self dynamism might be somewhat in abeyance, somewhat weaker in its manifestations, in sleep, when by definition we will have no contact with a real person—and you will remember that the self was derived from very real people.

Even though this is true, only rather strikingly healthy people have rather explicit, quite simply meaningful, perhaps quite simply constructive, dreams. Most people dream things which, as they recall them on awakening, are fantastic and meaningless.

Some of this is due to the transition from sleep to wakening. The transition from a state of being asleep with some remembered dreams to the state of being awake is a great change in consciousness. One can dream in the most illogical, perhaps, literally in a ruleless, way. When we are conscious, however, we are more or less completely under the sway of the processes of consensually valid communicative thinking that we have had to learn. Therefore, in the very act of changing from one stage of consciousness to another, where different frames of reference are applied, many details of the dream are just too intricate to be fitted into the waking consciousness and they disappear or they get themselves simplified. There is a real barrier in this very transition of consciousness that makes us somewhat obscure in our relation to that which went on when we were asleep.

Besides that, while the self is relatively dormant in sleep it does not disappear, it is a perduring aspect of personality and the dissociated impulses must, by fantastic means in many cases, follow a principle which is very strikingly manifested in the waking life in many of the mental disorders; the character of the interpersonal phenomena which are manifested in sleep is often regressive in the sense that it is of an earlier stage of development.

I have tried to suggest to you that the awareness of the infant is of a very diffuse and unspecified kind. We may, therefore, say that the maximum regression of prehending processes is to a sort of an amorphous universe in which one has one's being—doubtless, a fairly early infantile mental state. If there were necessity, one could revert in dreams to that sort of attack upon one's problems. Seemingly quite insignificant changes in this vague sort of center-of-the-universe picture might mean very great things at the adult day-consciousness level.

Regression is not usually anything like so deep. There is no necessity for such profound recessions. One can drop back from too disturbing a clarity as to what is going on to a time in one's past when any such disturbing clarity had not been comprehended, and actions could go on then which adultly, in our waking state, would mean the satisfaction of a tendency, but which, as we recall the dream, just seem to be sort of childish.

Also, much is made in dreams of a process familiar to the children of many a home. Take the case of the boy caught getting into the jam. And mother says, "Willie, I told you not to touch that jam," and Willie says, "I didn't touch the jam; my hand did."

Also, in dreams one may show some displacing of feeling, and that again is an ancient habit. For example, when one is angry at the teacher who has quite unjustly punished one for somebody else's act, one does not show it, if one is wise and well controlled, but on the way home one can raise hob with some other schoolboy. The affect, you might say, has been carried for a while and deposited on a less dangerous object. And so in dreams, feeling may be moved around so that it does not focus too keenly the alertness on what is actually the case.

These processes occur to enable one to avoid the disturbing anxiety or the feeling of insecurity which will suspend sleep. They usually become notable in the period of adolescence when the problems of adaptation to others become pressing. Let me now proceed to a consideration of adolescents and chronologically adult people as we encounter them.

When we seek to formulate the syndromes [25] of maladjustment or mental disorder we have to consider two fields of data, two somewhat remarkable separate universes of phenomenal completeness, the—to use old-fashioned words—world of the subjective, and the world of the objective.

What does this person, this patient if you please, notice, and what else is there to be noticed by the ideally unhampered observer? The subjective, that which the person himself notices, has always to be communicated to the observer. We have been ingenious in devising apparatus and in refining observational techniques which show that the subject person, the patient, is experiencing something. Thus, for example, we may put a person in the circuit of a very delicate galvanometer, notice the resistance that his skin interposes to the passage of an electric current, and find that when certain stimuli are presented there is an abrupt change in this electrical resistance. It falls rapidly, many thousands of ohms, and we know that this change in skin resistance is intimately, if not absolutely, associated with some change in the integration of the person. Or

[25] The term *syndrome*, literally a concourse or concurrence, means a pattern of phenomena—signs and symptoms—which is frequently encountered, and the abstracting of which from the flux of events is presumed to be based on a valid insight into human life. It is much to be preferred in psychiatry to the term, *disease*. *Mental disorder* may be used, if mental refers to those aspects of living that are manifested in behavior and thought.

we may, with less refinement, have a way of counting the number of breaths which a person takes per minute, and we find that at a certain time this rate of breathing is markedly augmented. We know that at certain times a person stops breathing for a measurable interval. There is a brief inhibition of the impulses which make for breathing. We know that these phenomena mean that something has happened in our patient. And we know, if we have sufficiently refined our own instruments —in this case, our hearing—that there are times in which the tone of the voice loses its rich quality and becomes flat, monotonous as it were, and we know again that this, the moment that it occurs, represents the particular timing of some event in the configuration involving the person.

But all these ingenious instrumental expansions of our senses in interaction with people, and all the acuity which we can develop from long contact with people, tells us only that something has happened. When it comes to testing the validity of our notion as to what has happened our only recourse is to listen for a long time to the reports of the patient as to what seems to him to be going on.

When we do this, we find some very interesting correlations; of a thousand people we find that 942, for example, report that when we said so and so, they experienced so and so. And the instruments in the meanwhile recorded a shift in the resistance of the skin and a change in the breath rhythm. But when it comes to discovering what that person experienced subjectively, what meaning the situation had for him, we have only the report, the attempt to communicate by the use of words and gestures to us, of something that is extraordinarily private.

The facts are that it is only by the skilful use of our most specialized tool of communication that we can seem to overcome the privacy of these so personal worlds. By responsive speech we are able to bridge the gap with inferences of high probability as to what is actually the case.

You may remember in the first hour that I suggested to you

that our perceptions of the physical universe are always separated from that physical universe by the act of perceiving. I went on to say that in the realm of interpersonal relations, the mediation between the personal situation outside us, namely, our idea of that personal situation, is much more complex. We again recur here to this point and suggest that the best that speech—by far our most refined instrument of communication, a tool for relating ourselves meaningfully to another person—can bring about is an understanding of the other person which has high probability of correctness.

High probability of correctness is very different, indeed, from absolute certainty. The moment that one introduces the concept of probability one realizes that it may approach one hundred per cent as a limit, but that it never gets to that limit; that it may approach zero as a limit, but it is never quite that low. Probability is always uncertainty, but it is sometimes very little uncertainty and sometimes very great uncertainty, and to understand the other fellow in his most intimate relationship with us, the best we can achieve is a partial understanding of what is going on. If we are wise and clever, this may have high probability of being correct.

Now the syndromes which are most useful in the diagnosis of personal situations, come more and more clearly to appear to be statements of the past, the momentary present, and the future of the career of the person who is our subject. The career that we are discussing is made up of the events which have connected, now connect, and will presently connect him with the lives of other persons.[26]

[26] The term *diagnosis*—literally a discrimination, and medically a deciding as to the character of the situation before one—is in the study of personality inextricably involved with *prognosis*—literally a foreknowing—the formulation of the probable outcome. Kraepelin's famous classification of the functional psychoses had an all but absolute prognostic slant. Current internal medical diagnosis is more inclined to consider the multiplicity of events that *may* influence the outcome—thus tending to set diagnosis apart from prognosis. Personality problems involve an even greater number of unpredictable factors than do most problems of internal medicine. The use of statistical ex-

These useful syndromes are different from the category of mental and nervous diseases which are taught to the medical student even to this day. They are perhaps somewhat more like the statements about this and that one which are heard in the privacy of the home, among intimate friends. The point we make here is that the ancient preoccupation of psychiatrists was a diagnosis of mental disorder, which had every now and then to be revised. From this field, the interest has moved on to considerations of how people could be classified. All that is out of sympathy with the central view of this series of lectures, to the effect that the subject of psychiatry is the study of inter-personal relations. Dementia præcox, schizophrenia, neuras-thenia—these things are the privilege of the person who has them, in blissful separation from any suggestion of the social communality. The symptoms are ordinarily discussed as if they are static characteristics of a thing, very different indeed from statements about "How does Mr. A. act with Mr. B.?" "What goes on in the situation integrated between Mr. A. and Mr. B.?"

As I say, as one shifts the emphasis in psychiatry from the study of alleged personalities with alleged disorders to that which beyond any doubt is scientifically accessible; namely, what goes on in the situation with this person, then this panoply of neurasthenia, dementia præcox, anxiety neuroses, and so on, fade out of the picture. The picture becomes somewhat simpler and at times much more complex.

It becomes somewhat simpler in that one is relieved of the necessity of maintaining a God-like objectivity as if literally from an ivory tower. It becomes much more complex because one really has to notice what is going on and to derive some

---

perience as a basis for prognostic formulations is, therefore, a very dubious performance.

It is well-known among physicians that all persons suffering tuberculous meningitis die. A patient at the Sheppard and Enoch Pratt Hospital, so diagnosed by three outstanding internists—and confirmed by the laboratory—recovered. The internists became unhappy about their diagnosis. The patient has been doing well for ten years.

inferences at to the past, the present and the future of the career-line from these participantly observed events.

If I say neurasthenia is a condition characterized by pain in the neck, great readiness for fatigue, and preoccupation with fancied disorders, often of the genitals, which cannot be explained on any organic basis, the medical man feels that he has been told something useful to him. If I say that as a student of personality I cannot find any virtue in the conception, neurasthenia, that is another matter, much less satisfying.

The person who has an acute belly-ache followed by a feeling of extreme sickness, great anxiety, fear of death, and so on, calls the family physician, who takes his temperature and a blood specimen, pokes him around, hits some very tender spots in the abdomen and says, "Johnny, you have appendicitis." Johnny is greatly relieved to hear this word "appendicitis." It is not entirely a matter of verbal magic, if you please. When the doctor says, "Oh, this is appendicitis," this indicates that the doctor knows what he is talking about. Even if the patient is very much worried, here is the doctor, representative of medical science, who regards the thing much as he regards the weather—it is clearly not anything to be much excited about.

The new viewpoint of psychiatry teaches us that we cannot parallel the performances implied in the medical diagnosis, and, however enthusiastic the patient or his relatives may be about having a scientific name for the trouble, we must discontinue the finalist performances by which, for example, we have been classifying large groups of our fellows who are chronic inhabitants of mental hospitals. They are there. Something is the matter with them, but we should no longer feel happy because we have applied a label to them.

The first group of our syndromes pertain to the relatively uninterrupted career-lines of people; the second group, to more or less clearly episodic changes in direction. The first group, therefore, appear to be diagnoses of personality; the second, of disorders of personality. Actually, the first group refer to degrees of development and the second to a blend of the developmental factors with the vicissitudes of the person in his communal existence with others.

We have seen how the culture in which we chance to live comes finally to have great prescriptive power over our thoughts and behavior, not only because other people, the carriers of the culture, thwart, humiliate, punish and reward us, and facilitate our securing satisfaction and maintaining a sense of personal security, but finally in preadolescence and adolescence because some of these other people become highly significant to us.

Our first syndrome is made up of phenomena which appear at first sight to contradict these considerations. There are people among us whose integration of interpersonal situations is chiefly characterized by lack of duration. These people live through a great number of fugitive, fleeting, involvements with other people—and even with the more tangible of the institutions of the particular society in which they have their being. They are disappointing to everyone who is interested in them. They are themselves always disappointed in other people—but this does not make them bitter, nor does it excite them to inquiry as to what may be the matter. Without troubling to think it out, they exemplify the saying that all the world is queer, except . . . . They move through life giving many of the appearances of human beings; they just miss being human—and they do not lack fluency in verbal behavior. They almost always say the right thing. They often say it well. But it signifies very little.

The striking things about these people are their inability to profit from what we would consider to be their experience, and their disregard for the future. The intelligence factor is not involved. They experience life differently from others and their insight into reality is correspondingly different. Not only is it different, but it is far more imperfect than the average.

Here and now may be grasped quite well. The past is vague and the future is of no real interest.

These are the non-integrative, the so-called *psychopathic*, personalities [27] who are superlative in social nuisance value and of great theoretical interest for psychiatry. This latter interest arises from their peculiarly qualified insight into their personal reality—and that of others—which implies an extraordinary peculiarity of their self dynamism. It is so difficult and disconcerting to deal with them that but little valuable data has been accumulated.[28] I believe that the first essential in a research in this field is the application of the techniques used in the study of anthropoids. This will give us useful clues towards the elucidation of language behavior in the psychopath, and thus we may come to unravel their relatively vestigial self.

Secondly, in these syndromes, we come upon the *self-absorbed*, or fantastic person. To those of you who are given to reading about psychoanalysis, this is the person whose relations with others and with the more objective institutions of society are shot through with "wishful thinking"—for me, a difficult concept.

The prototype of these people is to be sought in early childhood. To make this clear, I must say something as to the prehension [29] and perception of significant people, as we conceive

[27] Comment on two patients of the category appears in Regression: . . . *State Hospital Quart.* (1926) 11:208–217, 387–394, and 651–668. The (1925) view expressed in footnote 13 is in part erroneous. An "unconsciously determined inability to profit from experience" is now seen to be equivalent to *biological* defect. The factors of personality exterior to awareness do not arrange difficulties of this sort; the self dynamism is the 'part' that interferes.

[28] Kraepelin classified psychopathic personalities under seven rubrics: the excitable; the unstable; the impulsive; the egocentric; the liars and swindlers; the antisocial; and the quarrelsome. Eugen Kahn—*Psychopathic Personalities* [tr. by H. F. Dunbar]; New Haven, Yale University Press, 1931 (521 pp.)—has a most elaborate classification, some of which doubtless pertains to the people whom I am discussing. See in particular, Partridge, George E., Current Conception of Psychopathic Personality. *Amer. J. Psychiatry* (1930) 10[o.s. 87]:53–99. See, also, Henderson, David K., *Psychopathic States;* New York, Norton, 1939 (178 pp.); and Partridge, George E., A Study of 50 Cases of Psychopathic Personality. *Amer. J. Psychiatry* (1928) 7[o.s. 84]:953–973.

[29] To prehend is to have potential information or misinformation about

them to develop in infancy. The nipple is probably first prehended as a part of one's vague cosmic entity. It gradually stands out as an attribute of the Good Mother. There gradually evolves another complexus of impressions which—because of the empathic linkage—is the Bad Mother. Objectively, to us, the person concerned is the mother; to the infant, these are two vaguely limited but entirely distinct people. The discrimination of the Good Mother pattern of events and the Bad Mother pattern of events constitutes a primary bifurcation of interpersonal experience, evidences of which persist in most people, throughout life.

In later infancy there is a synthesis of experience which dulls this primary discrimination and gradually evolves an adequate perception of the mother as a person who is sometimes good— giving satisfactions and security—and sometimes bad. The fantasies of childhood show, however, that the earlier formulations have not disintegrated. For that matter, many of the puzzling excesses in the child's emotional reactions arise from the continuance of these dynamic factors. But for practical purposes, the child has learnt that mother is not as good as was the lost Good Mother, nor as bad as the other one. There is loss and gain.

The loss, being a privation, is more vivid than is the gain. I believe that we can safely read back into these early times, the usual ways of dealing with irreparable losses of this kind; and if so, we may feel sure that constructive fantasy appears only after mere representative fantasy has worn itself out. The child fogs the undesirable aspects of mother with recollections of the Good Mother; thus reinstating security and satisfaction enough to sleep in peace and to remedy slights and frustrations. This gradually fades from waking life, as better adaptations to the more real mother are invented. It probably persists in the preliminary stages of falling asleep.

---

something; to perceive is to have information or misinformation in or readily accessible to awareness.

In people who show our self-absorbed type of perform-ances, however, the element of representative fantasy continues as a major ingredient of life. All sorts of interpersonal prehensions are fogged into what is called 'wishful' distortions or misinformation about people. These people have no grey; everything tends to be black *or* white. Their friends are simply wonderful people. People whom they dislike are just simply impossible. Their "love" is melodramatic to a degree that confounds its object—excepting the object be another self-absorbed person. Together, by a sustained miracle of accommodating—or ignoring—the individualistic misconceptions of each other, two of these folk can have quite a good time. With the rest of us, however, they are apt to be disappointed, wounded, misunderstood. And we, if we care to study the processes at work, cannot but marvel at the failure of learning which has left their capacity for fantastic, self-centered, illusion so utterly unaffected by a life-long series of educative events. These people integrate situations with foggy embodiments projected upon us from their fantasies about themselves.

Let us now look at a type of organization which represents less blandly a cosmic centering in the person concerned. We shall call this syndrome of characteristics that of the *incorrigible* person, choosing this none too satisfactory term for the reason that these people have actively evaded or resisted the educative influences that in more fortunate people lead to a more practical organization of the self dynamism. I may suggest their characteristics by saying that they integrate more durable situations only with people whom they regard as their inferiors. Towards all others, their basic attitude is hostile, unfriendly, or morose and forbidding. It is clear that these people have a grave defect in the field of security; often inculcated by a parent who just would not be satisfied with the child.

The syndrome makes clear appearance in the juvenile development. These young folk cannot progress to the stage of give-and-take, of competition and self-satisfying compromise.

The incorrigible person does not attack the really strong. He has failed in the most significant of efforts to overcome dissatisfaction with him. The scar of this failure remains and he is forewarned from contests that might renew the pain. Authority—paradigmatic of the disapproving parent—is anathema to him, but to smooth-working, competent, authority he interposes no objection. To authority that is exercised with any uncertainty, any irrational contradictions, any 'stupidity,' the incorrigible person is intolerant and intolerable. If he is intelligent, he shows a genius for finding defects in the exercise of social controls, and for making trouble about it. He is a thorn in the side of teachers. From school, he proceeds into the larger world, to put "stuffed shirts" where they belong.

The fourth syndrome that I shall present you is the *negativistic* person. These are the people, to keep to our earlier figure, who have no black or white, but only grey. They are in many ways antithetic to the self-absorbed person; their selves are organized on the basis of appraisals that make them insignificant—until their constructive fantasy hit upon negation as a device for forcing notice if not approval. If mother says "It's time for little Willie to go to bed" and little Willie goes; that is one thing. It may be but one of unnumbered brushings of little Willie out of the way. If now, instead of going to bed, little Willie says "No" and reinforces his non-cooperation with all means at his disposal, his significance in his world may become at least briefly, very great.

I shall not digress to consider various reactions to the child's negation: the submersion in "sweetness and light," the submission to tantrums, and so on and so forth. I wish rather to indicate the typical negativistic syndrome which has its origin in the discovery that it is better to be a problem child than a mere necessary evil.

Insecurity in the negativistic is met with an assertion of refusal. If such a person feels any tendency towards minimizing him or taking him for granted, he resists a suggestion, or refutes a statement, or differs with an opinion, or in some other nugatory way accentuates his significance in the interpersonal situation. If he is keenly insecure, he may be simply uncooperative in everything, to such an extent that the other fellow can but go away.

The negativistic way of life is apt to be highly educative, and it thus comes about that many prevailingly negativistic people get to be quite expert in some field—even that of conciliation. Being highly competent, it is no longer necessary to feel insecure in situations in which they are recognized as the expert, and their long experience with divergent views comes in handy.

It was necessary for me to present the negativistic category before mentioning a syndrome of the interpersonal phenomena which is in many ways a super-incorrigibility, and in some ways a super-negativism. This, our fifth syndrome, I shall call that of *the stammerer*. These people make use of vocal behavior—or misbehavior—not for communication but for defiance and domination. They have discovered a magic of articulate sounds that really works. By demonstrating their inability to produce a word—and to desist from effort at producing it —they immobilize the other person and arrest the flow of process in the world. This is a power operation of no mean proportions. It represents a grave disorder of development at the time when sheerly magic operations were being abandoned and the consensual validation of verbal behavior was beginning. The disorder of speech is but one of several striking phenomena in this syndrome, about which, however, I shall say no more at this point.

It is to be noted that these first five of our syndromes are of early origin in the development of personality. They all come from the time of predominantly autistic verbal behavior. They are deviations of growth that are not chiefly a result of verbal communication between parent and child, teacher and pupil. They occur before the mediate acculturation of the

juvenile era, which includes, among many other important ac-
complishments, the learning of things through the written and
printed form of the language; and in particular, learning about
legendary people who embody ideals, mores, and norms of the
particular culture-complex.

One learns, for example, of Hans Brinker's feats. We learn
of him through the mediation of speech, but he becomes an
immediate ingredient of our thinking. We do not expect to
meet him, as we did Uncle Herbert; but he is just as significant.
He more or less adequately represents, perhaps by his very ab-
stractness, his purely traditional existence, traits of character
that are praiseworthy. As something greater and less than life,
Hans Brinker becomes a denizen of the self.

The syndromes that present distortions of development after
this spread of acculturation are of a greater complexity than
are the first five. I shall present them in the order of complexity,
which is naturally the order of developmental stage chiefly
concerned in each.

The sixth syndrome may be called the *ambition-ridden* personality. These people have to use everyone with whom they
are integrated. If you are no good for advancing his interest,
the ambition-ridden person can find someone who is, with
whom to enjoy whatever other satisfaction he had been having
in your company. Some of them are scrupulous about some
ideals, some of them are almost wholly unscrupulous. Some
are clever at avoiding dangerous competition; some have to
compete with everybody. Your personal experience will fill
in this picture, for there is no dearth of these folk among us.

We come to a seventh syndrome, the *asocial*. Please note
that the term is asocial, not antisocial. Antisocial is a nuisance-
word which carries a penumbra of confusion: it is used indis-
criminately to refer to the asocial, the incorrigible, and the
psychopathic. The asocial are by no manner of means brigands,
criminals, or people who are always rude without provocation.
Many asocial people are among the more delightful folks I

have known. They are the people whose integrations with others are assumed by them to be of no special moment *to* the other person, and to be of the duration of his convenience only. Some of them show considerable error of judgment as to the other fellow's convenience, being as we say, so sensitive that they are put off by quite insignificant things and withdraw long before one would lose them. Some of them are quite obtuse and drift along with us long after we have been discouraged as to the possibility of intimacy with them.

They may be thought to be extraordinarily lacking in self-esteem, and in one way this is quite correct. They often esteem themselves, quite properly, quite highly—many of them are competent people. But they have not grasped the possibility that they themselves may be valued, cherished, by others. All that category of experience is missing from their self dynamism. The approvals which are incorporated are chiefly the products of mediate acculturation, and not of direct early experience. It is not strange, therefore, that these people often have highly formulated and rigidly held ideals of behavior. This does not exempt them from loneliness, and many of them have no difficulty in overlooking shortcomings in themselves and others with whom they have relations.

For an eighth syndrome, we may consider the *inadequate person*, including under this rubric all those people who integrate situations of dependency with others, and the people who derive their feeling of personal significance from identification with some extravagantly over-valued 'cause.' Some of these people have been obedient children of a dominating parent. They go on through life needing a strong person to make decisions for them. Some of them learned their helplessness and clinging-vine adaptation from a parental example. Some of them took over a justifying invalidism from a similar source.

A ninth syndrome may be named the *homosexual*, although this term has accumulated so great a freight of misunderstanding that I could wish for something less ambiguous. These are the people whose earlier experience has erected a barrier to integrations with persons of the other sex. The barrier may be relative or absolute. It may be highly specific in regard of the type of situation concerned, or it may be quite general—as in the 'woman hater' who really dislikes the presence of any woman. We would say that his barrier was absolute and general in its effect. We encounter men who preferred to play with girls, in the juvenile era, and whose most enjoyable companionship is still with women but who cannot integrate sexual situations with them. We encounter men who have no use for women except for integrating sexual situations with them— and, believe me, these situations include nothing of love. I need not say that parallel deviations appear in women, though the cultural definitions of rôle adds and subtracts features from the phenomena that we encounter.

Some of these people, in preadolescence or later, learn to integrate sexual situations with persons of their own sex. Some of these are relations of love, and are stable and durable. Some are devoid of love and are very transient. Some are relations of hatred, durable or otherwise as the determining circumstances dictate.

Many of these people discharge their lustful impulses by self-manipulation, with or without explicit fantasy of another person. Some of them depend chiefly on processes that go on in sleep. A marginal group follows the heterosexual pattern of genital behavior with women of a particularly highly differentiated type, and some of these integrations are relationships of love, and wholly durable.

Our tenth syndrome, the last that I shall indicate, is really a congeries of syndromes, but it has enough of consistency to merit its title of the *chronically adolescent*. These are the people who never find the right love object. Some of them are driven by lust, and go on seeking the right person, always disappointed with anyone who has been available. Some of them become cynical and adopt lustful performances as an ideal indoor sport. Some of them are celibate, withdrawn from genital behavior, and—as I said earlier—in real danger as to personal stability. They all pursue the ideal and they find it not.

These are some of the more outstanding diagnostic syndromes which appear in the series of interpersonal relations through which one passes. They tell us of the past and permit shrewd guesses—predictions of high probability—as to the future integrations which the person will show. More significant for the clinical practice of psychiatry, they provide the meaning for otherwise mystifying episodes that occur in the lives of those who experience mental disorder. For the broader aspects of psychiatry, they are reference-frames for understanding what will and what will not work, in connection with a particular person.

LECTURE
IV

Explanatory Conceptions

IT HAS been said that the history of mankind depicts a spiral progress; the course of events returns at increasing interval to the neighborhood of the starting point.[30] There is more than a little evidence in favor of such a view regarding the history of each person's ideas, and from this I must hope for justification for taking you back now to yet another sojourn along the co-ordinate of individual physiology. I have now to point out that the pursuit of satisfactions and the maintenance of security—the great motors of human behavior and thought—have physiological substrates that must be considered in any attempt at explaining states of mental disorder or maladjustment.

The rôle of muscle tissue in adjustment is rather obvious when the moving of material objects is concerned. Muscles contract and do work in moving the bones and the tissues they support. That is rudimentary. But what of the continuing tension or *tonus* of each muscle? Some muscles are never completely relaxed; most muscles are in a state of considerable tonus throughout our periods of deepest sleep. Moreover, this tonus

[30] C. Delisle Burns—*The Horizon of Experience;* New York, Norton, 1936 (372 pp.)—shows a table of the rhythm of development of the Western civilization: new horizons, 800–400 B.C.; Greek-Roman System, 400 B.C.–A.D. 400; new horizons [the Dark Ages], A.D. 400–800; Medieval System, A.D. 800–1400; new horizons, A.D. 1400–1600; Renaissance System A.D. 1600–1900; and new horizons, A.D. 1900–. He remarks that the rate of rhythm seems to become shorter. "But the Renaissance System, with which we are familiar, is really only a continuance of the Medieval, as the Roman was of the Greek. The only breakdown as great as ours was that of A.D. 400–800, the Dark Ages."

changes rather generally throughout the major muscular systems of the body, without direct relationship to demands for work and movement. A person who is tense—has rather high tone in the skeletal musculature—on laughing in amusement, undergoes a swift and general reduction of this tonus. A person who is engaged in friendly conversation, unexpectedly severely criticized, undergoes a rapid increase in the tone of most of the skeletal muscles. This clearly has something to do with one's feeling of comfort and discomfort.

The facts seem to indicate that tonic changes in the unstriped, involuntary, muscles of the viscera—the internal organs of the body—are, from birth onward, intimately related to the experiencing of desires, needs for satisfaction. Heightened tone of the stomach wall is called out by depletion of our chemical supplies, and the occurrence of vigorous contractions in these tense muscles gives rise to the 'pangs of hunger.' The taking of food—the ingestion of which probably leads to a release of nutritive substance stored in the liver—promptly relieves the excess tone and the contractions quiet down to the churning of the stomach contents. Hunger, in a way of speaking, is from the first influx of food, more a matter of the oral dynamism than of the stomach. In infants, at least, once this dynamism has discharged itself, alertness disappears, vigilance is withdrawn from circumambient reality, and sleep supervenes. Throughout life the pursuit of satisfactions is physiologically provoked by increased tone in some unstriped muscles; and the securing of the satisfactions is a relaxation of this tone, with a tendency towards the diminution of attention, alertness, and vigilance, and an approach to sleep.

In this satisfaction-securing behavior, the striped, skeletal, muscles are of relatively instrumental value. They do what is necessary and then relax. This picture is adequate for the earlier phases of untroubled infancy. It is no longer relevant when acculturation has come to include prohibitions and disapprovals.

When the infant begins to need security—primarily a security from noxious emotional states empathized from the personal environment—the skeletal muscles take on a new function. The oral dynamism has been the channel for performances needed to appease hunger—and pain and other discomforts. It may be presumed that its function in emitting the cry has been quite automatic. This may not have worked too well, and delayed response to the cry may be one of the first experiences that tend to focus alertness. But in any case, the oral dynamism is not now effective in securing relief from the discomfort set up by empathy; on some occasions, it is simply ineffectual, and on other occasions, its activity is accompanied by increase of the empathized discomfort. This leads gradually to a differentiation of empathized from other discomforts, and to the *inhibition* of the cry as a universal tool. The inhibiting of a complex pattern of behavior is not as simple as was its automatic initiation. Some of the movements are cut off, but the increase of tone in the appropriate muscles may not be inhibited. The experience of empathized hostility, or unfriendly prohibition, or, as it later comes to be observed, a forbidding gesture, becomes colored by and associated with heightened tone in some striped muscles—at first those concerned with the cry.

The course of acculturation, in so far as it pertains to toilet habits, is also a learning to suffer increasing tension in the bladder and rectum, and to resist the automatic relaxation of the sphincter muscles concerned in retaining the urine and feces. Failures in this are often accompanied by empathized discomfort, and success is often the occasion of empathized comfort—which is added to the satisfaction from relief of the tension.

The whole course of acculturation is replete with forbidding gestures and indications of approval. The forbidding gestures—scowls, frowns, expressions of embarrassments, certain tones of voice, certain variations in enunciation, for example—inspire a feeling of insecurity and the self comes into being in learning to avoid the acts which provoke them—and in performing the acts which bring about approval or, at least, cause no disapproval. The parents' and other older people's "patterns of behavior-toward-a-child are generally far from simple; their restraints and facilitations of behavior are usually much less adequate than is the case in their interpersonal relations with compeers. All too generally they inculcate a great deal that is incoherent and incapable of unitary integration. Almost universally they encourage the continuance of autistic-magical processes in the field of speech behavior—'You are a naughty boy; say that you are sorry,' for example, includes being-naughty as an addition to conceptual 'me' that has its real basis in empathized hostile-disapproving attitudes of the authoritarian individual, with somatic heightenings of muscle tonus; while saying-I-am-sorry comes to have the power of reducing or dissipating the hostile-disapproving attitude, without in any way undoing the activity which comes presently to be seen to be the exciting cause for the disapproval. When one considers how much of this sort of thing almost every child experiences, it does not seem so peculiar (or inevitable) that, while some considerable proportion of our people develop aptitudes for manipulating machinery and scientific concepts in a practical way, very few people show much 'sense' in interpersonal relations, and almost everyone deals with other people with a wonderful blend of magic, illusions, and incoherent irrelevancy. Childhood is the incubator of man's evil genius for rationalizing, a special aspect of the delusion of unique individuality which is necessitated by the peculiar limitations of conceptual 'me' and 'you' as a governor of one's perceptions, a reference frame that determines the accessibility of one's experience to awareness."

"One has information only to the extent that one has tended to communicate one's states of being, one's experience."

"Much of the child's life goes on without any necessity for

alertness. Needs call out adjustive movements and achieve satisfactions without particular attention from the authorities, and therefore without implicit or explicit communicative processes. They tend to be unnoticed, to remain outside of the realm of information and misinformation, outside of the growing elaboration of conceptual 'me' and 'you.' These adjustive performances are a part of the experience of the organism, are a part of the growth process, and contribute, like all other experience, to the refinement and differentiation of behavior of the individual. But they are a part of experience the memory of which is not readily accessible to subsequent states of awareness. As one proceeds toward adulthood one's more lucid states of consciousness tend more and more completely to be concerned with experiences definitely involving the conceptual 'me' and 'you'—experiences about which there has been at least a tendency to communicate. It is usual to be able to recall a great deal of one's experience of which one was clearly aware at the time it occurred; it generally requires a special set of circumstances, a peculiarly characterized interpersonal situation, to provoke the mnemonic reproduction of previously unnoticed experience." [31]

The psychiatrist, as he listens to his informant, "must realize that he is participating in speech behavior that pertains chiefly to the conceptual 'me' and 'you,' with corresponding manifestation of the factors that have distorted and continue to complicate the interpersonal relations of the subject personality. As one who speaks, he is keenly aware that he is using linguistic processes in a configuration in which the hearer enters most significantly into the outcome of the attempt at communication.

"In the interpersonal contexts through which the writer has passed, it is recurrently necessary to dissipate the importance

[31] Sullivan, Harry Stack. A Note on the Implications of Psychiatry . . . . for Investigations in the Social Sciences. *Amer. J. Sociol.* (1937) 42:848-861. The quotations that follow are also from this paper.

of statements allegedly indicative of various aspects of reality, but actually far too complex to accomplish anything more than self-deception of the speaker. Some insight has developed as to the function performed by uncommunicative, unintelligible, and misleading statements in allegedly communicative interpersonal contexts. These have been observed to occur when the integration is *parataxic*; [32] that is, when, besides the interpersonal situation as defined within the awareness of the speaker, there is a concomitant interpersonal situation quite different as to its principal integrating tendencies, of which the speaker is more or less completely unaware.

"Besides the two-group integrated of psychiatrist and subject there is in the parataxic situations also an illusory two-group integrated of psychiatrist-distorted-to-accommodate-a-special-'you'-pattern and subject-reliving-an-earlier-unresolved - integration - and - manifesting - the - corresponding - special-'me'-pattern. The shift of communicative processes from one to another of these concomitant integrations may be frequent or only occasional; in any case, the alertness of the speaker is usually sufficient to insure the weaving of word patterns and other linguistic elements into grammatical speech. There, therefore, ensues an apparently coherent discussion, and one usually rather clearly addressed to the hearer." [33]

This is a succinct expression of the theory; I wish now to expand various of its terms. The performances of a person arise from a complex of factors, and our observation of these performances is influenced by our own previous experience. When we talk professionally with a person—whom I shall now call 'the patient'—the speech behavior occurs in a situation including the two of us and an indefinite and shifting group of illu-

[32] This term, I believe, was first utilized in a psychiatric sense by Dom Thomas V. Moore, M.D., The Parataxes. *Psychoanalytic Rev.* (1921) 7:252–283.

[33] This conception is made much more explicit in *Psychiatry: Introduction to the Study of Interpersonal Relations* Chapter I. The Data of Psychiatry. PSYCHIATRY (1938) 1:121–134.

sions and impressions as to each other. The patient, newly come to me, is strongly influenced by his impression as to what a psychiatrist is like, and by statements told him about me. If he observes no surprising discrepancy between his expectation and the person he finds, he will proceed on these implicit assumptions. I cannot know what they are, but I must discover them as best I can. Otherwise, I shall have little or no valid basis for observing the interpersonal processes and formulating an impression of the complexities in them which constitute his maladjustment or mental disorder.

It is often useful to inquire as to what brought him to me; who advised it, and for what purpose. If he comes from someone well-known to me, I may have a shrewd guess as to what was said about me. That is by no means a knowledge of the expectation created in the patient—the elements of his previous experience and his relationship with the referring person are complicating factors. If, however, he says "Dr. A. said that I had schizophrenia and that you were the person to cure me of it," I have certain surmises which can be tested almost at once. I surmise that his term, schizophrenia, is almost entirely autistic; I surmise either that Dr. A. is misquoted as to the 'cure,' or that Dr. A. produced a dubious impression as to his honesty. This last surmise arises from the fact that I know that Dr. A. does not believe that a schizophrenic state can progress to recovery.

One can now go on to uncovering the *noticed* difficulties of the patient in his relations with others. The autistic term, 'schizophrenia,' may be a useful fixed point in the shifting field of our discourse. Its appearance preceded our integration and connects the present with the time before consulting Dr. A. I seek an impression of that time by inquiring as to what took the patient to see Dr. A. Let us suppose that he replies "My father took me; he thought something was the matter with me." I then inquire "And what made him think so?" The patient states that he does not know, but "Father said I was acting funny; I know I didn't want to go out of the house." Had there been any marked change here; did his dislike for leaving the house appear suddenly? He guesses so, he hated to have people stare at him, so he stayed at home. Why did people stare at him? He does not know—and is obviously keenly uncomfortable. Were they acquaintances or strangers? He rather morosely says he does not know. I comment, looking at him, that I see no reason why people should stare at him. In most cases, at this point, he will either show relief from tension or show suspicion of my good faith.

The manner in which my remarks are made may perhaps be suggested if I state certain of the preconceptions that underlie the psychiatric interview. First, the patient is a stranger and is to be treated as a stranger. There is every reason for his being here; but there is no reason whatever for presuming on any friendly or unfriendly attitude. He comes to an alleged expert whose expertness is to show itself, if at all, *in uncovering the processes at work in the patient's relations with others—*not in omniscience, omnipotence, magical reassurance, persuasion, or exhortation.

Secondly, the interrogation proceeds in so far as possible from a given point in a direction easy for the patient to follow. If he cannot foresee the direction of inquiry, his responses lose known orientation and become relatively uninterpretable. If, on foreseeing the direction, there are shifts in his bodily tensions, their source is not wholly private. Consider, in our example, the substitution of "Did people stare at you," or "What made you think that people were staring at you," for the question "Why did people stare at you." The first is thoroughly disconcerting, thoroughly disorganizing to the direction of inquiry. Suppose I ask you your age, and, having been told, ask if it is so, or why you think it is so. The patient has clearly shown his belief—or his intention that I shall understand—that people stared at him. I am in no position to contradict this, even if I wished to do so. Moreover, he is probably in no condition to yield his conviction, or his intention that I shall share it.

It is not by any means just a misapprehension on his part, to be brushed aside by some feeble conversational magic. The father probably wore out his patience in just such attempts at "reasoning" with his son. Also, the disruption of our directed inquiry would put us back at the beginning, if in fact it did not awaken grave suspicions in him about me.

A third preconception underlying the interrogation is to the effect that little can be learned as to 'what manner of man is this' by direct questioning. If I ask a person if he believes in evolution, he is apt to answer generically 'Yes,' 'No,' or 'What?'. This tells me nothing. If he elaborates his answer, I *may* catch on to—develop insight into—what the term, evolution, means to him, and as to the complicating beliefs that he also entertains. The result, in dealing with a stranger, is much more certainly obtained by other devices; namely, the synthesis of indicative statements that have been made by him in highly personal references, rather than in discussion of abstract concepts. By and large, one's beliefs in abstract concepts are far from guiding principles in interpersonal relations. Consider the widespread belief in forgiving offenses and injuries, and the parallel faith in the magic of apology.

Many of the positive statements volunteered by an informant require testing by an inquiry into his supporting ideation. Our patient may say, "People stare at me because I am so ugly." If I find him remarkably unattractive in appearance, I may be inclined to accept this as an unfortunate idea based on all too real a foundation. Suppose, however, that I am true to my presupposition; without denial or affirmation, seek to uncover the patient's views as to his personal appearance; and learn that, to him, his significant ugliness consists in a change that has recently taken place in his mouth, such that his lips have become Negroid. This matters; my reference-frame for pulchritude is simply irrelevant.

A fourth preconception is the general dynamic view of interpersonal relations. Nothing is static, everything changes—

changes in velocity or changes in organization. In the psychiatric interview, we expect, we desire, and we must if possible
quickly perceive, changes in the organization of the interpersonal situation. This is additional to the changes in direction and the speed of interpersonal processes. The organization
of the situation changes as some of the parataxic elements
change. The possibility of such a change appeared, for example, when I said to our patient that I saw no reason for people's staring at him. He grew less tense—his security increased
—because I enfeebled a shadowy conviction that I was experiencing the alleged factor making for staring. Or he grew
suspicious—more tense and less secure—because a conviction
appeared to the effect that I was trying to deceive him. The
situation was simplified in the first case; complicated in the second.

A fifth preconception may be illustrated at this point. One
assumes that everyone is much more simply human than unique,
and that no matter what ails the patient, he is *mostly* a person
like the psychiatrist. This implies that a great many of the
techniques of interpersonal performance continue to be just
as applicable here as elsewhere. I am not pleased by the shift of
our situation towards greater complexity. I 'discourage' the
suspiciousness of me, not by some omniscient "aha! so you now
distrust me," but by showing irritation. The discouraging is
really our old friend, the forbidding gesture, which communicates more in a moment than any bright remarks would in an
hour; with the great advantage that it does not require formulation by the patient—he does not have to 'think'. The irritation is communicated by a change of voice. I ask in a less neutral and somewhat unfriendly manner "Perhaps you can say
something about it [the staring]?" If this fails, we are at an
impasse in this attempt. One then picks up a new line of approach.

Another preconception is to the effect that, in an indefinite
field, one accommodates to the apparent prevailing tendencies.

When, in other words, my patient will say nothing further about the cause of the staring and is obviously unfriendly, I accept the fact that this line of inquiry is for the present ended. I have been defeated in an inquiry and it is important that I avoid any irrational performance called out by the rebuff. I do not retire with an Olympian "Oh, very well; it is of no moment." I do not punish with some "Well, it's your loss, if you can't talk." I do not fold my psychic hands in mute acceptance of a juvenile 'the patient will not cooperate.' I have shown irritation in an effort to disintegrate the new hostile parataxis. I take up another line of inquiry, but I hold the expression of irritation until we are moving along a new line—until there is a simple human reason for changing.[34]

The seventh and last of the preconceptions which I shall mention bears directly on the growth of information about oneself—or *in* one's self dynamism. In general, one cannot accomplish good by increasing a patient's anxiety. Any question, and in particular, any explanatory statement—interpretation—that arouses anxiety is apt to prove worse than useless. At the same time, we must come to formulations that are of rather high probability. This means that the patient must obtain new insight into himself, for otherwise the psychiatrist has no confirmation of his surmises and they are therapeutically quite useless.

The preconception to which I am leading is this: personality tends towards the state that we call mental health or interpersonal adjustive success, handicaps by way of acculturation notwithstanding. The basic direction of the organism is forward. Regardless of the warp incorporated in the self, the psychiatrist, given sufficient insight and skill, may expect favorable changes to ensue from his study of the patient's situation. The disappointing outcomes and the difficulty encountered in successful

[34] The patient, too, knows that I am more simply human and like him than different. He has experienced innumerable impostures and has been 'taken in' by many of them; but his like everyone's efforts at communication imply the conviction of similarity, and the less this conviction is strained, the better.

therapy are referable to the culture-conditioned selves concerned—the patient's self, the psychiatrist's self, and the other selves that are significant in the course of the therapeutic situation. Some people are ill-equipped for life by defect of ability—particularly the intelligence factor. If now they have been trained to expect some day to be President, the maladjustment which they present may be prohibitively difficult of attack—primarily because of difficulty of communication, and of elaborating information. Some people have been educated and otherwise acculturated for life in a social order that has swiftly undergone profound change after they had reached chronological adulthood. For these, there may no longer be enough probable lifetime for the great reorganization that is necessitated by the new order. Somewhat parallel to this is the case of the person who for years has lived a simplified existence as a patient in an institution for the mentally disordered. For many of these, the social order has changed so much, while they were out of touch with it, that the reintegration from regressive change is discouraged. But these are exceptional situations, far from the case of most people who seek psychiatric help, and far indeed from the case of those who might benefit from the wider utilization of psychiatry.[35]

Having again said something of handicaps arising from or otherwise related to acculturation, it may be wise at this point to remind you that acculturation is necessary for the human estate. Growth implies incorporation of chemical substances

[35] To minimize their misunderstanding this conception, let me recast it—as far as possible—in the terms used by (Freudian) psychoanalysts. This conception denies categorically the possibility of a death instinct. Excepting in so far as cultural conditioning may lead indirectly to injury or destruction of the person, it questions any explanation of phenomena in terms of a drive towards self-destruction. It states that only the energy of the Id impulses is available for maintaining the therapeutic situation and for overcoming the difficulties encountered in therapy—the 'resistance' and the 'repetition compulsion.'

Therapeutic results are the expansion of the self dynamism and the simplification of living which results from this. I shall not attempt to express this in terms of the Ego and the Super-ego. I have not found these conceptions useful in formulating problems.

for the somatic organization, and of cultural entities for the personality. Deficiencies in either field may be disastrous. Noxious entities may be incorporated from either field. The body, at birth, has some capacity for selective relationship with environing physico-chemical entities; this capacity is, however, tenuous and increases greatly during infancy and childhood. The personality also, in the beginning, may be presumed to have certain limiting capacities. We have seen how the self comes presently to govern its own growth. Some people grow up in environments deficient in iodine, and, therefore, are distorted in the fashion that we call cretinism. Some people grow up in environments the other people of which are deficient in self-respect, and, therefore, are distorted in the fashion that I have called hateful. But certain chemicals are necessary for the continuance of life itself, and some culture is necessary for the appearance of humanness. Deficiencies and incongruities in acculturation are the handicaps, not acculturation itself.

To carry this parallelism a bit further; as a person seeks within varying limits to correct deficiencies in diet, so also one seeks for experience which will correct his deficiencies in acculturation. This is another way of saying that there is a tendency to achieve mental health.

Also, as the evil effects of dietary deficiencies appear so insidiously that they often remain undiagnosed until some intercurrent disorder brings them to light, so too the evils of personality handicap are usually revealed by a crisis in living, which in turn constitutes an episode of mental disorder.

It is my purpose now to develop in rudimentary outline the more significant of the syndromes which are seen in these episodes. The first syndrome to which I shall refer may come as something of a surprise. It is the episode of "love."

This "*love*" is an effect of culture patterns that still have great force; that, four generations ago, could scarcely be escaped unless one were of extraordinary ability or remarkable ugliness. These patterns bear with the greatest force upon the young. There is no end of talk about love, the movies are full of it, the newspapers recount varied facets of these situations, romantic fiction arises almost exclusively from it, and all the other boys and girls seem to be involved in it. Yet only the preadolescent and the adolescent have matured the capacity to love. Those who, regardless of chronological age, are not yet that mature, cannot experience it. Under social pressure, however, they do their best to conform and go through the motions of falling in love. As their need for security is great, the performance is as dramatically convincing as possible—to themselves and to others. Their demonstrations of emotion, occasionally knowingly fraudulent but often also self-deceptive, may be spectacular, quite beyond the real thing.

I can best illustrate the differences between "love" and love by recounting an extreme instance from the group of schizophrenics. A young man goes one night to the movies, alone, as usual. He often does this when he finds he cannot "concentrate" on his studies—in which he is doing less and less satisfactory work. He often falls asleep over his books but even with nine or ten hours of sleep, he awakens less and less rested. Sleeping is becoming his major activity; he can't seem to get enough of it. Yet he can't put the books aside and just go to bed; he knows he is not doing good work—and he is very ambitious to be a success. The movie is better than just chucking the book, and it is about the only thing he can do, at night, except an occasional solitary walk. He has long since given up his efforts to be one of the boys, to play games and converse with others. They don't seem to find him interesting; in fact, some of them have made fun of him, quite openly. At least, he is pretty sure that this happened, and that none of them have much respect for him—but he does not think about that if he can help it.

This particular evening, as the platinum-blonde heroine is revealed to the ecstatic audience in a moment of ingenuous helplessness. something happens to our boy. He has an 'electric' feeling; he is jolted out of his all too usual gloomy calm; he realizes that here is the Perfect Woman. He is in "love."

He sits through a second showing of the film, aflame with mounting excitement. He goes out and walks the streets—walks, in fact, far out into the country. Dawn finds him writing a letter to his love. He may or may not mail it. If he does entrust it to the mailbox, in all likelihood the postman ultimately brings him a photograph—straight from Hollywood. But in any case, his life is changed. The gloom is gone. He is warmed by an inner fire. He spends long hours in fantasy about the dear one. Studies cease to have any relevance. And the people who were once sources of self-abasement, are now of no moment whatever. They wonder what has happened to him; he does not notice them at all. The 'affair' may go on for months —as our boy moves on to the schizophrenic dénouement. All the reality of the love-object is photographic. He has no need even for the sloppy 'details' of her life distributed to the hungry world in the movie journals. Everything is provided by his revery processes; other people's views would garble his private perfection.

There are many variations on this theme of the fantastic love affair. Sometimes, the unwitting object is a classmate. Sometimes, as the revery grows and grows, the luckless youth is driven to reveal the state of affairs—to the astonishment, chagrin, and sometimes horror, of the girl. The events that then transpire do his tenuous self-esteem no good whatever and the psychosis, the severe mental disorder, frequently makes itself manifest in his performances immediately after the shock of the misunderstanding.

These are extreme examples, of a piece, however, with all the episodes of "love." That many of them go on to marriage is not surprising. That this is an important source of income and deference for psychiatrists also follows. The related patterns of our culture succeed all too frequently in coupling ill-assorted young people in what proves to be a singularly frustrating and unhappy relationship which sometimes leads to homicide; fairly frequently, to suicide; and increasingly often, to divorce, the damaged-goods situation, and the long tedium of alimony. There are also the children of these psychiatrically impossible marriages, pregnancy being one of the devices to which the interpersonally wretched often have recourse.

Let us now turn to another of these episodes which is related to the dynamism of grief. Grief is the way by which we detach our integrating tendencies from a lost significant person. It is as if our ability for integrating situations with fantastic persons would endanger our survival in the case of the death or other removal of anyone highly significant to one. We see this in "*grief*," chronic mourning, in which the survivor remains preoccupied with the departed one and carries on a semblance of life centered in the lost one, who still subsists and is functionally effective all the more ideally as a companion or lover because he is now but an illusion of the survivor.

Only superficially related to grief and mourning is the type of episode that we call *depression*. Depression is not a dynamism for the health-preserving release of integrative bonds which connect one to another. It is a chiefly destructive process. It cuts off impulses to integrate constructive situations with others. Only destructive situations are maintained, and these are extremely stereotyped. There is even a change in the physiology such that vital processes are slowed down and movements, particularly those of the large joints, are much reduced in speed and in frequency. The depressed person is preoccupied with a circle of ideas about evil, hopelessness, destruction, and damnation: "I am a great sinner; God has forsaken me; I am horribly punished; I have committed the unpardonable sin; I have lost my soul; I have destroyed my family; I am a great sinner," and so forth. The circle can be repeated day in and day out. It is all that the patient has to say; facial expression, sighs and groans make up the rest of the communicative activity.

Another form of episode is in some unclear fashion closely related to depression, although its signs and symptoms are in most particulars the very opposite. I refer here to *manic* and *hypomanic* states, in which there is a great outburst of fleeting impulses to integrate situations with others, a great variety of these abbreviated integrations, a great volubility—usually of low communicative effect, however, because there is great distractibility of the attention and what is called "flight of ideas"—and a corresponding acceleration of the physiological processes and increase in movements, particularly those of the large joints. The manic person is preoccupied with nothing; it is as if his attention shifted as frequently as possible, without rhyme or reason excepting the availability of some new distraction.

Depressed states frequently follow on states of manic excitement, perhaps after an interlude of approximately conventional behavior. The depressed episode may be the first; the manic, the following. The series, depression-excitement or excitement-normality-depression, once started, may go on for years. The people who show these types of disturbance in living often have a history of wide swings in their mood. One learns that they have been easily elated or begloomed; their mood has been mercurial. Moreover, to a noticeable if not to a statistically validated degree, they tend to be of a particular type of somatic organization; the body-build which Stockard termed *the lateral*. I have regarded these states as the manifestation of a peculiarity of the bodily constitution, but without any great conviction. It may, however, be noted that cocaine intoxication, in certain people, gives something of the hypomanic picture; and that mild poisoning with some other drugs —luminal, for example—produces some of the symptoms of depression.

It is easy to establish the fact of the serial order of manic and depressive states in the career-line of some people and, therefore, an entity called the *manic-depressive psychosis* is included in psychiatric diagnosis. There are many instances of disorder that do not closely approximate the manifestations of this entity, yet resemble it. These patients are often identified as suffering from a psychosis *allied to* the manic-depressive. Moreover, the pictures of the hypomanic state and states of depression have been generalized in attenuated form, so that some psychiatrists teach that the entity or group of allied entities, manic-depressive psychosis, includes certain "mild" states. A mild depression is often diagnosed to exist when a patient suffers a considerable diminution of energy and initiative, extending over a period from weeks to months in duration—yet is allegedly physically sound. A mild depression is sometimes diagnosed on the basis of physical complaints—weakness, debility, insomnia, vague to marked discomfort in the head, belly, or cardiac region—when no "organic" basis for the symptoms is discovered. Another diagnosis for this last mentioned picture is that of *neurasthenia*.

These diagnostic fringes to the manic-depressive entity require consideration from two standpoints. They give a very considerable leeway for psychiatric diagnostic prejudice to operate comfortably. They provide a convenient common ground for general medicine and psychiatry, in which common ground we may be certain about very little. The mild depression is diagnosed negatively, by the failure to demonstrate physiological factors making up a state of organic disease. In my opinion, this failure is, more often than not, the result of inadequacy of investigation. Many of the "mild depressions" and "neurasthenias" are deficiency states, malnutrition, and states of chronic intoxication. Insidiously developed ill-health is attended by increasing inertia, feelings of inadequacy and vague ailment. These attending symptoms have repercussions in the interpersonal performances, which in turn contribute signs and symptoms to the psychiatric picture.

The uncertainty and confusion of diagnosis reflected in these remarks is a strong argument for reformulating all diagnostic syndromes in terms of interpersonal processes. I shall not undertake to present a syndrome of interpersonal phenomena which would constitute a valid identification of manic-depressive psychosis. Instead, I shall speak of the *reactive depression,* another rubric in the accepted psychiatric classification. If one encounters a series of misfortunes and becomes depressed, after the pattern above described, this is presumed to be a much less serious mental disorder than is the obscurely initiated depression of the manic-depressive disorder. This, like a great many troublesome errors, seems rather obviously to stand to reason. If one should in the midst of a delightful experience, burst into tears, one is as certainly out of the ordinary as is one who does *not* weep at the loss of a parent. In either case, one has a lot to explain in order to maintain one's prestige and self-respect. This explaining—very generally rationalizing, appealing to mutually accepted prejudice—is perhaps the really significant factor in the relative seriousness of the alleged two kinds of depression. A person who has undergone a severe depression *which he cannot (understand or) rationalize* and which he and others certainly cannot forget, is by that very set of interpersonal factors made permanently insecure. If, on the other hand, he and his friends see as self-evident the "cause" of the depression, then there is a way of integrating the experience into the self without loss of prestige and uncertainty about his social and personal future.

Memory and recall deserve a word at this juncture. I have a theory of memory which has grown out of psychiatric experience, but which has not yet been formulated rigorously. Memory is the relatively enduring record of all the momentary states of the organismic configuration. In less abstract language, living beings *fix,* somewhere and somehow, meaningful traces of everything they live through, not as 'perceptions' or 'states of excitation of the cortex' or the like, but rather as the pattern of how the organism-and-significant-environment existed at the moment. I shall remember this moment as it exists, with all

its implications past, present, and future—most of these implications having been present as tensional elements, and not
as formulated statements. Let me illustrate: there is the spatial
orientation—this beautiful and acoustically excellent auditorium; the rostrum, the microphone and its related system
which tonight seems to be unmonitored, the audience as a certain amazingly large number of people, a friend who is deaf in
the ear nearest me, the stenotype reporter, and many and many
another detail of the geometric and local geographic situation
—coupled with the *most significant* first experience of the related spatial orientation at the start of the first lecture in this
series. There is the temporal orientation along several significant lines; the night after our unusually timed Thanksgiving,
the 'place' of the moment in the exposition that I had planned
for this lecture; the 'place' of the moment in a prehended
durability of the lumped attention of the audience and their
tolerance for my presentation; the 'place' in the attention-toler-
ance of certain more personally significant members of the
audience; and various other details. There is the orientation in
terms of my personal career-line; the lucidity of my formulation, the adequacy of its verbal expression—or rather, verbal
indication, for one has no time to be exact and precise, if one
is to cover these topics without exhausting the auditors—the
effect on this moment of gaps in the earlier presentations, the
'coming' ideas that should grow out of this, its relation to the
hoped-for success of the whole as an organization of all these
statements and indications in terms of changes in the general
audience, and new insights in the more personally significant
auditors—including, very significantly, myself. I have mentioned these orientations without reference to the zones of interaction that are involved. I have omitted reference to the
patterns of kinæsthetic and related data that exist in me, in
connection with them. I can but invite your attention to the
complex pattern of vocal—sound productive and sound receptive—past and future verbal and other voice-communica-

tive processes concerned, and the effective or partially ineffectual and unfortunate function of these patterns in terms of
what makes up this moment in each of you. I will only mention as yet other coördinates of the present moment, states of
my visceral and skeletal musculature as terms in relative satisfaction or dissatisfaction with the momentary situation and
with the accomplished and the potential performances of the
whole lecture, the series of lectures, and with events before
and to follow on the lecture. These are some of the items that
may be abstracted from the momentary state of the organism—
of a vast series of which one's memory is composed.

Recall is the functional activity of this organization of all of
one's organismic past. Recall is vividly manifest in many of the
details just presented. This auditorium is a recurrent, tempo-
rally durable item in my life. I *know* it. Awakening here after
having been carried in, sleeping, I would *recognize* it because
its traces in my memory would readily connect with the experience that I was undergoing. The aspect of recall that is not
quite so obvious, however, is fully as important. The recall
and recognition that I have mentioned occur within awareness.
What of the activity which adapts me to the microphone? I do
not wander out of its range. I maintain—with occasional error
—a level of amplified speech which will serve my purpose. The
memory of reverberation in this room this evening—appraised
carefully in the first few moments—as it affects me through the
auditory zone is operating smoothly, except when my fatigue
or irritation at an inadequacy of communication disturbs the
integration of the lecture-situation. This recall functions for
the most part outside of my awareness. There are many phenomena of recall that represent its functioning entirely beyond
the awareness of the person concerned. In other words, memory and recall are not restricted to the self. Recollection, recognition of and through recall, is another matter.

We do not consider disorders of memory, but only disorders
of recall and its subdivision, recollection. It may occur to you

that elderly people and those who suffer the injuries of cerebral arteriosclerosis are said to have defects or disorders of memory. The manifestations are of two orders. Relatively recent events are reputedly beyond recollection by the aged, while their memory of distant times is remarkable. To point to the explanation of this let me suggest that each of you may recall the first occasion on which you wore clothes of adult style; very few of you can recall in detail the last twenty times that you dressed. Recurring performances tend to become relatively automatic with a minimum of distinguishing characterization; if the actual demand in a situation includes the necessity for recalling the events of a given forenoon, the act and circumstances of dressing on that particular morning will recur. The recall will now meet a need, contribute to an adaptation. Otherwise, it is not forthcoming.

Difficulties of recall that arise from or are at least connected with disturbances of the brain may or may not carry with them a feeling of incompleteness, a sense of discomfort and inadequacy. This is also the case with the malfunction of recall which arises from fatigue, malnutrition and intoxication, and with that which is the result of multiple integration of one's situation—often experienced as a *conflict of motives*. The brain, particularly the cerebrum, neopallium, is the ultimate integrating apparatus of the organism; it serves the self system and the rest of the personality, and may be presumed—but not proven—to be almost exclusively concerned in the phenomenology of awareness. The central nervous system is also the most probable site of the principal factors of memory in the higher animals.[36]

[36] For the reason, primarily, that integrative representation of the historic momentary states of the organism may be presumed to occur here. One must not lose track of the "profiting from experience" which characterizes at least the whole of the animal kingdom—we are but beginning a comparable exploration of the vegetable world. Monocellular organisms show some phenomena of learning. The memory function may, therefore, be regarded as one of the aspects of (animal) life. Differentiation and specialization of functional activity culminates in the architectonically almost incredibly complex

If one cannot recall the name of an acquaintance, it may be because of fatigue which narrows the field of awareness; of intoxication or deficiency in nutritive substances, which impair the efficiency of organismic function; or of so-called psychical causes—factors in the immediate situation such as hostility to the acquaintance as a person (integrant) in the present situation, so that his presence is to an extent deleted or rendered merely potential by the defect of recall. It may be a particular instance of a general tendency to 'forget' all ordinal data. It may be a particular instance of a general tendency to forget names of people; this expressing a persistent characteristic of one's personality.[37]

The most astonishing of the disorders of recall are the *amnesias* which we encounter most frequently in self-absorbed people who have met insuperable difficulties in living. These folk live rather as if the world were a stage on which each performs, assisted by shadowy figures, for a shadowy audience including one luminously real person, the actor. It is not so strange, therefore, if, to them, recollections lack the brash reality to which the rest of us are accustomed; if they, instead, have a varying measure of uncertainty, so that some recollections of events have a rather dream-like or may-have-happened character. *Hysteria*, the mental disorder to which the self-absorbed are peculiarly liable, is the distortion of interpersonal relations which results from extensive amnesias. Let me indicate something of it by an imaginary instance. We have a

human central nervous system. Parallel with this goes a vast discrimination of the relevant factors in life-situations, and complexity of factorial integrations. This makes the central nervous system a very significant 'organ of mind' but not *the* organ of mind. Mind is a word referring to the organism, not to artificially separated parts.

[37] Let me point out, with these six of an indefinitely large number of explanatory hypotheses, the absurdity of *precocious interpretation*. There are some people who unhesitatingly express as the correct interpretation of a stranger's act, the one of several possible explanatory hypotheses which occurs to them. The interpretation is valid as a datum of magic omniscient performance useful in understanding the interpreter in his complex interpersonal situation. It may have very little to do with the person whose action is allegedly interpreted.

self-absorbed young man who finds himself married to a fiercely puritanical woman. He plays out the antiphony to her zeal very well, as long as speech serves the purpose. But he has need for sexual satisfactions in which she is wholly non-coöperative. We shall have him rebuffed one night; we shall have him roll over, turn his face to the wall, and think "This woman is driving me crazy with her damned morality." He falls asleep. He awakens with a cry; he clutches his wife in an excess of fear; he quivers, he stammers, he leaps about, he tears his hair, he beats his forehead. She calls a doctor. The doctor finds tachycardia—a fast pulse. The patient has a 'violent pain in his heart,' breaks out in a 'cold sweat,' rolls on the floor in pain and terror. A sedative is provided; he is lulled into quiet in bed; sleep finally supervenes. The most strenuous interrogation, during or after his attack, will uncover nothing of recollection of the thought that staged the drama. If by some transcendental magic a psychiatrist could ask "Did you not, before falling asleep last night, have the thought that your wife's morality is driving you crazy?," the patient may honestly— and indignantly—answer "Never; preposterous!" The most for which one might hope is that, afterwards, after the psychiatrist has left, our young man might recall the question and think "Now, that is queer, I do seem to recall thinking something about my wife, before I fell asleep." The attacks recur. They continue to be utterly inexplicable to the patient. The little detail, the preliminary thought which provoked the drama, is buried in amnesia. The fact that the doctor's comment about rapid pulse preceded the heart pains is also missing; the event cannot be recalled. These elements of memory are *repressed;* that is, they have lost their connection with the recollectable series of events. But both can be recalled in the peculiar situation which we call hypnosis.[38]

[38] Also, in hypnosis, anything else that suits the physician or other hypnotist can be "recalled," whether it happened or not—unless the hypnotist is careful to use no leading questions and give no other cues as to the "information" that he is expecting.

The dramatic 'maladies' of the hysteric are most varied. They include *anæsthesias*, losses of special senses. They include *paralyses*, loss of function of muscle-bone complexes. They include *visceral disturbances*—of the circulation, respiration, the gastric and the rectal function, the activity of the bladder, and of the genital apparatus. The "mild shell-shock"—attacks of disabling tremor—which was so dangerously contagious near the front line in the World War was hysterical. Many cases of "heart disease" have hysterical elements. Chronic coughs, some asthmatic conditions, and certain susceptibilities to "colds" are hysterical. There is hysterical indigestion, frequently complicated with diarrhœa. Frequent or difficult micturition may be hysterical, as are many cases of precocious orgasm. As a boy in grammar school, I had an illuminating experience with the hysterical possibilities. Having mixed a little red ink with a glass full of water, I was approached by a girl whom I disliked chiefly because of her remarkable cupidity. She had to know what it was; I said it was wine, and she had to have a drink of it. She thereon became most embarrassingly drunk. For fear of what might happen after the recess, I explained what it was. She thereon became poisoned. Not only did she defeat my efforts on her behalf for a half an hour, but then required the teacher's aid in surviving.

The hysterical interpersonal situation includes special disablements of a relatively clearly idea-born character which permit the securing of satisfactions or the protection of security without awareness of this meaning of the performances. Whether it is the highly moral person who makes sexual advances to a companion under cover of light sleep, or the "loving" person who revenges himself for any slight or thwarting by presently having an attack which makes life miserable for the other, the principle is the same. The other fellow is inhibited from attacking one's prestige or denying one's satisfactions by virtue of the complicating factor—the special state of light sleep, "One is not responsible for what happens in one's sleep"; or the attack, "You surely don't blame me for being sick."

Let us now look at quite a different type of performance, also often including signs and symptoms of physical disease. These patients, the *obsessional states*, too, have a variety of bodily ailments but their physical disorders are not simple tools in their interpersonal relations. They are supplements or aids in the maintenance of parataxic integrations. They do not protect prestige from easy attack, nor do they directly facilitate satisfactions. Often enough, they interfere seriously with bodily health, and thus undermine one's security and diminish the possibility of satisfactions. A frequent obsessional disability is the 'tense belly' with pylorospasm, hyperacidity, and sometimes gastric ulceration. There is usually a spastic constipation, with or without phases of diarrhœa. There may instead be cardiovascular phenomena, particularly hypertension. The patients are methodic, ritualistic, punctilious. The dietary restrictions imposed on them by well-meaning physicians may be carried out with such thoroughness as to induce malnutrition and deficiency disorders.

Interpersonal situations including an obsessional person are characterized by obscure power operations directed to the maintenance of control over everything that happens. I once had a patient, a good artist, who, however, hated to market his works. He lived in a two-story house and, one day, in coming downstairs, en route to a dealer's, was seized with the thought that he might fling himself over the rail and gravely injure or kill himself. The thought paralyzed further progression. He crept back to his studio and called his wife. He told her the awful experience . . . . To make a long story short, it was not long before his "fear of stairs" had immured him on the second floor. His wife, a rather domineering woman, was reduced to going for his commissions, delivering his work to the galleries, and bringing his food upstairs to him. He continued to do good work, but the necessities from his "fear" grew and grew until the wife was driven to call in a psychiatrist. He made rather prompt recovery—on the second floor of a mental hospital, with little but good, routine, institutional regimen. That is, he reverted to a simply quite obsessional condition, free from the disabling special fear of stairs. The wife thought he was basically improved.

I cannot leave the impression that mere pressure of circumstances will usually remedy the obsessional state. Perhaps it would, if we could carry the principle far enough in the right directions. The facts are not too encouraging, however, for obsessional states under threat of failure in their obscure power operations, often shift to even more grave disorder of living, as I shall presently illustrate. We have to expand their awareness as to the activities in which they are engaged, but this is extraordinarily difficult and usually fantastically time-consuming. The trouble arises from a very early, if not a lifelong, condition of profound insecurity. This has been made endurable by the perpetuation and refinement of personal magic, lineally descended from the late infantile and early verbal stages of personality development. These people cannot be comfortable as to their personal worth and as to the favorable attitude of others towards them. They have an abiding contempt for themselves, usually much more vividly manifested as an obscure to obvious contempt for others. The low level of self-esteem is concealed—very successfully concealed, in many cases—by the rôle of a powerful but subtle magician. The quiet grandeur of many of these patients is simply too staggering to occur to other people. A companion may, in temper, say "You always have to be right, don't you?" He does not realize that he has made a simple factual observation; the obsessional person is quietly omniscient and omnipotent. It has to be done in a subtle fashion; in the face of inescapable demonstration of error, he says "Of course; you are quite right." If you could prevent any such utterance, he would be terribly upset by the error. Instead, he passes grandly on, having by verbal magic reduced the situation to insignificance. When the state is severe, one can tell an obsessional person nothing; one can, however, provide data from which the information presently springs to the person's mind. I say to such patients, on particularly suitable occasions: "Quite often, when a person experiences such and such a series of events, it means such and such a motivation." This is usually, being offered with all humility, received politely and dismissed from attention while we go on with something important. Days to months later, the patient develops a surmise that there might be such a relationship. This is satisfactory; if he attempted to agree with me in the first place, my statement would have been metamorphosed in the process, if not in fact dissolved into sheer verbal fog. *He* has to be the one who knows, discovers, effects. My rôle, to match his ideal, would be that of one who 'only stands and waits'—a sort of admiring slave who never shows any unmistakable sign either of enslavement or freedom.

Sometimes the obsessional person is a tragic figure moving majestically through an awful world of inferior and malevolent people. Sometimes he is a great Christ-like figure who undergoes tortures in trying to "arrange" things as they have to be for his peace of mind, without interfering with anyone—in these cases, other people get nothing they want out of their integrations with the obsessional person. In the former case, they suffer and are provoked to cause suffering. Usually, any interference with the obsessional "arrangements" leads to withdrawal to an extremely detached, morose, or hurt position. Often, one cannot interfere, short of physical violence. This is typical of functional speech-disorder, in which, I am sure, the stutterer would follow one a mile rather than release one from waiting for the successful "arrangement" of the situation so that the word can be said.

The obsessional state is classically a state in which there is great activity of thought. The interpersonal relations are never simple, never free from great parataxic distortion, and they can be very strikingly illusory—particularly, of the Me-and-Myself type. These people are always "trying to make themselves" do this or that, or be this or that which is regarded as desirable —which they "ought" to do or be. One of them, told repeatedly in a series of consultative interviews that his fear of blushing could not be overcome by any effort of will, was nevertheless compelled each time to say "Don't you think I ought to stop thinking about myself so much." When they are relatively comfortable, they are often self-consciously observing their performances. As one of them put it, there are mental states like "Behold me, making my guests comfortable," "I am really being very agreeable," and so on.

These patients do not lack the drive toward mental health, but the growth of their awareness is wonderfully complicated. They notice and can report many an incident fraught with great possibilities of insight, but the report is so confounded with parataxic views as to what the other person was doing, that the hearer also is led astray. Under stress, they can overlook almost anything, or warp it unrecognizably to fit their determination as to what the situation must be. In this process, they often come to suffer severe visceral disturbances which take on the appearance of primary physical disease.

The son of a hateful, domineering, self-centered and self-seeking, ultrapenurious mother, and of a charmingly unreasonable and henpecked father, after a good many more obviously "suitable" contacts, married a woman some fifteen years his senior. The wife was a lady of great social charm, of broad interests, a philanthropist. She had been respected by his mother, and had herself always treated him in a definitely maternal way, very kindly. They had been acquainted for years. It was rather difficult to recall just how it had culminated in marriage; perhaps it was a result of the death of the patient's father, or merely of the son's realization that he was growing rather old. There had been some rather severe misgivings, and the consummation of the marriage was thoroughly unsatisfactory.

From the very beginning, there was a great disparity as to physical endearments. The wife was not interested at all. The man, however, could not adapt himself to this and often made endearing gestures—which were greeted with a tolerance that had obviously diminished over the years. The patient did not tell me this; it became evident as data accumulated. I learned also that, some years before consulting me, the patient had developed a gastric ulcer which had finally perforated, with grave hemorrhage. The patient volunteered the information that he had felt indifferent as to the outcome of treatment, at that time; quite willing, in fact, to die. The ulcer had healed, but there were still many symptoms of gastro-intestinal spasticity; diet and other hygienic requirements had to be followed quite rigidly. Despite meticulous care of himself, the patient still suffered quite a few attacks of gastro-intestinal disorder.

We worked intensively to clear up the severe obsessional state which he suffered. In about a hundred interviews, we came to a point at which it was possible to demonstrate, despite any power operations that the patient could muster, that the domestic life had long since come to include an unvarying manifest dislike of the patient by his wife. It was evident that she respected him; in fact, she did very well in maintaining appearances and in otherwise facilitating his career. But she clearly detested physical intimacy—and he was still, after fifteen years of discouraging, actively seeking it. As the patient came to recall clearly some of the unnumbered occasions on which he had pressed for some demonstration of pleasure in physical contact, always to be rebuffed—for some years, now, quite brutally—always withdrawing with concealed hurt and a "resolute effort" to put it out of his mind by considering how fine a person his wife was, how desirable a home they had, what standing they had in the community, and so forth, and so on; I say, as all this finally became clear and undisguised, it also became clear that on equally innumerable occasions he must have been filled with rage—of which he was only now beginning to be aware.

With the acceptance in awareness of the hopeless campaign to win over the wife to demonstrative behavior, the rebuffs, and the supplementary procedures by which he had been able to overlook his helplessness and avoid profiting from the recurrent humiliation, he became clear also about the rage and hatred that he experienced. The great "love" and contentment faded away and the couple came to live on a much less mutually provocative and painful basis. The gastro-intestinal spasticity correspondingly faded out of the picture and the patient finally 'recovered' from the disorder of alimentary function.

A number of rather parallel instances of spastic belly has led me to say that if one has to swallow resentment, one may be sure that it will give one indigestion. This may do as an allusion; what of the theory which underlies the occurrences? If you will devote all your attention, the next time you are suddenly angered, to noticing the movements and changes of tension that occur in your body, a clue may appear. You will notice a rather extensive group of phenomena; a suspension of exhalation of the breath, a change in tone of the facial muscles, a tension which may be referred to the diaphragm, and a tightening of the muscles of the abdominal wall. These phenomena are rather clearly represented in awareness. Changes in the distribution of the blood, changes in the rate of impalpable perspiration, and changes in the visceral tone will have no such vivid representation. Let us now suppose that, while you are made angry, this emotion and the situation factors pertaining to it arise from a dissociated tendency. Under this circumstance, the first group of changes, those well-represented in awareness, can scarcely be manifested in clear form. They would, so to speak, give the show away—or be involved in a rapidly developing attack of anxiety, which would complicate the experience beyond recognition. The group of substitutive processes which includes the obsessional states makes one, in general, proof against anxiety attacks under any but extraordinary circumstances. In patients belonging in this group, therefore, the skeletal and other clearly represented changes of tension and movement which accompany the working of dissociated systems are not manifested, and the changes of visceral tension (and movement) are markedly exaggerated—as if to drain off the excitation which would ordinarily effect the recognizable changes.

Besides this factor of drainage of "expressive" excitation into the visceral area, there is also the factor of duration of the unresolved situation. If one is aware that one is angry, in most cases one does something at least in fantasy, which tends to resolve the situation and discharge the impulse. If it is wise to inhibit all direct expression of anger, one can still have an imaginary situation in which, certain items being different, one can tell one's superior precisely what one thinks of him, even of his maternal parent. One feels better after this; the visceral resonance of the inhibited emotion is resolved. Consider now, however, the case of our patient—who went off smarting with rebuff and "told himself" what a fine wife he had. This clearly extends rather than resolves the somatic states connected with rage at his thwarting.

Some of us would be able to dispose of the emotional hangover and its visceral disturbances in sleep, by way of a dream. I surmise that it is only by this type of relief that patients in the group of substitutive disorders are able to live. But what one observes in them is something quite peculiar: their dreams are but obscurely related to the dissociated systems; the structure of the personality, the organization of self and non-self, is such that *no* clear representation is possible. Even at the time when by virtue of the inherent character of sleep itself, the person must feel relatively secure, the anxiety factor in the self dynamism is still effective. Clearly, even in sleep, the obsessional patient is not securing a fair return in repose and restitution for the time spent. Just as we saw our patient withdraw from rebuff with more or less concealed hurt—which means skeletal tension—which prohibits immediate relaxation; so also we expect to find that he needs a good deal of sleep, sleeps rather lightly, and is not too well rested in the morning, because security operations involving the self have also been going on during the night. This, the aspects of the problem which involve the self, is in addition to the effects of visceral tension, spasms and cramps, by which many an hour's repose is cancelled.

We have spent some time on these physical or at least bodily disorders of the obsessional patient. You must not suppose, however, that these patients have much to say about their symptoms. The contrary is the case; they are in fact often ashamed of being ill, and would be embarrassed by sympathy. They do not *use* their illness directly to achieve unacknowledged goals, as does the hysterical person. They are not preoccupied with their physical ill-health as are the *hypochondriacal* people. These latter, correspondingly, are much less obviously engaged in magical power operations in interpersonal situations than are the obsessional people. It is as if the hypochondriacal patient had abandoned the field of interpersonal relations as a source of security, excepting in one particular. He has to communicate data as to his symptoms; the illness, so to speak, becomes the presenting aspect of his personality. His interpersonal relations are chiefly influenced by the need to discuss the illness; he always gets around to it in any conversation; it is often about the only topic in which he has interest enough to sustain the effort of talking.

It might be thought that the hypochondriacal person, like the hysterical, is preying on sympathy. This also is not the case. It may be pleasanter to discuss one's ailments with a sympathetic, or at least an apparently attentive, listener; but discussed they must be, whether to a person obviously annoyed and bored, or even to a person who is delighted to hear of the suffering. This is one of the most illuminating features of the hypochondriacal state. The physical ailment, bizarrely enough, is a means for augmenting security in interpersonal relations. Without it, the patient would feel abased, inferior, and without any merit for the consideration of others. It is as if the source of chronic unworthiness which is obliterated as a subject of awareness by the obsessional routine, with concomitant disorders of tension and motility, is handled in hypochondriacal people on the level of obsession *with* the somatic symptoms and thinking about them. The source itself, however, being in the structure of the self dynamism—being a product of acculturation—is interpersonal in its origin and in its manifestations. Just as the obsessional person strives to overcome the promptings of this felt unworthiness by magical power over others; so does the hypochondriacal, by engaging others in discussion of the malady. Neither can withdraw from the world of people—even though, in their most aggravated states, the people concerned become highly illusory.

There is another of these substitutive states in which not the body but the world is treated as ailing. The *algolagnic* people seem to enjoy suffering, and passing it on to others. They have an astigmatic slant on life such that its unpleasant aspects are all that concern them. One of them, on his first trip abroad, rode on the "Coronation Scot" from Glasgow to London. He read a detective story throughout the journey, only thrice glancing out of the window. Finding himself observed, he remarked to his companion "Isn't the landscape boring." Asked as to the book in which he had seemed to be absorbed, he said that it was very tiresome. He mentioned in retrospect that the English trains were bad; the food, tasteless; the money entirely beyond his understanding. In brief, everything he noticed—or was observed to notice—was bad, wrong, or positively distressing. A grim possibility could be found behind any piece of good news; a high probability of evil lurked in every promise. Although an artist of great talent, he did practically no work because he was so distracted with the suffering caused him by life—with the suffering of his family, in case he could not find anything himself to suffer at the moment. These people, too, have to have a hearer; our particular artist had married a somewhat handicapped woman chiefly, I believe, to be sure of an audience.

Next in this series of substitutive states is the case of the *paranoid* individual. These folk regard themselves as the victims of specific, "deliberate," injury by other people. They are, in short, persecuted. The only durable integrations in which they are involved are situations in which they feel that the other person is doing them an injury. If they are seriously disordered, the others in their interpersonal relations tend to be highly illusory, often personalized abstract groups—the Masons, the Catholics, the Jews, or the Nazis, for example. Anyone in whom they are moved to be interested is soon discovered to be an agent of the persecuting agency—albeit sometimes an involuntary one.

People suffering the paranoid states can generally be provoked into expressing *ideas of grandeur*. Paranoid states are said to be characterized by ideas of persecution and of grandeur. This is somewhat misleading, because all substitutive processes include an extravagantly superior formulation of the self—for the good reason that they are all complex processes to overcome or at least obliterate from awareness an irremediable sense of inferiority, unworthiness, and incapacity to awaken positive attitudes in others. If one's efforts in this direction take the form of being persecuted, it is only natural that the rationalizing of this extraordinary state of affairs calls for some rather amazing explanatory beliefs. To have a whole group of people bent on one's injury or destruction may well be convincing evidence that one is a person of considerable importance. To document such an idea, one may have to go back a long way to the time in life when certainty was difficult or impossible. It thus comes about that many of them believe that they are not children of their alleged parents. They were exchanged, adopted, kidnapped. Their real parents are people of great importance, indeed. It is all part of some plot which they have finally discovered. It was a long time before they suspected, but finally they saw it all—and it explains a great many things that previously had mystified them.[39]

The paranoid, the algolagnic, the hypochondriacal, and the obsessional states are probably different patterns of much the same maladjustive processes. Patients manifest various blends of the four and some patients definitely alternate between one or another of them. Some hypochondriacal people become paranoid, and vice versa; and there may be more than one such transformation.

The processes which are woven into these four types of episodes are briefly, as follows. The early experience produced a prevailing negative self. There was not enough approbation. The negative attitude has interfered with the securing of interpersonal satisfactions. The projected low appraisal of suitable people has minimized every opportunity. The feeling of personal inferiority and unworthiness—which has to be concealed but is not thereby improved—has applied even in comparison with the already derogated others. The unsatisfied state, also more or less clearly represented in awareness—often as loneliness—is at times intolerable. Failure after failure undermines the vestiges of security which come from revery processes of a forward-looking type. They lose their utility, and a state bordering on despair supervenes.

The conviction grows that one is not fully capable of being human, and the intolerable insecurity that this entails deletes what is left of adaptive effort. One ceases to make positive or negative movements towards others. Random, relatively purposeless, restlessness becomes the expression of unsatisfied longings; sleep is disturbed and fatigue phenomena appear. The processes making for consensual validations are entirely sus-

[39] Persons who recall such fantasies need not be alarmed. They occur much more often in the early years than do paranoid developments in the later.

pended. Autistic features become more and more evident in
one's reveries. The reveries themselves are regressive; they are
oriented to constructive purpose, but the orientation takes the
direction of a search in the past. One goes back as it were, over
the course of one's development, seeking for a time in one's
life which was satisfactory. In this regression, one always comes
to something that is experienced as a way to start over again.
The regressive direction now changes. The autistically valid
but consensually inassimilable pattern now unfolds as an episode of mental disorder; it initiates a relatively stable maladjustive progression in interpersonal relations.

Various degrees of awareness attend these dramatic changes
of life-direction from a regression in the face of despair to a
progression along the line of one of our syndromes. The person
who is regressing in the realm of interpersonal relations, be he
ever so withdrawn from integration with real people, is not
out of the world. Events continue to impinge on him. Some
of these events are provocative of the revery processes, the
highly illusory interpersonal relations, that he manifests in the
regressive course. One of them may strike off a vivid alertness,
all the more impressive because of the narrowing of consciousness which is a phenomenon of fatigue. This impressive event,
perceived in the setting of an earlier state of development, may
unfold itself as the very cause of the forward movement. This
is the case with the unhappy person who "suddenly sees it all"
and emerges from regression into a quickly systematized paranoid state.

Awareness of the origin of the classical obsessional states
is as vague as that of the paranoid is dramatic. Sometimes, it is
true, a patient may recall, for example, that on setting out for
a difficult visit, she suddenly felt weak and thought "What if I
were to faint"—thereafter having a morbid fear, a *phobia*, of
fainting. But the obsessional state with phobias is nearer to the
hypochondriacal, and the first intrusions of the magic which
comes to characterize the classical maladjustment are seldom

within the patient's ability for recall. Correspondingly, the evolution of the obsessional maladjustment is gradual. The patient becomes more and more of a magician—sometimes with occasional dramatic additions to the patterns of power operations.

I cannot leave this part of our subject without brief reference to a closely related life-pattern which, too, arises as the solution of a regressive change. It differs from the four that we have been discussing in that it is often quite successful as a way of life. I refer to the *sublimatory reformulations* of interpersonal relations. When there is severe conflict within awareness; when, for example, one ardently desires something the having of which one sternly disapproves; one cannot but regress to some earlier stage of development. This may, at first glance, seem none too self-evident. An example is certainly in order and, in our particular culture, a conflict situation involving sexual integrations would be among the most frequent. There are, however, other equally distressing states of sustained conflict, and I shall illustrate one of them before proceeding further with the topic.

We shall imagine a man of rigidly ethical upbringing, whose wife has developed what we call an involutional psychosis with decidedly paranoid coloring. For various reasons he resists psychiatric advice to the effect that she should be cared for in a mental hospital. He insists on caring for her in the home, where, despite competent nursing, he is available—at least, in the evenings—for integration in a decidedly destructive situation with her. She devotes considerable talent to making him utterly miserable. He discovers, partly through her promptings, a keen desire for her early death. This revolts him; he is horrified that he can entertain such thoughts about a person whom he certainly has loved, even though she is now greatly changed. Neither the desire for her prompt demise nor his abhorrence of his desiring it will yield; he is torn with conflict. The "death-wish" was at first attended by severe anxiety;

that is all past now and it has easy access to awareness. The conflict is clearly within the self.[40]

I shall not use this case of conflict to illustrate either the inevitable regressive changes or the sublimatory reformulation. Let me instead present the case of an imaginary young woman who, for reasons already suggested, is but imperfectly able to love a man. We shall have her marry much the sort of person as the husband whom we have just discussed, a somewhat remote, highly ethical, character who has attracted her all the more because he seems to have his sexual desires so very well under control. The consummation of the marriage will be quite unsatisfactory; throughout the years that they will have spent together, there will have been few instances of sexual intimacy. The wife early manifests a trait that is disturbing to the husband; she is intensely envious of other women and, as he discovers after giving singularly little cause, most irrationally jealous of him. We shall have her a prey to conflict between a powerful desire to engage in a life of easy virtue with many of the men she encounters, and a strong disapproval of anything the least 'free and easy' in a woman's attitude to a man. We shall see her withdrawing from social affairs as a regressive movement to reduce the force of this conflict, and we shall have her meet a clergyman of a particular, not too uncommon, type. He is of remarkable physical presence, great charm of manner to charming women, and much given to good works in which the people who have succumbed to his charm find a place. He is, of course, most circumspect in his relations with these people. This does not alter the fact that every

[40] The sketch of this case may well displease the psychiatrist skilled in the study of interpersonal relations. I have presented it as it is perceived by the husband. We know that he cannot have loved his wife in any realistic fashion; she would have loved him and could not have developed the involutional mental disorder. Correspondingly, we presume that the hostile-destructive impulse towards her is of no recent origin. It existed a long time in dissociation. Only the change in the wife's behavior to a frank and sustained torturing of him stirred it so powerfully that his self dynamism and anxiety were no longer able to maintain the dissociation.

woman with whom he deals comes quickly to feel that he is powerfully drawn to her, but under 'perfect self-control.' Our patient embarks, under his tutelage, in a truly astonishing career of practical philanthropy, looking after fallen women in the city slums. Her life is filled with this; her conflict all but disappears. She carries on with a minimum of contact with the good man who started it all; she lives in comparative peace with her husband and her women acquaintances.

This is an instance of the sublimatory reformulation of the impulses that expressed themselves in fantasies of prostitution. The motive is denied direct and complete resolution, but, in association with a *socially sanctioned* form of activity—the philanthropic work—is liberally if vicariously satisfied *in part*. This is the principle of sublimation: a motive which is involved in painful conflict is combined with a social (culturally provided) technique of life which disguises its most conflict-provoking aspect and usually provides some representation for the opposing motive in the conflict. The career thus brought into being is often pursued with all the more energy because it combines a disguised satisfaction with the achievement of personal security. In a word, sublimatory reformulations, when they work, work beautifully.

Our lady, now immersed in good work, may be somewhat of a bore. We may find her so 'concentrated' on her philanthropy that she is definitely a 'person with a cause' which is presented in and out of season with singular disrespect for other people's interests and avocations. There may seem to be something quite unrealistic about it, and one may be justified in wondering what would happen if it suddenly fell through. This is the price which is paid for sublimatory reformulations; they are ways out of a severe conflict, reflecting a disabling maladjustment of interpersonal relations, and they do not, in solving the conflict, greatly enhance the adaptive repertory. Unlike the obsessional, hypochondriacal, algolagnic, and paranoid states, the manifestations of sublimation in the specifically restricted field of the interpersonal relations are directly productive of prestige. Like any of the others, it presents a bar to the integration of situations of simple intimacy and complete satisfaction. It is, like all of the others, a power operation, but one peculiarly distinguished because the power-giving activity is endorsed by the culture. Its relationship to the others is shown by its combination with them, and by occasional alternations, in some people.

As another illustration, let me recite in briefest outline the case of a patient to whom I owe a glimpse of what may have been real *narcissism*. This term, so far as I know, originated in the early years of psychoanalysis, when certainly it was used to refer to a very dubious conception. The idea is that the infant is full of primary self-love, he has no object-love. I will not quarrel with the absence of object-love. The alleged primary narcissism, however, is not our concern; we look to "secondary narcissism" which—to quote one authority—is a retreat from object-love, so that one is compelled to seek pleasure in one's own attributes, fantasies, and so forth.[41] Anyway, as I encountered this veteran of the World War, in St. Elizabeths Hospital, he seemed as completely self-satisfied and self-absorbed as I can conceive mortal to be. He was unquestionably the product of a paranoid state, but the grandeur seemed to be complete, without evidences of his suffering persecutions. His end suggests to me that he had achieved that omnipotence so constantly pursued by the people that we are

[41] I take up the term, narcissism, only to condemn it. As formulated by Freud—in 1914, I believe—the conception underwent sundry modifications and, I surmise, came finally to be regretted by him. There is a certain cautious tentativeness in his later writings—not often enough the characteristic of his more ambitious followers—which makes for uncertainty as to just how greatly he had come to change his mind.

See, for a view sympathetic to my position, the scholarly "Selfishness and Self-Love" by Erich Fromm. PSYCHIATRY (1939) 2:507–523. A parallel view was expressed by Lewis B. Hill in an address, "The Treatment of the Psychotic Ego" before the Joint Session of The American Psychiatric Association with its Section on Psychoanalysis and The American Psychoanalytic Association, St. Louis, 6 May 1936.

discussing. One day while walking—in sublime detachment and completeness—with a party of patients, he leapt under a moving street car and was killed instantly. I believe that this impulse arose from a sudden defect of security, that he 'expected' to demonstrate his power to remain unscathed, and that there was no suicidal intention.

The history of this patient was something as follows. He was a sheep-herd in the Ozarks. One day, God spoke to him, told him of the war, directed him to enlist, and gave him assurances of his safety in this connection. The soldier repeatedly was decorated for valor. Only on demobilization was it noticed that he was psychotic. You will observe here, in this fragmentary outline, a paranoid sublimation, so to speak. What we encounter more frequently is a paranoid development as the outcome of failure in a sublimatory movement.

We can learn a good deal about the self dynamism from study of sublimatory reformulations that fail. In brief, they teach us that the escape from conflict by the reformulation is not an intellectual, 'voluntary,' performance. It happens in the way that the other substitutive processes take place. In a regressive state, it occurs to one that one might be interested in some particular form of activity. The idea 'grows on one.' Enthusiasm kindles. One moves forward again in the new interest. One has lost, or rapidly loses, anything but a memory —or an occasional exacerbation—of the impulses which stirred the severe conflict. The disappearance is, however, not without a trace. There are some peculiar new ingredients in the self dynamism, in the shape of more or less obscure taboos. These avoidances, which are frequently quite ritualistic, are based on situations which actually provoked the most troublesome instances of the conflict, in the days before the reformulation of life activity had taken place. It is rather as if the person arranges that the solution shall not be exposed to any very severe test, and is able to profit from experience in providing an unwitting protection. It was not possible to avoid the situations now avoided, until some components of the previously conflict-provoking motivation had been provided the socially approved mode of discharge. The taboo is an index of the impossibility of dissociating the motive, and an evidence that the reformulation *could* fail.

The relationship of the ritual avoidance in sublimation to the rituals and compulsive acts which are a part of many obsessional states amounts to a symbolic identity. The difference is one of degree, but degree of clarity of reference—in turn, an index of the depth of regression at which the solution was found. We do not shed much light on the situation by saying that a compulsive stepping on every third crack in the pavement is a ritual to avoid a situation like one in which one once had severe conflict. The meaning is shrouded by its origin in a deeply regressive state, when the representation of the conflict had lost resemblance to its 'objective reality.' If we demand of a person showing either the taboo of the sublimatory process or the compulsive act, an explanation of the why, we shall be told that it keeps his mind untroubled, or something to that general effect. This statement is fully responsive.

The compulsion to power operations and tests of—magic—strength in all obsessional people, to ritual acts and avoidances in some of them, to discussion of his symptoms by the hypochondriac, to expressions of derogation and suffering by the algolagnic, and to involvement with people who must be regarded as persecutors by the paranoid, are in every case to be regarded also as manifestations of the sort of solution found in sublimatory reformulation, *with the exception* that social approval is lacking. They are all complex processes, processes in parataxic integrations, which avoid painful conflict within awareness by virtue of resymbolization of the goals of the impulses that were disapproved as prejudicial to self-respect and security. All that can be accomplished by any therapeutically intended attack on the compulsively repetitious activity, under the most favorable circumstances, would be a renewal of the conflict.

It inheres in the nature of being human that one will relinquish, so to speak, a relative security and undergo anew a previously intolerable conflict within awareness *only* if one perceives a probability of speedy relief. If circumstances make a sublimatory reformulation ineffectual; as, for example, when a young person attempts the sublimation of all sexual motivation, so that the preoccupation with the new goals becomes more and more intense as conflict occurs; the course of events is often towards a paranoid excitement. By this I mean that the 'good works' are pressed ever more feverishly, with less and less judgment—less and less attention to consensually valid standards—and correspondingly increased feeling of frustration by others. There is apt to come a time when, from fatigue and recurring regressive movement, a paranoid state is substituted for the sublimatory one. I may be able to show something of the natural history of the substitutive processes by referring to a young man in the case of whom a swift unraveling of a residual compulsion was accomplished. This was a patient whom I had first seen some eleven years previously. I had found him suffering a severe obsessional state and had referred him to a psychiatrist for therapy. This had proceeded, on a meagre schedule of interviews, in the interval. At a time when the psychiatrist had been ill for nearly a year, and unable to see the patient, I acceded to his importuning and arranged for one interview an hour and a half long.

He told me that he was entirely recovered except for one symptom which still bothered him. He had still to throw away the part of his food that his fingers touched—I had not previously heard of this symptom. Please do not consider what follows either an adequate account of our interview, or an indication of the way to handle these patients. I said, after the complaint was heavily documented, that the symptom must have a history; that it expressed something akin to a notion that the hands were poisonous or otherwise contaminating. There followed what I consider to be the conventional movements to befog the issue. I pressed the point. The patient presently recalled—with many doubts as to its relevance—that as a boy, aged ten, he had developed a fear of being poisoned as a result of touching varnished wood. By dint of much urging, this idea was tracked down to its first remembered manifestation in connection with a bowling alley where he worked. He had then begun an excessive washing of the hands and an avoidance of that part of a slice of bread and the like which he had handled.

I insisted that such an explanation was inadequate, that while his account was good as far as it went, it omitted the really significant data. This sort of fear could not originate without an interpersonal root. There must be something that he had forgotten which involved a person, which would explain the fear of poisoning by the wood of the bowling alley. Could he think of anyone who might be concerned; of anything that had happened between him and someone else, before the appearance of the fear of poisoning. You must realize that I was operating in the field of a relationship created between us many years before, and occasionally renewed by my refusals of opportunities to see him, at intervals over the intervening years. In brief, the patient, under great pressure, recalled—with the usual doubts as to relevance, protest, as to why he should recall, and so forth—a boy with whom he worked in the bowling alley.

Under my insistence, he remembered that he had grown to be great friends with this boy; they had grown to be quite remarkably intimate; they had come to lie in each other's arms and to fondle each other, at times—he recalled someone discovering this, and telling him that it was wrong. He knows he never did it again. He agrees with me that the worry about touching the wood of the alleys appeared *after* he had been made to realize that there was something wrong with the intimacy with the other boy; after, in fact, he had stopped it. Because his therapist was not to see him for at least another six weeks, I made no effort to carry the explanation further. I did not ask as to the rôle of his hands in the happy intimacy with his friend, nor as to any physical basis for the idea of poisoning by way of the mouth.[42]

This example emphasizes, rather in the breach, my next point; namely, the course of events which is often initiated by a sudden failure of a sublimatory process.[43] Taking our young man who is assumed to have sublimated all recognized manifestations of lustful, genital, integrative tendencies, let us confront him suddenly with an extremely attractive and most forthright person who firmly believes that lust should be satisfied and that its satisfaction is unqualifiedly good—also, that he is attractive and suitable for genital integration. We shall presume that, in this uncompromising situation, he 'succumbs,' and enters, if not wholeheartedly, at least quite effectively into the integration. He has a shockingly good time. If the element of shock—postprandial, as it were—were not to materialize, he would be greatly benefited.[44] This, however, is not what

[42] Vague, or seemingly vague, ideas of poison—in our culture—have often to be related to autistic thinking about the semen. Poisons are *powerful* agents. Semen, the life-creating liquid ejaculated in sexual orgasm, is an ultra-powerful agent. Its ejaculation, in its fortissimo of unique sensation, is one of the sublime—if evil-marked—powers of one's organism. Power, lust, and the doctrines of sexual sin—related to the dark power of the body that overcomes the roseate, spiritual, and not in the given case quite adequate power of whatever is *not* the body—this is truly *something*. Coupled with all this not too distorted autistic thinking, go a variety of superstitions about *strength*. One loses one's manhood by "excessive" orgasm. Orgasm weakens one—a monstrosity grown from the observation that satisfactions induce repose and sleep. Loss of the semen produces or facilitates loss of the mind. And hundreds of other heinous outrages on troubled youth.

[43] Before I have left the topic of sublimatory reformulations, let me refer to the significant contributions: Chassell, Joseph, Vicissitudes of Sublimation. PSYCHIATRY (1938) 1:221–232; and Levey, Harry B., A Critique of the Theory of Sublimation. PSYCHIATRY (1939) 2:239–270, and A Theory Concerning Free Creation in the Inventive Arts, to be published in the May issue of PSYCHIATRY (1940) vol. 3.

[44] Here, again, the psychiatrist will recognize a defect in the presentation.

we wish to discuss. We shall assume that evil early experience has done its work, and that, as a result, the aftermath is self-recrimination and severe conflict. A good deal of his unhappy state of mind will get itself communicated to the partner, who will be distressed and repelled. Perhaps something will be said that makes him think that, not only has he done the wrong thing, but then made a fool of himself.

One of the courses of events subsequent to this is the rapid development of a state which I have called *ecstatic absorption*. The patient, as it were, makes a rapid regression to a state in which dream-like revery processes pertaining to a God-like condition solve the acute abasement. The recession is facilitated by his increasingly ineffectual attempts to remedy the interpersonal situation by conversational efforts that are becoming increasingly autistic and correspondingly puzzling to the sexual partner—or other significant persons to whom they are addressed. The state itself has its root-experiences in earlier performances connected with falling asleep when one was feeling very insecure. The increasing inutility of speech, the prehended disconcertment of the auditor, also has an effect in cutting off the attempts to maintain relations with actual people, and the patient—having perhaps become quite incoherent and completely incomprehensible—gives up all efforts to talk to anyone. His awareness is now that of a twilight state between waking and dreaming; his facial expression is that of absorption in ecstatic 'inner' experiences, and his behavior is peculiar to the degree that he no longer eats or sleeps, or tends to any of the routines of life.

Obviously, ecstatic absorption is a transitory state. Before I discuss its usual outcome, I shall present the picture of an-

---

Assuming a community of cultural background—our friend is at home, dealing with denizens of his culture-matrix, and not abroad among not-too-human beings—this lust-object that we have imagined is rather too good to be true. A person who found such a person as our young man attractive and suitable for genital integration *could not* be so healthy. A person who is integrated by sublimatory states is more motivated by power drives and/or hostility, than by simple, uncomplicated lust.

other development which may follow the sudden failure of sublimation. We shall return to our young man, a prey to self-recrimination and conflict. We shall have him, this time, leave the partner without any painful discussion; with, instead, some few hurried words of appreciation—which none the less strike her as reflecting an obscure but curious frame of mind. He will 'put the thought of his experience out of mind' by dint of preoccupation with something. The next night, he will sleep badly, perhaps tossing through the night harassed by unpleasant dreams. The next afternoon, as fatigue increases, he will be very restless and will take a long walk. He may set out for any-where, but at some point, without warning, he will find that he is returning to see his sexual partner, that he is burning with desire to repeat the experience. And he will be terrified. *Panic*, or a state bordering on panic, supervenes.

Panic represents an acute failure of the dissociative power of the self. The mental state is best suggested by referring to a sort of experience which may have befallen anyone. If you have walked each day for years across a little bridge in the side-walk, and it one morning yields under your feet, suddenly gives way and sinks a few inches, the eruption into awareness that accompanies this experience—a blend of extremely un-pleasant visceral sensations with a boundless and practically contentless terror—*is* panic. All organized activity is lost. All thought is paralyzed. Panic is in fact disorganization of the personality. It arises from the utterly unforeseen failure of something completely trusted and vital for one's safety. Some essential aspect of the universe which one had long taken for granted, suddenly collapses; the disorganization that follows is probably the most appalling state that man can undergo. Panic, too, is a transitory state, and, unlike any of the maladaptive conditions I have discussed, a state wholly incompatible with life; it has nothing constructive or palliative about it.

The failure which is responsible for either ecstatic absorption or panic is not merely the collapse of a sublimatory reformulation. It is the failure of dissociations which were connected with, and made possible, the sublimation of the undissociated components of the sexual drives. It is important that one grasp precisely what is meant here, for there is a great deal of loose thinking about 'partial impulses' and 'components' of the broadly defined *libido* of Freud. To help in the clarification, let me revert to our woman who escaped prostitution fantasies by good works, at the behest of the attractive clergyman. It might look as if prostitution fantasies were a simple discharge by revery processes of a strong sexual drive. One often hears discussion of promiscuity, if not prostitution, as being the result of excessive lust. When, on inquiry, one discovers that the sexual partners of such a person are never very satisfactory; that promiscuous women are often frigid—have no orgasm; this simple explanation loses its force. In this culture, promiscuity is generally an outcome of dissociated, rather than of uninhibited, lust.

Our lady entertained fantasies of prostitution not because she simply lusted after many men, but because she had in dissociation a lust after women. She was of the homosexual personal syndrome, but whether by virtue of lack of any permissive acculturation, or of early experience which erected a strong barrier to integrations with members of her own sex, she had no awareness of the homosexual motivation. It existed in dissociation and, as is often the case under this particular circumstance, manifested chiefly in the complex relationship of jealousy. She had barriers which had prevented the evolution of satisfying genital situations with men; this culturally facilitated, however feeble, component had ready access to awareness; was, in fact, a part of the self dynamism. By utilizing its energy for the maintenance of heterosexual revery processes, which conflicted with her ideals of womanhood, a basic component in her self-respect, she none the less had a preoccupation which specifically facilitated the maintenance of the homosexual component in dissociation. Moreover, in this lesser conflict, she had an easy rationalization for any anxiety that she might experience in incipient homosexual integrations. She ran no risk of becoming aware of the dissociated motive, because she was fortified by the insecurity allegedly resulting from the prostitution fantasies. She had but to think "what would she think if she knew what goes on in my mind" to feel a sort of negative expansion of security—"She'll never suspect; I conceal it perfectly." The concealing passed as social necessity in connection with the fantasies; it served as an important attenuating, distance-producing, factor in the unnoted homosexual connection.

I can now point out the complexity of the sublimatory reformulations which are apt to fail in these dramatic and personally very dangerous fashions. The good works in which our lady found her calling kept her in intimate but socially detached contact with unfortunate women. To this extent, the sublimation of the heterosexual was a direct if attenuated satisfaction of the dissociated homosexual components of her genital drives. The social distance is defined by the culture and reinforced by a very necessary factor in the relationship which in a measure traverses the distance defined by social class; namely, the element of philanthropist doing good to others and being ennobled by the one-sided or one-way traffic in good. The nobility of the rôle makes difficult the appearance in consciousness of unworthy personal, physical, attractiveness. It can even be noticed, in abstract, 'objective,' fashion; in that case it had best be discussed with some compeer; this makes it less personal, a general and unimportant observation.

So, too, in the case of our young man, the evil effects of early experience did not merely necessitate a sublimatory reformulation of genital drives. There was also a barrier to women and the corresponding homosexual motivation existed in dissociation. It was the repercussion on the dissociating power of the self that made so dangerous the unpleasant aftermath of his unexpected sexual engagement. The ecstatic absorption is now seen to seek to accomplish a double function by isolating him from either woman or man. The panic appears clearly as the result of failure of all functional efficiency of the self dynamism. I can make the course of events somewhat clearer in the case of panic than in that of absorption; the end state may be almost identical.

Panic is disorganization. Personality reintegrates as swiftly as possible; often as a state of terror with extreme concentration of attention on escape from the poorly envisaged danger, and with every energy directed to flight. Unless something of this sort is possible, panic eventuates in circus movements, random activity, and finally incoördination of the skeletal muscles. In terror, the perception of the danger—the source of threat— is primitive, has the cosmic quality of the very early formulation of the Bad Mother. The whole world is threatening. Everyone is dangerous, hostile, and bent on one's destruction. There is no trace of coöperative, much less collaborative, attitude. The terror-stricken person is alone among deadly menaces, more or less blindly fighting for his survival against dreadful odds.

The extreme restriction of perception may be illustrated by reference to the frequent *delusionary* belief that one is being watched and followed. After panic has passed into terror, many patients believe themselves to be followed by people in automobiles. This comes about rather simply. All the cars that are noticed are behind one. As a car passes, it ceases to have any relevance whatever. It is no longer perceived. Therefore, no car passes one, and so long as there are cars behind one, and they stay behind one, it must be that they are menacing.

Even more disturbing than these errors of perception are the phenomena which arise from autonomous function of some zone of interaction, often the auditory apparatus.[45] Dissociated

[45] The auditory zone is intimately related to the oral zone, particularly in the coördinate function of communication. I have spoken of the partition of energy among the zones of interaction; the 'need to talk' and the need to hear are manifestations both of the tendency to enjoy any ability and of the bio-

impulses, when the self is functioning smoothly, discharge themselves in unnoticed acts. In people whose self integration is unstable, these acts may be a conspicuous part of behavior; in some cases, so prominent that consciousness is clouded at times to preserve security. These latter are the folk who engage in mediumistic and related performances, including automatic writing. In the state of *trance*, the medium may show speech behavior which is of considerable psychiatric interest. The voice-producing apparatus may shift in its pattern of function from the medium's waking speech to one or more markedly different speech patterns. A remarkable imitation of a deep-voiced man may be produced—as the voice of her "control"—not once but at intervals over years of a woman medium's life. The same medium may at times manifest two or more of these pseudo-personalities, by way of different patterns of vocalization, and maintain rather high consistency in these subsidiary patterns over months or years. I mention this to emphasize the degree to which the oral zone—supported by the auditory—can be taken over as it were, as the channel of behavior for dissociated systems.

In the phase of terror following panic which I am discussing, it is usually the auditory zone which becomes intermittently autonomous. The phenomenon of auditory or other *hallucinosis* represents the noticed activity of one of the zones of interaction as the expression of a dissociated system. One hears voices, spoken statements which pertain to the experiential structure of the dissociated integrating tendency. These hal-

---

logically inhering need to reduce tension by the expenditure of the supply of excitation.

David M. Levy has done invaluable pioneering work in this connection. See Fingersucking and Accessory Movements in Early Infancy: An Etiological Study. *Amer. J. Psychiatry* (1928) 7[o.s. 84]:881–918; Experiments on the Sucking Reflex and Social Behavior of Dogs. *Amer. J. Orthopsychiatry* (1934) 4:203–224; A Note on Pecking in Chickens. *Psychoanalytic Quart.* (1935) 4:612–613; and On Instinct-Satiation: An Experiment on the Pecking Behavior of Chickens. *J. General Psychol.* (1938) 18:327–348.

lucinated remarks carry with them many indications of the
non-existent speaker's personality. The hallucinated utterances
come rather quickly to be statements of particular illusory persons or personifications—God, the Devil, the President, one's
deceased mother, and the like. The experience of hallucinosis
is initially deeply disturbing. In patients who have suffered
auditory hallucination for years, "the voices" may become
commonplaces of life, of about the same importance as ordinary conversation.

It must be evident that the theory of hallucinosis is of much
significance in psychiatry. To facilitate a grasp on the several
types of process that are concerned, let me say something about
the phenomena of the *tic*. Besides speech, we have gesture as
a form of communicative behavior and, related to gesture, there
are the postural changes, particularly of the face, by which we
give more or less witting signs of emotional states. The tic is
the autonomous activity of some part of this gestural or ex-
pressional apparatus, sometimes of a whole pattern—winking
of an eye or the shrugging of a shoulder, for example—but
often of but an uninterpretably small part of the pattern. Without any reason apparent to the person, but with some relationship to the interpersonal situation, the muscles concerned perform a personally meaningless action. There is awareness of the
activity, but no perception of anything meaningful about it.
The awareness of the movement can be absent; the person with
a tic often becomes so accustomed to it that its occurrence is
no longer noticed.

The automatism—tic, automatic writing, hallucination—is
expressive of a dissociated tendency to integrate some particular interpersonal situation. Unlike our original presentation
of entirely unnoticed behavior, however, these actions are—or
may easily be—accessible to awareness. The difference is significant, but is one of degree rather than of kind. Thus, one can
be led to notice manifestations of completely dissociated im-

pulses, but one can not be led to perceive the meaning in them. Once having been led to notice them, they are much more apt to be noticed thereafter. In other words, they take on somewhat of the nature of the tic and other forms of automatism *within* awareness. The first directing of attention to one of them is almost invariably quite unpleasant, disconcerting or disturbing. Their subsequent intrusion upon awareness is also at least annoying. All this is quite exterior to their meaning, which, as I have said, cannot ordinarily be elucidated.

We have more than this inferential data if we reconsider the case of our young man who had to reject the part of his food which he had touched. In that case we were able to sketch the rough outlines of experience which had eventuated in the peculiarity of his behavior. The not very clearly formulated notion that his fingers were or might be contaminating was accessible to awareness. He was inclined to regard the habitual rejection of the pieces of bread that he had held as a symptom of his peculiar or abnormal mental state, his 'trouble.' He was led under strong situational pressure to retrace the evolution of the symptom—a very disquieting performance, beyond doubt. The sequence appears to have proceeded from malfeasance of his hands in lustful behavior with a chum, to a substitution *within awareness* of a fear that his hands would poison him as a result of touching the varnished wood at the place of employment, which gradually faded into an habitual but compulsive avoidance of food that he had touched—with the feeling that *other men noticed* the feeding peculiarity and might think he was funny or queer on that account. It is almost as if the final presenting state of awareness about the symptom had retained the second and last terms of a meaningful statement of his unsatisfied desires and had become puzzling and relatively undisturbing by deleting the first, third, and so on, terms of the statement. The particular tendency system under discussion was not fully dissociated from awareness. It was much nearer to clear representation than is the meaning of a tic. Yet nothing recognizably oral-genital had any longer any access at all.[46]

The relevant consideration is roughly the following. When a system of integrating tendencies includes so much energy that it cannot be dissociated—and conflict and anxiety continue—the self dynamism may achieve approximate security by a process of *resymbolization*. The conflict provokes a regressive process and the tendency system undergoes a backward shift along the line of its historic evolution. At some stage in the process, some of its most conflict-provoking components are reduced to elements that, projected in the more adult awareness, would be relatively general and non-specific in meaning. They are adopted as a troublesome, 'irrational' ingredient of life, a symptom, and *by timely appearance* they serve to ward off clear awareness, conflict, and severe anxiety. This is the general formula for compulsive acts, rituals, and taboos.

In the *schizophrenic state*, which we are considering as the sequel to panic, this relatively convenient solution of conflict by resymbolizing and substitution has failed and all that remains of security operations by the self dynamism is a disowning of the now far too meaningful symptoms. Schizophrenia

[46] It may seem that I take considerable liberty in suggesting that there was in this patient a dissociated, an imperfectly dissociated, system of tendencies to the utilization of the mouth in homosexual genital integrations. Consider the following excerpt from my fourth consultative interview with him, eleven years earlier. "To be absolutely frank and candid with you——when I was about six I committed the sin of sodomy——[meaning what?] Oh, God, Doctor, that is disgusting—I don't know just what to say, I can't express—you understand. [You know what you mean; am I supposed to be shocked?] Well, we were playing under the front porch of one of my friends—and a boy much older than either me or my friend—and he was urinating—and—I saw —his brother—take this other boy's penis in his mouth. Now, I didn't know what a horrible thing that was then—and the other boy was older than I—told me that there was nothing wrong with doing that—and committed that error —and that is something that I've been sorry for and would do anything—to wipe out that fact—but it's there. . . . . I haven't told anyone else that, but you and . . . . [his Father Confessor] as he put it, God had forgotten about that, and I ought to, as well."

The final remark indicates the substitution of unabsolvable 'guilt,' as one of the events along the experiential history of his symptom. The overscrupulous are one of the harassments of the clergy.

is a term meaning literally a fragmentation of the mind. The state is factually a splitting of the control of awareness. In all other conditions a monopoly of the self dynamism, awareness in schizophrenic states includes that which is in the self system and also that which attends the autonomous functional activity of the hallucinating zones of interaction. Put in other words, in nonschizophrenic states, awareness—at least awareness of personal meaning—of the situations in which one exists is restricted to integrations brought about by tendencies incorporated in the self dynamism. Nothing else but conflict and anxiety can be present in awareness. In schizophrenic states, on the other hand, a state of conflict has as it were been universalized, the conflict-provoking tendency systems being accorded independent personality with power greater than that of the self. Instead of anxiety, there is fear and often terror. So far as the self functions, the patient is engaged in (regressive) magic operations in an attempt to protect himself, to regain some measure of security in the face of mighty threats, portents, and performances in a world that has become wholly irrational and incomprehensible.

If I have made myself only moderately clear, thus far, you may be wondering why the schizophrenic person goes on suffering the terrifying experiences, when everything would be solved by accepting the dissociated tendencies into the self. This is a rather natural question, if one has lost hold of the interpersonal principle, and instead is thinking of the self as a thing and the dissociated as another thing, the two being the units which make a personality.[47] To 'accept a dissociated

---

[47] As the *ego*, the *super-ego*, and the *id* are sometimes understood by some psychoanalysts to be the three units—hydraulically, mechanically, topographically, or allegorically. I originally adopted the term, *dynamism*, to escape some of the dangers of slipping from a mechanistic analogy into a thinking about mechanism. This usage has spread somewhat, chiefly through the offices of Healy, William, Bronner, A. F., and Bowers, A. M., *The Structure and Meaning of Psychoanalysis as Related to Personality and Behavior;* New York, Knopf, 1930 (xx and 482 and xxiv pp.).

William V. Silverberg, in the introduction to a current study of The Jew

tendency system into the self' is tantamount to undergoing an extensive change in personality, implying a marked change in the sorts of interpersonal situations in which one will have one's being. Not only is there this element of great change, but also there is no possibility of foresight as to the direction and extent of the change. Finally, one could not foretell that this change will be tolerable; there is every prospect of its including serious conflict, for the self dynamism includes powerful tendency systems which are responsible for the character of the present life course. The metamorphosis is scarcely an attractive prospect, even theoretically. Practically, there is no such prospect; there is only the stable course of life in contrast with terrors and anxieties, easily referable to the unknown.

It comes about, therefore, that the schizophrenic person, even though he is aware—in the disowned, 'they,' fashion—of tendencies which manifestly involve him in rather durable integrations incongruous with his past experience and foreign to his at least dimly formulated career-line, cannot easily reintegrate a unitary awareness. Moreover, he cannot accept the manifestations disowned as the performances of others, of the "they" who communicate abuses and disturbing suggestions to him, who make him experience disagreeable and disgusting sensations, and who otherwise through the hallucinosis destroy his peace of mind, perplex and puzzle him, and by fatigue and other interferences reduce him to deeply regressed states of being. Everything in his 'personal awarenesses'—for he now has two—repudiates any suggestion that the experiences are not real, or that they arise from his unrecognized needs and desires.

If he has fortunate experience with the more real people whom he encounters in his disturbed state, the fury of the hallucinosis may decrease, the welter of delusional perceptions may diminish, and something approximating a stable maladjustment of a deeply regressive sort may supervene. The regression of

and His Fellowmen, has indicated that *ego*, *superego* and *id* must be understood as different *modes of functioning;* they make sense in no other way.

personality processes in these fairly quiescent states is such that the patient lives in a world and participates in interpersonal relations, all of which are dreamlike in varying degrees. As this is most clearly observable in the states which we call *schizophrenic perplexity*, I shall give an excerpt of an interview with such a patient. During the interview, the patient suddenly experienced a need to void urine. On his return to his room—where we were talking—the following took place.

"Well, I don't quite understand—what it means to go in there——to pass urine. It's your nature, I suppose, and. Well, for some reason or another, it's—it affects me very much—the —I don't know just how to explain—it affects me—well, just like—giving my—feelings away—to, say—you, instead of—this girl. [He drifts into drowsy preoccupation; is aroused, and presently continues with the following.] Yesterday afternoon—[Yes!] I was—in there—shooting some pool—[Continue!] I was in there shooting French——and——I—touches. What's-his-name puts the 3-ball in the pocket; and the 4-ball —(deep sigh)—and a—I touched the 4-ball, and no more than I did it, and I urinated some in my pants.——And—I'd like to see my girl—we—it was—If I understand it—in a certain way —I—suppose it was more or less this—being around here, and maybe I thought—Miss B.—I suppose she's French—[Miss B. is the black-haired nurse in charge of the ward, towards whom he lately has made some obscure sexual advances] or maybe the feelings—that everybody around here—I had sort of been in contact with and—anyway, as soon as I touched the 4-ball, I couldn't hold my urine.—And then,—after I had urinated, I—I started to write a letter—to the—girl I was talking about ['my girl'; a fantastic love-object]. I didn't write —I took it out and started to, but it was pitch dark in here, so I didn't bother. [Why didn't you turn on the light?]—I never thought about it."

This excerpt shows the classical schizophrenic *spread of meaning*. Matters which are utter commonplaces of life may

be as it were dislocated from their place in the routine of living and elevated into focal awareness—with corresponding
necessity to 'do something' about them, a start at which is to
perceive their "meaning." This patient, having had a disturb-
ingly sudden awareness that he must pass urine, is preoccupied
with what the act means. This is no idle philosophizing. Patients who have come to trust one—part of the time—often
ask questions like "What does it mean when you rub your
nose?", or "What does it mean when people cross the right leg
over the left?", or "What does it mean when a person sits
down to the right of one?". The excerpt gives at least shadowy
indication of what is responsible for the puzzlement as to the
meaning of urinating. The patient progressed, through a phase
of drowsy preoccupation from which the demand implied in
my presence aroused him, to an obscure statement which might
be translated: 'I have a tension which I think should be connected with my heterosexual love object. This need to urinate
arises. I do so and the tension is gone; as if it had been connected with you instead of her.' He came to recount an incident which included involuntary urination. He was playing
pool with some other male patient. He touched the 4-ball and
as a schizophrenic result, urinated. The translation of his obscure remarks might run something as follows: 'I was growing
tense in this game with what's-his-name and the 4-ball in some
way associated itself with Miss B. and I touched it and the
tension became overwhelming and I had an orgasm and I felt
I'd better separate myself from this disturbing personal environment by renewing mediate contact with my girl.'

The excerpt is chiefly concerned with *regressive genital*
activity. The pattern of action in the sexual orgasm of the male
is a coördination of heightened tonus of the prostatic sphincter,
secretory activity of the glands of Cowper, increased tone and
finally emptying of the seminal vesicles into the prostatic
urethra, synchronous emptying of the prostatic gland into the
same area, and finally the occurrence of rhythmical expulsive

contractions of the urethra. These latter are attended by keen sentience rather different from the sentience connected with the expulsion of the last few drops of urine—to accomplish which the prostatic urethra also contracts rhythmically. The difference again is more of degree than kind, and its extraordinary aspects are less the result of the complex processes that are coördinated, than of the sudden release of greatly heightened tone. The contractions of the urethra in orgasm are much more powerful than are those concerned in policing the urethra at the end of urination. But the history of the urethral component of the orgasm greatly antedates the occurrence of orgasm. In the dream-like regressed states, the emergence of a few drops of urine into the prostatic urethra—the event which underlies a strong urge to relieve oneself—sets off the emptying contractions, and the whole can be and often is perceived as a *sexual* phenomenon. These particular regressive changes often take incipiently schizophrenic patients to the medical man. The urologist who finds nothing the matter is all too traditional. The quack is yet another story.

Just a word more as to the indications of dream-like symbol operations which appear in the excerpt. These pertain to the impulses that have provoked conflict. There is the amazing significance of the 4-ball, its relation to French, to Miss B. who is mistaken to be French in origin, her significance as a relief from the pressure of the prevailingly male environment, factors making her unsatisfactory as an illusory sex-object, and the movement to be rid of the actual by absorption in the illusory integration with 'my girl'—a lady who in fact scarcely knew of the patient's existence.

Not only is much of the schizophrenic thinking identical with the symbol operations that are encountered ordinarily in sleep, but the disorder of speech communication in schizophrenia is also paralleled only in ordinary situations where conversation is being submerged by drowsiness or sleep. The schizophrenic peculiarities of speech are chiefly of two orders, called respectively *stereotypy* and the use of *neologisms*. In the first of these much the same thing is said repeatedly, as if it would function with relevance in many different connections. In the latter, new 'words' are created and used as if they were communicative. The two phenomena have in common the defect of consensual validation, the profound parataxic dislocation of the auditor to whom one hears oneself address remarks. In the stereotypy, there is an impractical concentration of meaning in the expression, somewhat the reverse of the extraordinary spread of meaning in happenings in the 'outer' world. In the neologism, a dream-like condensation of several meaningful elements has occurred without the patient's noticing it; as a result of which the new word seems utterly valid, regardless of its inadequate function in communication. Some of the meaning which has been conglomerated in the neologism comes from the tendencies that had provoked conflict, and the inadequate function of the neologism is, therefore, to some extent necessary and satisfactory in that it permits a degree of —autistic—expression without any resulting necessity for an exchange of intelligence—information—and the associated processes of consensual validation. This brings us close to the topic of insight, the bridge that will carry us over into a grasp of conceptions useful in the remedy of mental disorder.[48]

Before leaving the subject of schizophrenic states, we must look rather more closely at the onset and outcome of these grave developments. Before I can make myself entirely clear, however, I must explain to the medically trained members of the audience that my use of the term schizophrenic is not equivalent to a reference to *dementia præcox*. By this, I mean that my conception of schizophrenic states excludes a certain

[48] The fourth lecture of the series was given under the title "Explanatory and Therapeutic Conceptions." In revising the extensive material for publication, it seemed best to divide the subject. [*Editors' note:* Sullivan in his original series gave a fifth lecture on "Prospective Developments and Research." It appears at the end of Lecture V here in abbreviated form. He had planned to expand this later but never did.]

indefinitely large number of the patients who are lumped under Kraepelin's rubric, and under most modern revisions of it. At the 1929 meeting of the Association for Research in Mental and Nervous Diseases, I pointed out the great difference in outcome respectively of acute and of insidious onset of the disorder in superficially similar schizophrenic patients.[49] I did not then stress the differences which appeared in the interpersonal relations of most of the patients with insidious onset. I was still too preoccupied with the seemingly parallel—because inadequately observed and analyzed—outcome of some twenty odd per cent of all these patients, regardless of type of onset. This is the more difficult to justify, for Hadley had demonstrated in 1924, that the 'deterioration' of some chronic schizophrenics is anything but a disintegration of personality.[50] Moreover, I had observed several remarkable social recoveries in patients who had spent years in catatonic states, and had developed some ability for quickly arousing some patients who had been following an uninterruptedly downward course for several years.

In brief, I have come to the opinion that there are two unrelated syndromes confused under the rubric of *dementia præcox*, or—as it is often used synonymously—schizophrenia. One syndrome is the congeries of signs and symptoms pertaining to an organic, degenerative disease usually of insidious development. These patients are finally discovered to be psychotic, although no one can say how long the state has been develop-

---

[49] Sullivan, Harry Stack, The Relation of Onset to Outcome in Schizophrenia. *Schizophrenia (Dementia Præcox)*; Baltimore, Williams and Wilkins (1931) 10:111–118.

This paper summarizes the conclusions of a report to the Neuro-Psychiatric Section of the Baltimore City Medical Society, "Prognostic Implications of the Type of Onset in Schizophrenia," 6 March 1930. The further development of my views is the outcome of subsequent study of patients who showed the simpler substitutive maladjustments as a persistent state, with schizophrenic episodes at times of great situational stress.

[50] Hadley, Ernest E., Is the Prevailing Content of the Hebephrenic Dementia Præcox of an Anal Erotic Character? Report of Study in Hebephrenia, 2 June 1924. Unpublished.

ing. Their outlook is very poor—even, I surmise, under the treatments by partial decortication which now enjoy such vogue.[51] I am content that this syndrome be called *dementia præcox*.

The other syndrome is the one about which I am offering some data. It is primarily a disorder of living, not of the organic substrate. The person concerned becomes schizophrenic—as one episode in his career among others—for situational reasons and more or less abruptly. He may have had months or years of maladjustive living, of one or another of the sorts that I have mentioned. He may have seemed to himself to have been getting along all right, until a few days or weeks before the appearance of frank schizophrenic phenomena. In any case, he knows what has been happening to him. He has not gradually and inattentively drifted into a world of vague philosophizings in lieu of interpersonal relations, or a world of more or less pleasant fantasy quite like that of early childhood. He has come to where we find him by a course that has at times been fraught with fear, terror, or literal panic. At some particular time which he will never forget, the structure of his world was torn apart and dreadful, previously scarcely conceivable, events injected themselves. It may be that he soon finds a way in which to patch up a semblance of his previous living; like my patient who, having accidentally discharged a gun in the direction of a beloved uncle, underwent some days of mutism and refusal of food, but then became approximately as usual until he met rebuff in both sexual and security adjustments, whereupon a prolonged schizophrenic episode appeared. It may be that he

[51] I refer here to the Freeman lobotomy, the metrazol and camphor convulsive treatments, the electroshock, the block method, and so forth. These sundry procedures, to my way of thinking, produce 'beneficial' results by reducing the patient's capacity for being human. The philosophy is something to the effect that it is better to be a contented imbecile than a schizophrenic. If it were not for the fact that schizophrenics—in my sense—can and do recover; and that some extraordinarily gifted and, therefore, socially significant people suffer schizophrenic episodes; I would not feel so bitter about the therapeutic situation in general and the decortication treatments in particular.

finds a way of life such that the schizophrenic episode stands alone, only marking a turning point from which a not very changed career-line has proceeded successfully.[52]

One is definitely schizophrenic when the regression of one's security operations, enforced by parataxic interpersonal relations, actually menaces one's survival. Whether one shall continue to be typically schizophrenic or not is, I believe, wholly determined by situational factors. In other words, I hold that there are *no types* of schizophrenia, but only some rather typical courses of events that are to be observed in schizophrenic states. This view is widely at variance with the Kraepelinian psychiatry and its derivatives; at least four types are recognized in the standard classification. These are enumerated as catatonic, paranoid, hebephrenic, and simple. Some overlapping of these types has always been admitted. Lewis, who made something of a survey of current investigations, comments, for example, "Catatonic features may also occur occasionally, even periodically in some patients, during a lifetime course of hebephrenia, in fact the two reactions are so frequently combined that I prefer to call this class of disorders the 'catatonic-hebephrenic' group." [53]

[52] This constructive effect of schizophrenic disorder, on which I published a paper in 1924, was at the same time under study by Rev. Anton T. Boisen, at the Worcester (Mass.) State Hospital. For a statement of his matured judgments see *The Exploration of the Inner World: A Study of Mental Disorder and Religious Experience;* Chicago and New York, Willet, Clark, 1936 (xi and 322 pp.).

For a fairly comprehensive bibliography on the lumped disorders see Lewis, Nolan D. C., *Research in Dementia Præcox;* New York, National Committee for Mental Hygiene, 1936 (xi and 320 pp.). The most recent significant error arising from confusing the two syndromes appears in the work of Kurt Goldstein and his followers. See his *The Organism: A Holistic Approach to Biology;* New York, American Book, 1939 (xvii and 533 pp.) and The Significance of Special Mental Tests for Diagnosis and Prognosis in Schizophrenia. *Amer. J. Psychiatry* (1939) 96:575–588.

[53] "Research in Dementia Præcox" includes in its text many expressions of opinion that are equally illuminating as to the sad state of psychiatric thinking. The passage quoted—p. 36—is followed by reference to disorders initially of the 'paranoid type' that "seen a few weeks or months later . . . . [were] obviously hebephrenia. *As it is extremely unlikely that any mental disorder changes its type fundamentally,* this means that we have too little knowledge

If the course of one's interpersonal relations comes finally to a schizophrenic state, and this continues without complication, one manifests a pattern of peculiarities which may be called the *catatonic state*. The variation of details in the pattern of catatonic interpersonal relations is great. Its adequate delineation is, however, of no little importance, for the prospects of ultimate restitution to ordinary life continue to be relatively good only so long as the schizophrenic state is uncomplicated. I shall, therefore, attempt a further description, and supplement this by illustrating the changes that may be taken to indicate an unfortunate course.

In the catatonic state, the patient, as a self-conscious person, is profoundly preoccupied with regaining a feeling of security. The processes by which the self dynamism pursues this goal are of the sort rarely manifested after early childhood, except in sleep. Put somewhat more exactly, the integrations which manifest the self dynamism are like those in which a person under three years of age might be expected to be involved. The picture is complicated by the fact that an indefinitely great part of the relevant experience undergone by the patient over the years continues to be in evidence. These integrations include as other people, parataxic illusions after the pattern of the Good Mother, the Bad Mother, the Good Father, and the Bad Father. In so far as subsequent acculturation continues to be effective, it gives to these illusory people various attributes derived from religious beliefs and the particular mythology which the patient has absorbed. The goals of the integrations are security; the performances are almost exclusively power operations. The experience which the patient undergoes is of the most awesome, universal character; he seems to be living in the midst of struggle between personified cosmic forces of good and evil, surrounded by animistically enlivened natural

to enable us to make scientific differential diagnoses." The italics are mine. Note the absence of consensually validated thought in the pronouncement. All that is evident is the author's conviction that mental disorders have fundamental types.

objects which are engaged in ominous performances that it is terribly necessary—and impossible—to understand. He is buffeted about. He must make efforts. He is incapable of thought. The compelling directions that are given him are contradictory and incomprehensible. He clings to life by a thread. He finally thinks that he is dead; that this is the state after death; that he awaits resurrection or the salvation of his soul. Ancient myths of redemption and rebirth seem to reappear, not because the patient has tapped some racial unconscious, but because he has regressed to the state in which only an early type of abstract thinking can be active. He is dead but clearly is not through with life. The remnants of religious teachings appear as an explanation. He will be saved from the failures and faults of his past life. Then he will live again.

Acts and ideas reminiscent of the whole history of man's elaboration of magic and of religion appear in these catatonic states. The abysmal insecurity is the driving force. The deep regression of personality processes is the moulding influence.[54]

In the midst of this dreadful experience, the patient is beyond the commonplace acts by which we live. He takes no food or drink. He notices nothing of the emunctory processes. He does not talk. He does not recognize the personal meaning of other people's actions in his behalf. He may show little activity; may lie nude with eyes closed, mouth finally shut, hands clenched, most of the skeletal muscles in a state of tonic contraction. He may engage in strange, often rhythmical, movements. He may undergo sudden eruptions of excitement, occasionally pass from mute catatonic *stupor* into violent *excitement* with seemingly quite random activity. Other people may

[54] For more details about schizophrenic content, see Storch, Alfred, *The Primitive Archaic Forms of Inner Experiences and Thought in Schizophrenia* [Tr. by Clara Willard]; New York, Nervous and Mental Disease Publishing Co. 1924 (xii and 111 pp.). Reiss, Eduard, Über schizophrene Denkstörung. *Zeitschr. f. d. ges. Neurol. u Psychiat.* (1922) 78:479–487, discusses the relationship of catatonic to primitive (infantile) thought processes. Both authors are carried away by speculations which lack the sound foundations that will be provided by research into the ontogenetic beginnings of personality.

be harmed. He may kill himself. This, however, is all by misadventure. There is no personally oriented hostility nor self-
destructive motivation.

Now, however, let us consider the case in which a personal
orientation of the awesome phenomena *is* found. In other
words, the patient, caught up in the spread of meaning, magic,
and transcendental forces, suddenly 'understands' it all as the
work of some other concrete person or persons. This is an
ominous development in that the schizophrenic state is taking
on a paranoid coloring. If the suffering of the patient is markedly diminished thereby, we shall observe the evolution of a
paranoid schizophrenic state. These conditions are of relatively much less favorable outcome. They tend to be permanent distortions of the interpersonal relations, though the
unpleasantness of the patient's experience gradually fades and
a quite comfortable way of life may ultimately ensue.

The paranoid outcome of incipient or catatonic schizophrenic states is to be distinguished from a paranoid coloring of
the onset of the psychosis. One has also to keep in mind that
schizophrenic processes may erupt in the course of a chronic
paranoid state which was previously relatively free from such
processes. This case, too, requires special consideration. The
estimation of probabilities as to outcome—and as to the proper
limits of therapeutic approach—involves a nice appraisal of the
actual course of events in which the patient has been involved.

Rather fugitive convictions that one is being subjected to
persecutory or destructive influences are almost always incidents in the incipient schizophrenic state. The patient for a
long time has felt unhappy over his inadequacies, has believed
that others did not respect him, that they disliked his company
and perhaps talked in a derogatory fashion about him. This has
made him more and more seclusive. He has kept more and more
to himself and has suffered increasingly from loneliness. In
desperation, he may have put on a bold front and become somewhat exalted, or oddly jovial and overactive. As his processes

of consensual validation are failing, his efforts in interpersonal
relations can scarcely be other than increasingly unfortunate.
He appears more and more preoccupied, inattentive, or given
to puzzlement, misunderstanding, and misinterpretation. Interested and well-intending companions become convinced that
something is wrong with him, that he does not know what
he is doing. This is but natural, as his responses to questions are
becoming more and more unintelligibly autistic. By this time,
if he is still making some outward efforts at keeping in touch
with others, he is certain to have received miscellaneous bits of
advice, many of which have been warped into queer misunderstandings, some of which may have been carried out in a peculiar fashion, with even more disconcerting outcome. The patient sooner or later will have to withdraw from efforts to deal
with his compeers. If he is living at home, he stays more and
more indoors, often seeming to need the company of one of his
parents yet becoming less and less communicative, perhaps
more and more morose and unpleasant.

At this point, a definite persecutory formula is apt to erupt
into the patient's awareness. His mother has been putting poison
in his food; a friend is trying to make him homosexual; people
are reading his mind and printing stories about him in the newspaper. With the expression of these persecutory thoughts, there
may be an 'appropriate' emotion. On the other hand, the emotion may seem wholly 'inappropriate,' as when the patient, in-
forming his mother that he believes she is poisoning him, grins
with obvious embarrassment, and eats his meals thereafter,
with outbursts of mirthless laughter; when, with tense and
awkward excitement, the patient announces to an astounded
friend that he is ready to submit to the other's sexual pleasure;
or when, with what must be taken to be an obscurely angry
helplessness, he tells an acquaintance that he has seen the piece
in the evening paper. The *apparent* incongruity of expressed
emotion and the related idea is most impressive; it is often taken
to be pathognomonic of schizophrenic states, and theories of

the disorder have been built around it.[55] I wonder that negative instances are so easily ignored, that the parallel in one's remembered dreams is overlooked, and that recollections of one's own behavior in awkward situations are not associated with this seemingly fundamental peculiarity of the schizophrenic.

The principal difference between the persecutory coloring of incipient and catatonic schizophrenic states on the one hand, and the ominous paranoid schizophrenic states, on the other, shows itself most obviously in connection with this 'inappropriate' emotional life. The parataxic complexity of the interpersonal relations of the catatonic state is such that very little indeed is manifested in a simple, conventional way. The appearance of any impulse is apt to be followed immediately by some negating impulse. In the act of expressing an idea, a whole series of contradictory or otherwise complicating ideas may occur. About the least that such a patient need expect is that only one pair of contradictory propositions shall be in mind at a time. It is not strange that patients are often 'blocked' in the act of speaking, nor that they often give up the struggle and become entirely mute. The stress of this sort of life is very great. For those whose personal history permits it, the elaboration of a paranoid distortion of the past, present, and future comes as a welcome relief. Instead of an exhausting and extremely embarrassing flow of belief and doubt, proof and dis-

[55] One reads of "disjunctures of affectivity," of "affect congruous with the patient's peculiar content which cannot be shared by the observer, or actual affective incongruity with the content of the moment." Whatever the latter cryptic statement means it seems to imply a separation of the 'observer' and the patient. In 1927, I reported the results of 23 months of intensive work with a patient previously diagnosed variously as *dementia præcox* simple type, paranoidal *dementia præcox*, and—at the Henry Phipps Psychiatric Clinic—schizophrenic reaction type with first catatonic and later paranoid features. That the patient was schizophrenic is beyond question; he was studied at the Sheppard and Enoch Pratt Hospital for some five years. This patient at one time or another in the course of our work, expressed well-nigh the gamut of human emotion, never in any instance that I studied with anything but a simple relation to the content in awareness at the time, or clearly evidenced as verging on awareness. *Publications of the Association for Research in Nervous and Mental Diseases* (1928) 5:141–158.

proof, and a blend of erratically shifting personalities involving each person with whom they are integrated, the paranoid systematization of experience is relatively firm and dependable. It is an improvement, so far as the security of the patient is concerned, not only on the catatonic state, but on the previous uncomfortable prepsychotic existence. Therein lies its most evil potentiality. It can lead to nothing conducive of personal development; quite the contrary. But it can and does give a pay-as-you-go security. The cost is an adoption of hate in the place of a never-quite-realized love. The result of this substitution of hate in place of love as the goal of interpersonal relations is the gradual disintegration of the patient. Before I develop this theme, however, let me remark that, once a persecuting person has been found, and a detailed retrospective account of the persecutory experience has been elaborated, the 'incongruity' of emotion in relation to ideas ceases to complicate the schizophrenic picture. There is rage (fighting fear), hatred (impotent fear), or an unwilling respect—perhaps progressing in this very order to, as the disintegration of the patient becomes marked, a final quite amiable vassalage.[56] The paranoid development, in contrast to the schizophrenic state, is a much simpler negative-destructive attitude to the persons involved in more or less intimate—significant—relations with the patient.

The differentiation of the paranoid development from the persecutory colorings of incipient and catatonic schizophrenic states is dependent on the appearance in the course of the schizophrenic phenomena of a retrospective and prospective falsification of experience pertaining to a person or a personified group. The falsifications are of a piece with those previously discussed in our consideration of paranoid substitutive

---

[56] As stated elsewhere, vassalage is used to refer to the more completely dependent-identification situations in which one of the people concerned seems to act as if he were the source of decisive impulses, while the other (or others) act as if they were but effector organizations for realizing these impulses. This sort of situation grades through limited dependency relations and restricted identification-attachments to lucid (consensually valid) subordinations to competent leadership or example. *Amer. J. Sociol.* (1939) 44:936.

states, plus the extremes of parataxic concomitance which the schizophrenic suffers. The term, *systematization,* is used in this connection. One systematizes a belief by suppressing all negative or doubt-provoking instances, and by bolstering an inherently inadequate account of one's experience with rationalizations in the service of an unrecognized purpose. If the rationalizations are feeble, the belief is said to be poorly systematized; if they are of the sort that would be apt to work with a jury of one's peers, the belief is rather well systematized.[57]

It must be evident that one's beliefs are not necessarily at all closely related to one's manifest interpersonal processes and that the transfer of blame for the results of one's inadequacies does not remove or reduce the manifestation of the tendencies concerned. It decreases the feeling of insecurity and to that extent contributes to the dissociating power of the self dynamism, and by this, it reduces the probability that powerful tendency systems will escape from dissociation and precipitate conflict, regressive change, and perhaps frank schizophrenic phenomena. A paranoid systematization is, therefore, markedly beneficial to the peace of mind of the person chiefly concerned, and its achievement in the course of a schizophrenic disorder is so great an improvement in security that it is seldom relinquished. I am of the opinion that only the most skilful of therapeutic approaches—or the most brutally direct and well-aimed of assaults on the self system—are apt to alter the balance of

[57] While dream-processes are too highly individuated to be apt to impress twelve of one's fellows, it is quite otherwise with rationalizations.

The psychiatrist has to be 'very realistic' about these twelve of one's fellows, for they may be the judges of whether or not he has committed *tort* or *felony* on the patient. Persons suffering paranoid states with minimal schizophrenic processes are often considered to be *sane* and entitled to all the freedom from interferences with personal liberty guaranteed by our government. There is an impressive number of homicides that have been committed by paranoid persons discharged from the custody of mental hospitals by juries of their peers. It is more than annoying that the victim is sometimes the very psychiatrist who had attempted to protect the community by resisting the writ of *habeas corpus.*

power in the direction of again receiving the dissociated tendencies into awareness, so that they may be worked over for good or ill. It is for this reason that the paranoid development in a schizophrenic state has to be regarded as of bad omen.

It might be interesting, at this point, to mention one of the extraordinary situations with which I have dealt. Dr. Paul Ewerhardt and I were some years ago confronted with the problem of diagnosing—with view to determining if a committing of his person or property was desirable—the mental state of an extraordinarily talented soldier of fortune. The father had extracted a promise from the patient that he would spend not more than three days in the Sheppard and Enoch Pratt Hospital, and 'coöperate' with the psychiatrist in discovering if he were of sound mind. We interrogated him for a three and a two hour period, the first day. We demonstrated nothing, even as we became convinced that the patient was suffering a paranoid state. The fact that he had been in the Secret Service of one Great Power, engaged in fomenting disorders among the alien subjects of another, made the task no easier. His work entitled him to believe that his life had been in danger—was still, for he had not retired from this work, but was visiting in the United States because, correctly or otherwise, he felt it had been wise to absent himself for a time from the scene of his operations.

He slept well the first night in the hospital and came fresh and enthusiastic to the interrogation the second forenoon. It, too, in about two and one-half hours, was wholly inconclusive. Dr. Ewerhardt had then to absent himself and I was tired enough of the patient's discourses to turn to other things for a while. In the late afternoon, however, he asked to see me. The exact reason for this, I shall never know.

On entering the office, and seeing me make it safe from eavesdropping, he drew me an odd diagram on a piece of paper. This, he explained, was the symbol of an association he enjoyed with a scientist with whom he had had casual contact on one occasion, abroad. I learned that these two people were about the most important people on earth. They exercised vast powers achieved by command over natural forces, through the instrumentality of hypnotism, and were soon to achieve what we now know as the ambition of Mr. Hitler, hegemony of the world. They were in constant communion, across the continent, by telepathy. Both were imperiled by a horde of secret agents who were all around us. In brief, the patient revealed a well-systematized paranoid state, with but incidental schizophrenic remnants in its structure. He revealed it because, he said, he had received an unmistakable command to do so immediately.

Before I leave the topic of paranoid developments, I shall pay some attention to one of our more venerable psychiatric terms; namely, *paranoia;* and the conception to which it pertains. According to the accepted definition, a person who suffers paranoia is mentally disordered in his reasoning, only. From the interpersonal viewpoint, this definition is absurd. What then of the traditional diagnosis of paranoia? Paranoia must be recognized to be an ideal construction, an abstraction from psychiatric experience. As such, to the extent that it is useful in organizing thought, formulating one's psychiatric observations, it is justifiable. The trouble has been that the ideal, artificial, and in fact impossible, character of the concept of paranoia has been overlooked. Paranoia, defined as an ideal pole in the field of paranoid states, immediately calls to mind as its antipole an equally ideal conception of *utter* schizophrenia. All patients in the large group of paranoid states may be located at some point between an ideal state of pure delusion without admixed autistic processes, and an ideal state in which nothing consensually valid exists. Neither of the polar states can have more than this relevance to psychiatry. It is already evident that the more paranoid a person may be, at a particular moment, the less schizophrenic are his interpersonal relations, and we shall presently see that it works the other way around.

The person diagnosed as a case of paranoia is an intellectually gifted individual whose systematizations make his self system impregnable to any disturbing influence emanating from the situation with the psychiatrist. It is not a case of his reason being disordered; quite the contrary, his reasoning is equal to divesting any communication of its power to stir dissociated tendencies and provoke conflict within awareness.

This does not mean that the more purely paranoid state is a comfortable way of life, a sort of eccentric state of mental health. The paranoid person must be integrated in paranoid interpersonal relations, otherwise the power of the dissociated tendencies comes to exceed the dissociating power of the self, with anxiety, conflict within awareness, or panic, and probable eruption of schizophrenic processes. Whether it is writing bitter and troublesome letters to his Congressman, or starting law-suits, or pestering psychiatrists, or intimidating neighbors; the paranoid person cannot merely repose in his persecutions and grandeur, but must show characteristic interpersonal activity.

I come now to the other unfortunate outcome of schizophrenic states, the *hebephrenic dilapidation*. This change may appear very early in the course of a schizophrenic state. It may occur as the termination of a prolonged catatonic state. It finally appears in any long-continued schizophrenic condition that has not tended markedly to recovery. After a term of years most of the patients who have suffered paranoid schizophrenic states become indistinguishable from the condition of those in whom the hebephrenic change appeared early. When it appears, the hebephrenic state is apt to prove permanent, although even this is not absolute—as demonstrated by the cure of one patient by Kempf, and the 'spontaneous' recovery of a few that I have studied.

The outstanding characteristics of the hebephrenic state, the signs ordinarily enumerated as its description, are a marked seclusiveness—avoidance of any companionship; a disintegration of language processes—the speech is described as scattered, incoherent, vague, unconnected, or showing poverty of ideas; a marked reduction of emotional rapport so that the patient gives the impression of dilapidation or impoverishment of the emotional aspects of life; and the following two kinds of disturbance of behavior. Occasionally, these patients, in most obscure contexts, perform strange, impulsive, and 'senseless' actions. They also, in any significant interpersonal context, show mannerisms. To these descriptive features, the statements are often added that these patients suffer vivid but changeable auditory and visual hallucinations, which may vary greatly in intensity from one period to another; and that they entertain changeable, fantastic, bizarre, or "silly" delusions. The Meyerian psychiatrists refer to an "empty dilapidation" of the habit patterns, with a "childish deterioration." A great deal is heard about the deterioration in which schizophrenic patients often come to spend the remainder of their lives, and I shall have a word to offer about it, later.

I wish now to deal particularly with the *mannerisms* of the hebephrenic patient. Mannerisms, hebephrenic or otherwise, come about by the stereotyping of a gesture or some other interpersonally significant pattern of movement. The activity becomes relatively rigid in the way it occurs, no longer delicately adaptable to the circumstances of the particular occasion. The person who is careful always to speak with an Oxford accent which the hearer finds tiresome is mannered in speech. His relatively rigid patterns of enunciation will affect one in a significantly different way than does the speech of a person long associated with people of the Oxonian dialectic peculiarities. The mannerism will be experienced as an irritating overcomplication, something stilted, artificial, or fraudulent. The usual tendency to suppress troublesome differences in conventional behavior is missing. There is rather an insistent effort as if to assert the particular presumptively prestigeful difference. We accommodate rather rapidly to the 'genuine' peculiarities of the stranger, but the nuisance value of mannerisms grows rather than fades.

While patients in the hebephrenic state often show extraordinarily mannered speech, may be peculiarly stilted in their utterances, and sometimes talk in a fashion that can scarcely fail to convey an element of inappropriate disdain for the hearer, these of their mannerisms are not of prime theoretical importance. Even their sometimes almost entirely stereotyped remarks and their often tedious use of neologisms are by no means pathognomonic. The mannerisms that are perhaps the most striking and significant features of the hebephrenic state appear in the field of nonvocal quasi-communicative gestures. I say quasi because the mannerism does not express anything that is accessible to the patient's awareness—it represents a dissociated impulse—and because the meaning is often obscured by the regressive character of the gesture.

We have already encountered this phenomenon in discussing the tic. We proceeded from that subject to further consideration of my patient who did not eat food that his fingers had touched, an avoidance which we might call a *symptomatic act*. The action was noticed by the patient, was regarded by him as a symptom of his trouble, and it stood for an imperfectly dissociated group of tendencies to integrate particular kinds of strongly disapproved interpersonal relations. If now we regard some few of the many peculiarities of behavior that may be observed in catatonic patients, the place of the term, mannerism, in this field of automatisms and relatively automatic action should become plain. A patient, for example, walked in a curious fashion, apparently as a result of extreme eversion of the feet. This postural peculiarity, on further study, was seen to be a necessary consequence of a persistent adduction of the buttocks. The history showed that he had suffered at one stage of the illness from cravings for pederasty; sensations in the anal zone associated with fear of attack and loathing of the idea of submitting to the procedure. With the development of the peculiarity in locomotion, the distress from these cravings faded out of the picture.

Another patient, when approached by anyone, closes his mouth in a peculiar fashion such that all the mucosa of the lips is pulled into the mouth, and the inverted lips are held between the teeth. This patient has thus been relieved of intense oral cravings, including the belief that his lips had grown thick like those of a Negro. I may remark here that great changes of persistent postural tone in the oral zone of interaction are one of the most frequently encountered phenomena in more promising catatonic patients. It is not uncommon to observe great differences in the amount of mucosa that is habitually everted, in each of the various phases through which the patient passes. Some patients show relatively persisting alterations of the mouth that are almost impossible to imitate, even briefly.

Catatonic patients may keep their fists so habitually clenched for such long periods that organic changes ensue, and the fingers cannot be extended unless the flexor tendons are lengthened by surgical operation.

Many catatonic mannerisms are much more subtle than these. One of my recovered patients, in the early phases of his catatonic state, distorted each 'g' in his writing. The lower loop was always so elongated that it crossed several lines of his script. Many of these patients show relatively persistent innovations in punctuation, capitalization, and even in spelling. This brings us close to the autistic neologisms, already discussed. Some at least of these may be catatonic mannerisms in speaking. We may now return to the quasi-communicative mannerisms of the hebephrenic patient,[58] and discuss the way

[58] The discussion of automatic acts should include comment on habitual movements. Some considerable number of people scratch the head, pick the nose, bore the ears, and the like, with only vestigial awareness of the performance—if they are alone or feel secure with the people present. Some schizophrenics actually rub off a strip of hair by persistently scratching the head. Many schizophrenics touch their heads very gingerly, or arrest a movement just before touching the scalp, often with peculiar movements of the face—which might be called a grimace. These performances may be called manner-

in which these differ from all the other superficially similar performances.

The remarkable thing about hebephrenic mannerisms is their meaning. Not only do they represent the autonomous activity of impulses dissociated from awareness, but they represent the activity of impulses that were once a part of the self dynamism, the dissociating system. In the hebephrenic state, what remains of the self system maintains more or less of a feeling of security by excluding from awareness various impulses which were a part of the prepsychotic self. These impulses had a part in the conflict and chaos of the catatonic state. They were then on the side of angels, opposed to the impulses the manifestations of which horrified or terrified the patient. Now, they themselves are in much the same relationship to the patient's awareness. If they tend strongly to integrate an interpersonal situation, the patient becomes acutely anxious, often becomes seriously disturbed, perhaps acutely hallucinated, excited, assaultive, and more or less randomly destructive.

The clue to this situation is to be found in close study of the hebephrenic way of life. The patient usually shows more ingenuity in avoiding personal attention from others than in anything else. His seclusiveness is no mere withdrawal from discouragement, humiliation, and feelings of being disliked. He avoids all semblances of intimacy with anyone because his peace of mind is seriously discomposed by even the most rudimentary relation with any real person. The people with whom he maintains protean interpersonal relations are animistic natural objects and other simulacra born of a very great recession of personal development. The regression may be so great that

isms, but are better considered to be schizophrenic distortions of habitual movements. See, as to the origin of some habitual movements, Levy, David M., Finger-sucking and Accessory Movements in Early Infancy; reference footnote 45, page 67. See also, Krout, Maurice H., A Preliminary Note on Some Obscure Symbolic Muscular Responses of Diagnostic Value in the Study of Normal Subjects. *Amer. J. Psychiatry* (1931) 11 [o.s. 88]:29–71.

very little exists in awareness except elaborations of sentience connected with the physiological processes of the patient's body. All that remains of acculturation and of integrative tendencies that once had high satisfaction value is in dissociation, expressing itself in the mannerisms, if at all. Real people endanger this state. They provoke the unwelcome integrative activity and they interfere with the activity by virtue of which the hebephrenic self is in its lowly measure secure.

I believe that the alleged emptiness of the hebephrenic is one manifestation of these security processes; the silliness, another. What little data I have from my own work with these patients seem wholly congruent with the findings of Hadley and of Kempf. The hebephrenic has shed the troublesome demands of living among people. He cannot escape the proximity of people, but he can, often in a sort of crudely humorous way, belittle them to his own level of existence—just so they leave him alone and do not stir up any of the past that has ceased to harass him.

On the wards of larger mental hospitals, one sometimes can listen in, as it were, to a 'conversation' between two of the dilapidated patients who have come to find each other's company inoffensive. The remarks of each are made with due regard for the principle that only one person should be speaking at a time. There may be considerable intonational coloring, as if, for example, questions were being asked and answered, or as if one had reminded the other of something astonishing to him. The remarks, however, have but the most remote, if any, connection with those of the other. Each is talking to himself, but is doing it in a sort of double solitaire played after the fashion of conventional language behavior.

The intrusion of someone to whom long habituation has not occurred, who moreover shows interest in the patient, and pays attention to anything said, is quite another matter. Mannerisms rather in abeyance during the 'conversation,' become conspicuous. There may be a forbidding display of anger. The patient may resentfully move away. If not, he will probably laugh in a 'silly' fashion, from time to time, and discourage the intruder by the incoherence and irrelevance of his utterances. The silliness, 'senseless grinning,' and the like, seem to be called out by obscene, belittling thoughts that occur to the patient. He is by no means devoid of humor, even if his 'refinement' is conspicuous by its absence. I think, also, that he is far from 'empty' of revery processes and practical thinking. His incentives are not at all adapted to our habitual mode of life; one of his chief concerns seems to be the preservation of the status quo, regardless of other people's pressure.

Here, again, my picture of hebephrenic dilapidation will not be complete without brief comments first, on the necessities that confront these patients, and then on the general pattern of their course. This state is not by any means one merely of contented vegetation to the accompaniment of primitive autistic reveries and the simplest of zonal satisfactions. Many patients in a hebephrenic state seem for long periods to be contented, if left alone. All of them may have episodes of extreme agitation and violence, the provoking circumstances of which are entirely obscure. They are all busily hallucinated at least part of the time, the 'voices' are usually accepted in good part, but under some circumstances become unpleasant and thoroughly disturbing. Many of the patients talk *with* the hallucinated voices, have long felt compelled to maintain amicable relations with the illusory "they" whom they hear, and have in fact sunk into the hebephrenic state in gradual relinquishment of any independent existence.

Whether, once this hebephrenic change has begun, the patient will continue to sink in the scale of personal evolution, or will come finally to a relatively stable condition, is, so far as I can determine, beyond early prediction. If the dilapidation progresses, the end-state of the patient is practically indistinguishable from that of the probably organic deterioration called *dementia præcox, simple type*. These patients undergo a progressive shrinkage of initiative, a disintegration of social habits, including communication, and a seeming evaporation of any interest in events impinging on them.

It has been demonstrated in a few cases of hebephrenic change that it is not irreversible. By great and well-directed effort, a patient has sometimes been brought back—by prolonged treatment with a stormy course—to the catatonic state or even to a measure of social rehabilitation. Therapeutic effort has sometimes been successful in relieving a hebephrenic patient of some particularly disturbing aspect of his problems, with improved institutional adjustment of the plateau type suggested above. On the other hand, attempts at therapy are often wholly ineffectual. After a patient has been out of contact with the ordinary courses of life for several years, it is often entirely impractical to expect more than an institutional adaptation to be possible for him.

Before I conclude this presentation of explanatory conceptions I must touch very briefly on the topic of the involutional states, after saying a few words about the *psychotic accompaniments* of various organic diseases and degenerations. An example may show a principle that is useful in this latter connection. *Paresis* is both a disintegration of the central nervous system as a result of its invasion by the microorganism causing syphilis, and also a mental disorder of more or less characterizable course—or courses. As the central integrating system is impaired, the interpersonal processes necessarily undergo changes. These changes include the altered attitudes of others as actually reflected to the patient and as distorted by the insidious changes affecting his integration of sentience and elaboration of information. The tendencies to stable maladjustment after the pattern determined by his career are clouded by the progressive organic change, and the paretic psychosis thus comes to be a blend of rather rapid disintegrative change with—most frequently—a grandiose expansiveness that becomes more and more boundlessly unreasonable. Almost any symptoms of interpersonal difficulties can appear as relatively transient phenemona in the picture.

Another important member of this group is the so-called *alcoholic psychosis*. The excessive use of liquor is not in the same class as is an infection. One usually drinks a long time before there are any demonstrable organic changes from chronic alcohol poisoning. Sometimes relatively non-personal factors intervene in an alcoholic career and precipitate the peculiar *delirium tremens*. The alcoholic psychosis, however, is not an acute internal medical problem. It is a rather characteristic deviation of the life course, determined by the patient's career among others, as it in turn has been altered by the specific effect on interpersonal relations of intoxicating amounts of liquor. The outcome is almost invariably a paranoid state with but little schizophrenic coloring. The delusions are very frequently centered around the emotion of jealousy with a conviction of the infidelity of the husband or wife.

Finally, quite frequently, in women around the time of the menopause and occasionally in men around the age of sixty, a so-called *involutional psychosis* may appear. These states are usually considered to be allied to the manic-depressive psychosis. I believe that this is not always the case in women and but seldom the case with men. The forms of the involutional illness are principally two: the agitated depression, which seems to be a depression with rather fixed schizophrenic features; and the *world-disaster psychosis*, essentially schizophrenic, and sometimes encountered in schizophrenic states occurring before age 25. As I can scarcely present enough of a picture of the schizophrenic state, I shall illustrate the world-disaster psychosis by a brief statement about such a 23 year old patient who made an excellent recovery.

This young man was deeply attached to his mother and very strictly disciplined by his father. He did well in school, took an interest in sports, and mixed well with other boys. After finishing high school and a brief special course, he secured a job away from home. This work was a seasonal position; the rest of the time he lived at home and worked on the farm. His father died suddenly of apoplexy, and the mental disorder began before the funeral. The following are selected quotations from our conferences.

"It is too late to do anything—I am worse now than I was when I came—I ate my stomach up and . . . . the real thing is I never believed in God—I believed, but I just kept putting it off, putting it off—I could have saved all this easily—I didn't do right—Everything is all gone now—I am not gone but— the whole earth is gone, almost. . . . . I won't see my mother any more. I am worse and worse. I keep going wrong all the time. Might as well have went to prison in the first [place], I would have been worse, I would have been better off. I am the worst sinner on earth. . . . ." Patient then explained that he had swallowed the filling out of an incisor tooth, as a result of which he had ruined his stomach, and was ruining the world. Said he now could not sleep at night; his room-mates called him disagreeable names all night long.

"I would have been all right if I had stayed at home. I was all right before I came up here [to the hospital]. Never will get back home now, will I? I wish I was back home. I can't get back home though. The world is coming to an end; that was caused by my coming here. [Swallowing the piece of tooth] caused me to eat up my stomach, insides; it ate itself up. I know that's what did it. I am worse than the Devil, ain't I? I haven't any feelings, hardly. . . . . I have brought crime on the world. I know it . . . . [The place where he worked] is all burned up . . . . I liked working in town. . . . . Dad said I ought to stay home and help him on the farm. . . . . The whole world is talking about me. Say I am the worst scoundrel. Dummy, small, bastard, yellow, dirt, and everything. . . . . Somebody dies every day on my account. People killing themselves all day long. The city is all tore up. . . . . I was a member of the church, took interest in everything, helped people. Just all at once I just got this stuff in my stomach and all over my hands and spread it through the air and that's how things started. The further I went the further it spread. Ought to have had better sense than to have come to a city. I couldn't tell you to save my life [what the stuff was]; I know it was some kind of stuff in my teeth. Just got nervous, kept sucking my teeth, and—ate my insides up. I haven't got any insides. They are inside there, but not in working order. I know when I eat it all goes to water, and everything. My bowels never move any more, since I left home . . . . if I lived, every-one else would get that. [If I] bury myself or starve myself for other people, it would be all right. . . . . There isn't any-thing in the world to eat. Everybody is starving to death and I just caused every bit of it myself. . . . . [The voices] call me 'bum' and all that. They call me every low name they could. . . . . I am losing weight all the time. The more I eat, why, the more people I send to hell. . . . . I am eating the Lord's body everytime I eat. . . . . The Lord said to me 'Well, you should live—you have got to die for the rest of the world'; and I didn't do it. . . . . Something is missing every day. . . . . [Today it is] some of my clothes. And I wasn't supposed to eat and I have been eating all the time [since being fed by the nasal tube, after refusing served meals]. Everything is gone, everything I own in the world is gone. I let the world come to an end. . . . . I was the one that was supposed to save the world, and I didn't do it. . . . . Every time I eat it gets colder all the time. . . . . I haven't any insides, any intestines. I haven't any lungs. I am dead, that's all, about dead. Should have starved myself. . . . . I am getting worse all the time, weaker. I ought to go home. Ought never to have come [to the hospital] at all. I think I'll—I think I'll go home. Should have been home long ago. . . . . I can go home now. . . . . Might as well go home, hadn't I? Don't do me any good to stay here; only doing harm to other people. People don't want me here. . . . I ought to go home. I know I should go home and tend to my own business. I know that people are suffering on my account [yawns]. I know I shouldn't eat, yet I keep on doing it."

When he was well advanced in reintegration of personality, this patient said: "I used to think I destroyed the world. I thought people were suffering on my account. . . . . Something on my mind caused it, probably my father's death. . . . . Felt afterwards maybe I could have been a better son to him, probably. My other brother was his favorite son. They used to get along good, but I never could get along with father; we'd work together and have a fuss. I had a pretty hard time with my father. He used to beat me, get a switch and whip me—for talking to him rather rough, or not doing something right, the way he wanted it done. It was mostly his disposition; that kind of a man, gruff, never explained anything. . . . . I used to tell him I was going away and never coming back any more. . . . . I would go to the city and after awhile he would write me to come home. I would go home, and it would be the same thing again. I would get more work done than the other brother, but he would get along better. He could take the car and go away if he wanted to. . . . . I used to go out and work and get giddy and sick . . . . especially in the hot sun; I used to almost have sun stroke at one time—about [the age of] 15, 16, 17—I was wearing long pants, I know. Always felt worried at home on the farm. Didn't like the work and didn't get along with father."

This young man was of a very strongly moral cast, and his psychosis was precipitated by the sudden—and shockingly welcome—death of his father. The involutional illness in the fifth, sixth, and seventh decades of life is frequently the outcome of a career of interpersonal frustration through the instrumentality of a rigid moral system acquired in the early years but energized in adolescence by the coming of lust. In many, if not in all of those who presently manifest this disorder, there has been throughout the adult years, an imperfect sublimatory handling of the more powerful integrating tendencies, with no instances of frank failure, but with many approaches thereto —and often, I believe, a sustained course of almost frankly meaningful revery processes which are entirely concealed from everyone else, and regarded as a secret vice. The psychosis is precipitated, in women, by realization that the time for fully meaningful sex life is at an end. In men, I surmise that the precipitating factor is the waning of illusions of potency. In other words, they too find that fantasy of full meaningful sex behavior after the established pattern is no longer possible. It is notable that the involutional disorder in men is almost always prefaced by an obscure gradual deterioration of physical health. Fairly frequently, there is a history of some disturbing event, such as loss of money, immediately before the health began to fail.

As a final contribution to the picture of schizophrenia, I shall here digress to illustrate the dramatic failure of the sort of career that might otherwise have terminated some years later in an involutional state. This is the case of a teacher whose work entailed an almost pastoral relation with adult students, mostly women. He was of impeccable virtue, but secretly he had for many years enjoyed a rather remarkable fantasy. He accompanied himself in his conferences with these students, with an illusory stallion who made most gloriously free with the women. As he entered the sixth decade of life, he passed swiftly into a state of utter terror—as the stallion broke loose from his 'imaginary' character, became real and autonomous, and even made free with the person of the teacher, himself. Admitted in a frantic excitement, with lurid hallucinosis, ideas of poisoning, utter refusal of food and drink, mutism, and continued catatonic activity, the patient rapidly exhausted his vitality and progressed into grave physical condition. Under treatment, however, he reintegrated a more adequate personal life which has kept him in comfortable circumstances for some fifteen years past.

The world-disaster psychosis is of no such abruptly self-disintegrating a character as was this psychosis of our teacher. It often first comes to notice by way of a panicky period on awakening during the night. The patient is more or less confused as to persons and objects in his environment, and convinced that something terrible is happening. Someone may be killing the family. The building may be afire. An earthquake, or an explosion, has happened. It is only after this acute disturbance passes that the more settled, preexistent content —such as bowel-change and world-disaster, a peculiarly frequent combination—rises to expression. The course of the disorder is deeply regressive, the behavior often manifests a great deal of hatred, and there is frequently a continuing preoccupation with the excrement, the patient becoming not only untidy but definitely coprophilic. The general type of nihilistic delusion is to the effect that the patient has destroyed everything, everyone, or at least the members of his family. The outlook for recovery is very poor.

The other type of involutional mental disorder, the *agitated depression*, occurs much more frequently. When fully developed, this is a picture of stereotyped depressive ideas, often of having committed the unpardonable sin—which cannot always be recalled—as a result of which the soul is lost and one is to be put to death. There is a recurrent or even a sustained state of apprehension, with wringing of the hands, moaning, groaning, and the utterance of woe—oh my God, oh my God, oh my God; and the like. The motor agitation may continue well into the night, so that the patient obtains but little sleep. There are apt to be ideas opposed to taking enough nourishment. The patients are often rather blindly resistive, yet given to clutching on to passers-by from whom reassurance is begged. Nothing of reassurance is possible. The patient becomes preoccupied the moment that she finds that one is not bringing her a message of doom. Fearing greatly that they will be killed, feeling that they are being or are about to be tortured, these patients are the most actively suicidal of all the mentally disordered.

I must bring to a close this sketch of the more important of our explanatory conceptions. I trust that, if nothing else has been accomplished, I have made clear that there are few fixed mental disorder entities; that instead far the greater number but manifest particular directions in which the field of interpersonal relations may be disturbed. The degree of disturbance in the case of any particular patient may become relatively unvarying; or, under stress of situational factors, may change from one relatively unvarying to another relatively persisting degree. Along the direction in which these disturbances can occur, we find it useful to formulate a series of definitions. These 'typical' states are naturally those points in the series at which many patients reach a relatively unvarying condition. There are other patients who do not approximate a 'type' but are somewhere in the series between two 'types.' The disturbances are ways of meeting the necessities of life as they are determined by one's history *and* the present interpersonal situation. The past conditions the particular events which precipitated the episode of mental disorder *and, with the foresight of the patient,* which is itself a function of the past, determines the type of disorder in interpersonal relations in which an equilibrium may be approximated. Events which alter the patient's anticipations of the future may open the way for a further development of the personality and a movement towards mental health. Other events may close these possibilities, so that the disturbed interpersonal relations are held as the only possible way to go on living. Suicide, intended or by misadventure, may end it all. Prolonged separation from more conventional life, and deep regression and disintegration of culturally conditioned interests and activities may fix the patient in the institutional setting, comfortably adapted to a rôle of some usefulness, or as a chronic nursing problem.

Therapeutic Conceptions

THE PURPOSE of psychiatry is the understanding of living to the end that it may be facilitated. The goal may be viewed from the standpoint of treating mentally disordered patients. Even from this viewpoint, one cannot but realize that the social order itself is an important factor with which one must reckon in formulating therapeutic aims and the procedures for their realization. If the psychiatrist is able to maintain his perspective, he comes sooner or later to see that there is another perhaps even more significant standpoint from which to consider the ways and means by which the purpose of psychiatry can be achieved. I refer here to contemplating the social order, not merely as it sets the limits within which the patient's interpersonal relations may succeed, but rather as the mediate source from which spring his problems which are themselves signs of difficulties in the social order. Yesteryear, it might seem that this broader viewpoint should be reserved for the philosopher, or for the psychiatrist who had retired from the toil which is still the common lot of most of us. Today, the acceleration of social process has become so great that almost every psychiatrist has some occasion to realize that the first viewpoint is too narrow; that the level of general insecurity is rising, that the social order is in a sense itself gravely disturbed, and that psychiatry as a therapeutic art is confronted with new tasks that require a change of orientation and the perfection of new techniques.

I must necessarily confine myself, chiefly to that which we have learned in our efforts to participate helpfully in the lives of the mentally disordered. The broader aspects of therapy are scarcely ready for generalization. We can form some conceptions that are useful in dealing with relatively well-organized groups; for example, the armed forces, or the workers employed in the larger industries. We can formulate a number of principles that should be generally useful in the unhappy contingency of serious national emergency. But I, certainly, can offer nothing particularly inspiring for the general benefit of our people in their particular present state. I must say that I feel deeply disquieted by what I perceive to be the general attitude towards the course of world events. It seems as if our most remarkable development of education had failed to inculcate any deep sense of civic responsibility based on a clear understanding of the absolute dependence of personal welfare —of those of us who wish to continue our democracy—on the welfare of the nation as a whole and on the adequacy of its defensive personnel *and* matériel. This failure is manifest in the futile, the trivial and the positively harmful activities with which a great many of our people are responding to the increasing uncertainty, insecurity, and discouragement that is coming to be the common lot.

I make no apology for introducing this gloomy view as a preface to my consideration of benevolent psychiatric procedures. No other group of our citizens has a greater stake in the future of these United States than have the psychiatrists who are students of interpersonal relations. Our psychiatry emerged here in the peculiar setting of our national life; it has developed along lines of promise for reciprocal service in the evolution of ever-increasing human dignity, fraternity, and opportunity. It had looked forward with growing confidence to the time when the incidence of grave maladjustments of living would be greatly reduced by virtue of our increasing civilization. A crisis in world-events now imperils all this, and one may well wonder if the emergence of our psychiatry was not much too late in the era of realizing democratic ideals.

The therapeutic conceptions of modern psychiatry arise directly from the work of Freud, Meyer, and White. Were it not for Freud's formulations, we would probably still be frustrated by the obvious discontinuities in the stream of consciousness. Had it not been for Meyer's insistence that mental disorders are to be considered as dynamic patterns, as types of reaction to the demands of life, we might still be working in the laboratory on problems of neurophysiology and endocrinology. But it was White's ineffable zeal in teaching us to "determine what the patient is trying to do," his indomitable energy in training and in encouraging psychiatric investigators, and his vision and sagacity in the executive, administrative, and promotional aspects of psychiatry in the broader sense, that gave us most of our profit from Freud and from Meyer. Called early from a clinical career to the far more demanding application of his insight to the management of legislators, educators and physicians, Dr. White—convinced that psychiatry has to serve in order that it may study—found his 'patients' everywhere. His practice of psychiatry interpenetrated every aspect of his life. He came to be the very opposite of insular in his psychiatric formulations; he needed no special language and his appraisals of the work of others erred generally on the positive side.[59]

Early convinced of the lawful operation of the human mind, and of the usefulness of determinism as a premise for the study of human conduct, Dr. White received his first clinical orientation from Boris Sidis, and his first great research enthusiasm from Sigmund Freud. As Abraham A. Brill was shortly to become Freud's American protagonist, so Dr. White immediately became the champion of open-mindedness toward psychoanalysis among leaders of psychiatric thought. To him goes

[59] See, for his bibliography, *The Autobiography of a Purpose;* reference footnote 1, p. 1.

first honor for maintaining the healthy eclecticism that has characterized American psychiatry and that has carried it far beyond psychiatry elsewhere in the world. To his credit principally, and to that of Brill, Chapman, Meyer, Kirby and Oberndorf, is the fact that we regard psychoanalysis as one of the psychiatric techniques and require medical and psychiatric training as a preliminary to training for psychoanalytic practice. The foresight of these early students of Freud has greatly impressed me as I have observed the course of events in the period from my first personal experience with psychoanalysis in 1915 to the present.

I can scarcely avoid a tendency to be autobiographical at this point. My psychoanalytic reading began with Hart's *The Psychology of Insanity*; Jung's *The Psychology of Dementia Præcox*, and Freud's *Three Contributions to the Theory of Sex* followed; thereafter Jung's *Psychology of the Unconscious*, Ferenczi's *Contributions to Psychoanalysis*, Freud's *Traumdeutung*, and *The Psychopathology of Everyday Life*. There then came Kempf's *Psychopathology* with its case reports in importance second to none. It is my impression that, aside from Freud's discussion of the Schreiber case, and Groddeck's *Das Buch vom Es*—the ego is essentially passive; we are lived by unknown and uncontrollable forces—my subsequent reading of more purely psychoanalytic contributions has fallen under the law of diminishing returns.[60]

[60] Hart, Bernard, *The Psychology of Insanity;* Cambridge, Cambridge University Press, 1912 (ix and 176 pp.). Now in its 4 ed., N. Y., Macmillan, 1931 (ix and 191 pp.).
  Jung, Carl G., *The Psychology of Dementia Præcox;* N. Y., Nervous and Mental Disease Publishing Co., 1909 (xx and 153 pp.).
  Freud, Sigmund, *Drei Abhandlungen zur Sexual-theorie.* Tr. by A. A. Brill as *Three Contributions to the Theory of Sex* [3 ed.]; N. Y., Nervous and Mental Disease Publishing Co., 1930 (xiv and 104 pp.).
  Jung, Carl G., *Die Psychologie der unbewussten Prozesse.* Tr. by Beatrice Hinkle as *The Psychology of The Unconscious;* N. Y., Moffatt Yard, 1916 (lv and 566 pp.).
  Ferenczi, Sandor, *Contributions to Psychoanalysis* [Tr. by Ernest Jones]; Boston, Badger, 1919 (288 pp.).
  Freud, Sigmund, *Traumdeutung;* Leipzig, Deuticke, 1900 (4, 371 and 4 pp.).

The focus of my interest from before medical school having been the schizophrenic states, a detail to duty at St. Elizabeths Hospital in 1921 finally brought opportunity for a variety of observations in an atmosphere of brilliant clinical psychiatry. This opportunity was greatly expanded by my transfer to the Sheppard and Enoch Pratt Hospital where nothing need interfere with the most intensive and prolonged study of informative patients. By 1925, I had convinced myself of the inadequacy of *any* extant formulation of the schizophrenic states, and offered a preliminary statement of the conservative as contrasted with the destructive aspects of these conditions: "the conservative aspects . . . . are to be identified as *attempts by regression* to genetically older thought processes . . . . *successfully to reintegrate masses of life experience* which had failed of structuralization into a functional unity and finally [had] led by that very lack of structuralization to multiple dissociations in the field of relationships of the individual not only to external reality, including the social milieu, but [also] to his personal reality." [61]

Tr. by A. A. Brill as *The Interpretation of Dreams* [3 ed.]; London, Allen and Unwin, 1927 (510 pp.). 9 ed. revised; New York, Macmillan, 1933 (600 pp.). New ed. revised; Macmillan, 1939 (600 pp.).

Freud, Sigmund, *Zur Psychopathologie des Alltagslebens*; Berlin, Karger, 1907 (132 pp.). Tr. by A. A. Brill as *The Psychopathology of Everyday Life*; London, T. Fisher Unwin, 1914 (vii and 342 pp.).

Kempf, Edward J., *Psychopathology*; St. Louis, Mosby, 1920 (xxiii and 762 pp.).

Freud, Sigmund, Psychoanalytische Bemerkungen über einen Autobiographisch Beschriebenen Fall von Paranoia (Dementia Paranoides). *Jahrbuch f. Psychoanalytische Forschungen* (1911) 3:9–68; and, Nachtrag zu dem Autobiographisch Beschriebenen Falle von Paranoia (Dementia Paranoides). *Jahrbuch f. Psychoanalytische Forschungen* (1911) 3:588–590; both published in *Gesammelte Schriften* and translated as Psychoanalytic Notes Upon an Autobiographical Account of a Case of Paranoia (Dementia Paranoides). *Collected Papers*; London, Hogarth (1925) 3:387–470.

Groddeck, Georg; *Das Buch vom Es;* Leipzig, Internationaler Psychoanalytischer Verlag, 1925 [2 ed. 1926]. Tr. by L. Pierce Clark as *The Book of the It;* N. Y., Nervous and Mental Disease Publishing Co., 1928 (244 pp.).

[61] The quotation is from Schizophrenia: Its Conservative and Malignant Features. *Amer. J. Psychiatry* (1924) 4:77–91. Muncie's *Psychobiology and Psychiatry*—reference footnote 10, p. 4—includes an "Historical Survey in Bibliography of Development of the Concepts Underlying the Principal Re-

Dr. White often remarked that an understanding of the schizophrenic states would also solve a great many other psychiatric problems. Some ten years spent in studying these conditions convinced me of the interpersonal nature of the psychiatric field. Another ten years in office practice with the closely related substitutive states, obsessional and other, has refined and consolidated the earlier insights. It is from this background that I bring what I can offer of therapeutic conceptions, including matters of differential diagnosis and prognostication.

Diagnosis and prognosis cannot be dissociated from therapeutic considerations. This comes about not so much because different therapeutic efforts are required for the various disorders. Rather, it follows because the information which one requires for making a diagnosis is most readily secured in a situation oriented to treatment. Let me develop this topic. For many years it has been the rule that psychiatrists shall conduct an initial more or less formally routine mental examination of their patients. This is all but invariable in many of the State Hospitals systems, where the manual edited by Kirby as Director of the New York State Psychiatric Institute has been widely adopted.[62] There are practical considerations that ren-

action Sets . . ." which shows that nothing of significance in the field of schizophrenia—excepting Cotton's focal infection theory and Lewis' primary cardiovascular aplasia theory—has happened in America since Meyer, Jelliffe, and Hoch gave their résumé of dynamic conceptions in 1911. Meyer's "Fundamental Conceptions of Dementia Præcox" appeared in *Brit. Med. J.* (1906): 757–760; and also in *J. N. & M. Disease* (1907) 34:331–336; Freud's "Analyse eines Falles von Chronischen Paranoia," in *Neurol. Centralbl.* (1896) 15:442–448.

[62] Kirby, George H., *Guides for History Taking and Clinical Examination of Psychiatric Cases;* Utica, N. Y., State Hospital Press, 1921 (83 pp.). The plan of the examination is basically that formulated by Meyer, who preceded him in the same post. A modification of this outline is given in Henderson, D. K., and Gillespie, R. D., *A Text Book of Psychiatry* [3 ed.]; London, Oxford University Press, 1932 (ix and 595 pp.). Most textbooks include advice as to the psychiatric examination. See, for example, White, William A.; *Outlines of Psychiatry* [14 ed.]; N. Y., Nervous and Mental Disease Publishing Co., 1935 (vii and 494 pp.) and Noyes, Arthur, *Modern Clinical Psychiatry* [2 ed.]; Phila., Saunders, 1940 (570 pp.).

der this procedure desirable. Most hospitals are understaffed and much of this work has to be delegated to relatively inexperienced medical officers. Expeditious achievement of some information in all the important fields of possible abnormality is facilitated by the use of a routine. The administrator of any hospital may be confronted by legal action amounting to a requirement that he show cause for the further detention of any recently admitted patient. If he fails, for want of information convincing to the judge or jury, an action to recover damages for alleged illegal detention of the patient may follow. However closely a hospital administration may come to Dr. White's dictum that in case of doubt the welfare of the patients shall determine policy, the legal responsibility and the enduring public attitudes to mental hospitals combine to require an early documentation of the patient's need for hospital care.

The differences of the interrogation for history taking and establishment of the "mental status," from the therapeutic interview are chiefly the results of lack of time, inadequate experience, and erroneous preconceptions on the part of the examining physician. The examination in either case is often conducted on the assumption that one person is obtaining information from the other. Our interpersonal viewpoint indicates that this is decidedly too naive a view. The interview situation is never so simply one-sided. It is never one who gives and one who takes. While it may be hard to see, in some cases, there is always a measure of exchange of information, and some consensual validation of expressed views. This touches on the greatest fault of the interrogation. There is so little of validation that neither the physician nor the patient are apt to be accurately informed as to the views of the other. The patient often receives misinformation which substantiates a body of his erroneous beliefs. The psychiatrist is often misled into formulating a history and a description of the present state of the patient that is a complex product of objectively valid fact and the preconceptions of doctor and patient. These unfortunate results of the formally routine examination have led some administrators to assign more experienced psychiatrists to the admitting services. These admitting medical officers make a brief but searching interrogation of each new patient, and incorporate their impressions in an Admission Note. In so far as the experienced psychiatrist deliberately or unwittingly gives the patient some valid insight into what is to be expected in the hospital, this is a distinct improvement. I think, however, that I might well illustrate, at this point, the evil effects that can be attendant on a hurried interview.

I worked at one time with a youth of 17 who manifested a severe and ominous schizophrenic state. We had some hour-long conferences, the first few of which amounted to very little, so far as communication was concerned. There came finally an hour in which the patient, as the end of the hour approached, mentioned the sexual performances in which he had been engaged by a boarder who had subsequently married the patient's mother, shortly before the psychosis occurred. I was then working in the room in which clinical conferences of the hospital staff were held. As the patient ended his communication, and I was attempting in haste to convey reassurance to him, the first group of the staff came in. I had to interrupt, continuing my remarks as I walked with the patient to the entrance of the hospital wards. On his way from that door to the door of his ward, he eluded the attendant who had joined him as we parted, rushed into a sun room, whipped off his belt, tightened it around his throat, and fought off an attendant and a nurse until he collapsed from asphyxiation. The subsequent course of his mental disorder was uninterruptedly unfortunate and he has resided for years in a State hospital. I have not since then permitted a patient to enter upon the communication of a gravely disturbing experience unless I have plenty of time in which to validate his reassurance as to the effect of the communication on our further relations.

Any interview presumes the existence of interlocking culture patterns, some approximate identities in acculturation of the people concerned. The most notable of these elements is generally the language. The risk here is the ease of assuming a full identity where there is only a superficial similarity. I could give such examples without number. Let me instead approach the subject from the standpoint of psychiatric discussion. It has for years been conventional among more psychoanalytically oriented psychiatrists to speak of some conditions as having resulted from "mother fixation." I have worked with a good many male patients from whom I came ultimately to understand the peculiar relationship in which each had stood with his mother. Far from becoming able to see an approximate identity in the significant features I learned from every patient new depths of meaning in the pattern of the mother-son relationship. Instead of learning the 'effects of the mother complex' so that I could use it as a sort of master symbol in thinking, I have learnt to avoid these generalizations. The significance in personality development of particular courses of events with others seems more generally to inhere in nuances than in the gross pattern more easily put into words.

I suggested early in the fourth of these lectures that the interview situation presumes a gradual evolution of awareness of the people actually concerned. The patient loses parataxic concomitants with which the physician is at first invested. The physician gradually refines his impressions as to what manner of person the patient may be. One of the more important factors involved in this growth of awareness is the purpose of the interview itself as the patient comes to see it. This purpose sometimes seems to be the humiliation of the patient. This is most diligently to be avoided, if one has any interest in therapeutic possibilities.

The processes that go on in the interview situation are determined by the whole body of integrating tendencies that the interpersonal situation calls into play. The perceptions of each person concerned and the actual verbal exchange are mediated by the respective self systems. Everything else goes on outside of awareness, and, unless the psychiatrist is both of wide experience in living and relatively very secure in the interview situation, a good deal is apt to escape his notice. The psychiatrist's formulation of historic development and present state of the patient is then apt to be relatively inconsequential if not quite irrelevant.

What is said in an interview is the part of the speaker's more or less cogent streams of revery process which is not suppressed by the self system concerned. Remembering that the self dynamism is a growing integration useful in dealing with others for obtaining satisfactions and avoiding insecurity; knowing that its growth is restricted by the function of anxiety which excludes from awareness all the data which would expand the self at the cost of insecurity; it must be evident that the patient cannot know enough to explain his present difficulties. What with the witting suppression of some considerable part of that which does appear in the patient's awareness, it must also be clear that far more than an interrogation is needed if one is to secure relevant and highly significant data about the sources of peculiarity in a patient's interpersonal relations.

An ideal psychiatrist with wholly unrestricted experience in living, whose self dynamism would be coterminous with his personality, if alert and intelligent, could observe in a sufficiently extended contact with any patient a great many of the actual peculiarities of the interpersonal relations in which the patient took part. Even this impossibly competent psychiatrist, however, could not infer with high probability the actual sequence of significant experience which lay behind the observed peculiarities. The most that he could infer with high probability is that certain events must have, and that certain other events could not have, occurred.

These inferences would be useful in guiding him in his further interviews with the patient, to the end that information rather than misinformation would be obtained, and no serious insecurities provoked as the patient became more fully acquainted with his own history—underwent an expansion of his self.

The principal problem of the therapeutic interview is that of facilitating the accession to awareness of information which will clarify for the patient the more troublesome aspects of his life. This requires that one circumvent the inhibiting processes which, on direct attack, would manifest themselves in severe anxiety, or anger and resentment, with disintegration of the therapeutic situation. This phase of the work is based on the fact that one has information about one's experience only to the extent that one has tended to communicate it to another—or thought about it in the manner of communicative speech. Much of that which is ordinarily said to be *repressed* is merely unformulated. The revery processes concerned with it are either non-verbal or of a highly autistic character. They do not recall the experience; in fact, their form is chiefly determined by a need to avoid recall. They often proceed in states of abstraction or inattentive preoccupation.[63] In other cases, they are actively preoccupying, making up the relatively meaningless recurrent ideation of a substitutive state. If so, their experiential subject-matter is sufficiently disguised so that nothing of it is recalled.

Before I leave the topic of the interview, let me anticipate something of that which I must say about therapeutic conceptions, and mention here the principal factors making for success and for failure in the interview. The successful conversation establishes various *consensi*. The physician is able to arrive with the patient at an agreement as to the time order of events, as to sequent and consequent, as to cause and effect.

[63] Revery processes have received very little attention compared to that given the processes of consensually validated, logical thought. See, in particular, the two books of the late Varendonck, J., *The Psychology of Day-dreams*; London, Allen and Unwin, 1921 (367 pp.); and, *The Evolution of the Conscious Faculties*; London, Allen and Unwin, 1923 (259 pp.).

The interview progressively *enfeebles restraint* on the free development in awareness of clear statements of unpleasant, embarrassing, or otherwise anxiety-laden experiences. The interchange *substitutes socially sanctioned* for anxiety enforced restraints or supervisions of behavior. The patient who uncovers and becomes clearly aware of an impulse the direct manifestation of which would probably be disastrous, sees the possibility of finding partial or symbolic satisfactions. It occurs to the patient who entertains impulses that would be acceptable to but few other people that he may *segregate his integrations* to suitable occasions and objects, and discharge the complicating resentments aroused by his individuation, perhaps in games.

These results come partly from the interpretation of clearly documented facts, the building of inferential bridges that carry one from particular concrete instances to a generalized formulation, and partly from considering alternative hypotheses for misleading formulations.

There are a great many misunderstandings about interpretation and inference. Some psychiatrists, particularly some psychoanalysts, are prone to much interpretation of the material expressed by their patients. I have worked subsequently with patients who have received this kind of treatment. Thus, one of them reported that her analyst had complimented her on the classical character of her "free associating." I was told of this gratifying circumstance because I had objected to the patient's uncommunicative verbalizations during our interviews, insisting that while they doubtless had purpose and meaning, they in no way informed the patient or me of anything concerned either in the patient's general difficulty in living, or in the present interpersonal situation. The analyst had on occasion been intrigued by the reveries provoked in him by the flow of language, and, with charming naïveté, assumed that what was going on in his awareness must have some validity for the patient. He, thus, expounded to the patient the meaning of the uninterpretable content—often to the patient's astonishment, sometimes to her perturbation; but by and large, to her final conviction. In other words, she came usually to accept the interpretations. It did not seem strange that some of her difficulties had not been remedied.

The supply of interpretations, like that of advice, greatly exceeds the need for them. Every patient has enough of his own misinterpretations and may well be spared the uncritical autistic reveries of his physician. At the same time, some interpretations are indispensable, if therapeutic results are to be achieved in a reasonable length of time. The first test for any interpretation should be as to its adequacy: does it cover the data to which it is applied? The second test should be as to its exclusiveness: are there other equally plausible hypotheses that cover the data? If so, the proposed interpretation justifies no presumption of its validity and, in general, it should not be offered.[64]

The psychiatrist must be resistant to precocious conclusions. In many patients, almost any inference is acceptable which *does not* clarify the problem in point. There is no particular anxiety connected with accepting the psychiatrist's mistake.

A great deal of the revery processes of many people are made up of what I have called *not-processes*. The patient thinks a great deal about what is not the case. This is greatly tributary

---

[64] Some people seem to have great difficulty in developing alternative hypotheses for any given set of facts. The first thing that comes to mind seems to them to be self-evident. Anything else is self-evidently erroneous. They can scarcely listen to a presentation of contradictory data; they may be polite and hear one out, only to renew the presentation of their previous view. These are mostly people who do not discriminate any more than they can help. They work preferably with conventional patterns of people and situations and are annoyed or puzzled by novelty. They show the all-black-or-white that I have associated with the manic-depressive psychosis. People interested in formulating 'types' of people call them *extraverted* or *cyclo-thymic*. The latter term refers to the swings of mood that often characterize them; they are either up or down, mildly elated and expansive or gloomy and 'blue.' Neither their moods nor their interpersonal relations have subtlety, and they are lacking in the capacity for *perseveration*—the carrying over of expression from an unsuitable to a subsequent occasion.

This sort of person and the one whose security depends on creating an impresson of omniscience are alike unsuited to the rôle of psychiatrist.

to security, for anything *is* but *one* thing, but *is not* an infinity of other things. One can proceed, therefore, by the not-processes to contemplate innumerable formulations, thereby easily avoiding the *one* formula that would be illuminating—and anxiety-laden. It is salutary, therefore, to see that all statements are finally offered in a positive rather than a negative form. Not the one of a possible infinity of statements as to what the patient does not think, did not do, or does not feel; but the single statement of what he thinks, did, or feels.

Even positive statements by the patient are usually misleading, unless they pertain to a concrete course of relatively impersonal events. The most forthright account of a conversation or other interpersonal event is apt to include a number of parataxic elements projected on the others concerned. Many patients include in their accounts long contexts about the other person's thoughts, motives, and intentions. The motives ascribed to the others are usually motives into which the patient has but rudimentary insight, in his own case. His interpretations, which he takes for granted and without any doubt, are therefore wholly unreliable. Whether they be correct, approximate, or entirely erroneous is simply beyond determination. Their relevance in therapy lies in their unquestioned acceptance by the patient. Their occurrence is a significant feature of his difficulties in interpersonal relations.

The pursuit of accuracy may be in itself a major handicap to communication. Some patients talk at great length 'to make something clear,' but qualify their various propositions so abundantly that the statement as a whole means simply nothing. As these vocalizations are often produced with much color of emotion and in good rhetorical form, it is easy for the bored or somnolent psychiatrist to pick out the part that interests him and to elaborate it into a conviction that the patient has told him something in particular. When he subsequently refers to this alleged communication, the patient may flatly contradict him. On the other hand, the patient may hasten to agree, but again embark on a course of qualifications which terminates the situation in a verbal fog.

"Agreement" is often a device for maintaining the illusion of one's omniscience. Patients suffering the substitutive disorders are often most ingenious at preventing the accurate formulation of the events which made up a situation. If, despite all the patient's efforts—parataxic interpretation, qualification, specious generalizations, and erroneous placing of events in time—the physician comes to grasp the actual facts and expresses them, one of a few processes is apt to follow. The patient may say, in essence, "Yes; but—." The proposition is then befogged. The patient, after a pause, may say, "Yes; that is quite true." The proposition then vanishes from active attention; the patient has asserted an omniscient control over the facts, which renders them unimportant. Or the patient may ask aid in understanding the implications, or ask some more or less relevant questions, and so lose the proposition in the pursuit of some details. It then appears that he has misunderstood the physician in all essential respects, and one is back where one started.

Even when a consensus is achieved in an interview, it may be short-lived. The factors which entered into it need not survive the interpersonal situation of its occurrence. Something apparently fatally contradictory to it may occur to the patient as soon as he has left the physician's company. Moreover, a disintegrating process may put in appearance near the close of the interview itself. There are some patients, for example, who show a marked change of attitude as they rise to go, and ask as if from a different position "Have we accomplished anything, today, Doctor?" This is a movement by virtue of which the significance of the interview is minimized and only the physician's opinion about it is given any importance. If this movement is not countered, the patient represses anything significant from the interview into a sort of dream-like vagueness, such that it is none of his business. This shift of attitude at the end of the interview is particularly conducive of the more autistic sorts of performances. The patient 'produces' a stream of unintelligible and uncommunicative revery processes, from which the physician is by some kind of a miracle supposed to achieve the patient's 'cure.'

Somewhat related to this interpersonally meaningless production is the patient's preoccupation with what one *ought* to do. A great deal of time and effort is wasted in discussion of will-power, choice, and decision. These three terms which refer to products of acculturation in the home, endure and are functionally very important because they are potent terms of rationalization in our culture. They are, in fact, embodied in various institutions of law and religion; and all too often are powerful factors in the work of the psychiatrist, himself.

The psychoanalyst, for example, may instruct his patient to say instantly every littlest thing that comes into his mind. The patient then charges off in autistic revery which gets nowhere, therapeutically. The analyst, if he is not entertained by parallel autisms, may interpret this as "narcissistic self-gratification" on the part of the patient. The patient may counter with the statement that he was told to say what comes to his mind and that is all he can do. There is no doubt that patients and others often have fun with their thoughts—and sometimes with gullible companions. The point is not this fact in itself. It is that there may be nothing else which could happen in the given situation. In any case, there is nothing else as powerfully motivated as that which is happening. The reason for this lies in the situation, not in the perversity of the patient, or his 'narcissism.' The physician, the patient, and the parataxic concomitants make up the situation. The punishing type of interpretation may obviate any necessity for the physician's seeing wherein the 'self-gratification' is the action which suits the integration. The situation is not necessarily integrated to the achievement of a therapeutic goal, and the physician, because of his relative freedom from personal handicap, is the one who can do most towards altering the integration in a desirable fashion. This is one of the more important uses of interpretation; in the case in point, the interpretation may be merely a statement to the effect that the physician does not see any connection between the expressed stream of thought and the current interpersonal situation.

All therapeutic conferences are made up of various patterns of some five types of process. There are processes which illuminate the immediate interpersonal relationship. These include the revelation of parataxic or "transference" phenomena. There are processes which clarify the action in some recent interpersonal situation, perhaps one in a relatively durable relationship with some person often discussed in the interviews. There are processes which revert from present and current situations to relevant situations in the patient's more remote past. There are processes which represent the pursuit into the future of aspects of current situations, by way of constructive revery. And there are processes called out by various crisis situations, in or outside of the therapeutic situation, many of which amount to acute maladjustive movements—one group of which is a preoccupation with current events of but trifling relevancy.

The patient's struggles to do the right thing, to overcome certain tendencies, or to stop certain manifest actions are all to be placed in the first and last categories of these processes. They are either parataxic adaptations to the psychiatrist as a moral censor, or preoccupations to avoid anxiety or conflict. I know of no evidence of a force or power that may be called a *will*, in contradistinction to the vector addition of integrating tendencies. Situations call out motivation; if there is conflict of motivation outside of awareness, a compromise or a temporary domination of behavior and suppression of the weaker motive occurs. If the conflict is within awareness, the self system is involved, with the corresponding element of insecurity. In these cases, more complex products result, but these too are vector additions, not interventions of some sort of personal will-power.

Decision, about which many patients have much trouble—their indecisiveness—is intimately connected with the illusion of choice, in turn entangled with dogmatic assertions of "freedom of the will," and of one's ability to choose between good and evil. Let me first settle the question of dogma, which is in this case both religious and legal. Dogmatic statements are necessary ingredients of any system of thought which cannot be deduced from generally demonstrable events. When I say that a burned child avoids the fire, I do not deny the possibility of some complex exceptions, but I do assert the prevalence of a type of behavior that could be inferred from almost any one's experience with being burned. When I assert that evil is any unwarranted interference with life, on the other hand, I am offering a complex formula that has arisen from my unique career among others. I do not know how to state a generally useful rule for assessing the warranty for particular interferences with, say, another person's life or living.

It will be a long time indeed before any group of people shall have come to a fully rational way of life, and in the meanwhile, man must have normative rules to govern his behavior with others, especially in the fields most modified by culture. Dependent on the particular course of culture evolution, these rules may carry social or transcendental sanction, or a blend of the two. This is of but indirect concern to the psychiatrist. He is concerned when the rules and the underlying and supporting culture-complex are so incongruent and so peculiarly contradictory that they give rise in some people at least to states of mental disorder—and probably in everyone to some measure of insecurity. As the rules of religious systems are relatively static, tend to be highly resistant of change; and as those of legal systems are susceptible to episodic modification only, these two fields of normative prescription are the least apt to keep closely in step with the developing culture-complex.

In the Western culture, into the second decade of this century, there was no devastating divergence of the religious rules from the main trends of the culture-complex. With the short-lived emergence of the Communist idealism and the still-spreading reversion to Totalitarianism as a doctrine of the state, the practical solidarity of the Western culture was destroyed.[65] There are now many significant differences in the culture-patterns which are impressed on children in home and school, and through the channels of mediate acculturation. A great deal that was unquestionable has now become controversial, if not obsolete. Whereas once one 'belonged' or was an outcast, the question now is rather *where* one belongs than *does* one. Each party, group, and clique has its own normative rules, its own orthodox attitude to the religious and even the legal systems. The differences in these respects between the most extreme groups are greater than any differences of belief that have previously influenced the peoples of the world. The ideologies (dogmata) that find devout believers even among our own people are strange indeed to survivors of a time when one's "conscience" could be one's guide.

Decision and choice are functions of memory and prospective revery—which often eventuates in foresight. They are, however, interpersonal processes; they do not occur in the vacuum of an isolated individuality, and they correspondingly

[65] I must not digress to contemplate the historic currents that prepared the way for these changes, nor shall I defend the statement that these two of a complex pattern of events are the most significant. In the first place, persons immersed in rapid culture change can seldom make valid judgments as to the relative significance of presenting signs and symptoms; in the second, I am not competent to discuss the economic factors which are doubtless of great importance. I will say that economics has developed with singularly little interest in the persons who manifest economic behavior, and economists do not interest themselves particularly in the personal effects of economic factors. I wish that the latter, at least, might not continue indefinitely to be the case, for economic factors cannot but be important elements in personal as well as in social security.

include the function of the self system. To that extent, they are influenced by all the factors involved in the pursuit of security or its maintenance. They may be, and often are, symptomatic of mental disorder and signatory of overcomplicated interpersonal situations. When they happen to be the decisions of a person who has come to subscribe to an ideology foreign to the culture-pattern of his childhood, they may be complex indeed. The person who believes that he *voluntarily* cut loose from his earlier moorings and *by choice* accepted new dogmata, in which he has diligently indoctrinated himself, is quite certain to be a person who has suffered great insecurity. He is often a person whose self-organization is derogatory and hateful. The new movement has given him group support for the expression of ancient personal hostilities that are now directed against the group from which he has come. The new ideology rationalizes destructive activity to such effect that it seems almost, if not quite, constructive. The new ideology is especially palliative of conflict in its promise of a better world that is to rise from the debris to which the present order must first be reduced. In this Utopia, he and his fellows will be good and kind—for there will be no more injustice, and so forth. If his is one of the more radical groups, the activity of more remote memory in the synthesis of decisions and choice may be suppressed almost completely, and the activity of prospective revery channelled rigidly in the dogmatic pattern. In this case, except for his dealings with his fellow radicals, the man may act as if he had acquired the psychopathic type of personality discussed in the third lecture. He shows no durable grasp of his own reality or that of others, and his actions are controlled by the most immediate opportunism, without consideration of the probable future.

The apparent psychopathy of persons entertaining more radical views arises chiefly from the institutionalization of their feelings of difference. If one is alone in this feeling, a paranoid state or a schizophrenic development is apt to ensue.

If, however, one finds not only a fellow, but a group who have a however feeble rationalization for active hostility to the 'in-group,' one is spared the more serious disorders. This comes about in part unwittingly by virtue of the group solidarity, and in part because of peculiarities in the verbal interchange in all militant minority groups. The more autistic thoughts of each person in such a none too secure group are rejected or modified by the others, while the more or less credible transfers of blame are elaborated into workable expressions of hostility and destructiveness. The group approaches a paranoid attitude to everyone outside it, but saves its members from deep regression under pressure of conflict. The aspects of the member's self which once might have conflicted with the destructive motivation are disintegrated by the revaluation of his past experience, or suppressed by the group norms. It is chiefly for these reasons that his dealings with people not of the group are so like those of a psychopathic personality.

The position of the person who *perforce* subscribes to an ideology foreign to his past is rather more simple, but by no means so comfortable. He is in essence a stranger in a strange land, but one who is surrounded by powerful people, not by infra-human creatures. The net result is that he has to take on a rôle of cautious subservience, and to live in a state of constant but obviously externally-conditioned insecurity. If his personality is one that permits the suppression of hostile impulses, all may go fairly well. If, however, he be of the incorrigible type, it is probable that some incompetent in the ruling clique will arrange his 'liquidation.' [66]

[66] Of more current interest to the American psychiatrist is the place of the *liberal*, the person who is not blind to the unsatisfactory state of things as they are, but who is not sufficiently disturbed in his interpersonal relations to yearn for a radical Utopian solution either on the far side of chaos *or* to be achieved by reversing the current of social evolution and regressing to the "good old days"—the equally morbid wish of the *reactionary* "conservative." The rational, liberal position exposes one to extreme vicissitudes of security from attacks by both the reactionaries and the radicals in our technically democratic society—some outstanding characteristics of which pertain less to the achieve-

Choice and decision are the products within awareness of the vector addition of motives called out by a situation, plus the constructive revery processes pertaining to them. The constructive revery, if its end stages are clearly within awareness, is said to constitute foresight. In many people, on many occasions, there is no clear foresight but rather a consciousness of determination that seems to be a thing in itself, a manifestation of the 'will.' These are simply cases in which the self system intervenes to suppress awareness of the forward-looking revery processes. Their unnoted presence is often indicated by disquiet experienced after the 'determined' action is started. This is a variety of anxiety; the foresight still tends to occur, and the self system is restricting awareness in the usual fashion.

A grasp on these processes is fundamental to the durable benefit of many patients. I shall, therefore, go to some trouble to illustrate what I mean. Let me take, as an illustration, the occasion of the lecture on explanatory conceptions, which was perhaps most unduly prolonged. This has a history. The topics of the individual lectures of the series were established some six months ago. The plan comtemplated an hour for each of the five topics. There seeming to be no possibility of foreseeing the real composition of the audience, I drafted the outline for the first lecture with an audience of psychiatrists and social scientists in mind. The audience as encountered included a signifi-

---

ment of human dignity, opportunity, and fraternity than to the safeguarding of special privilege at whatever cost to others.

I have no hesitancy in expressing these views for I am clearly of the privileged class, as are all of my intimate friends. I feel radical as to certain of the underprivileged, who would seem to have potentialities far greater than their socially-defined rôle permits them to manifest. I feel most reserved as to reactionary and radical groups—in part because I know intimately some of their leaders. I do not believe that the destruction of values is a necessary or even probable preliminary to their renaissance, and I know regression, professionally. I feel particularly hostile to all those among us who are incapable of appreciating our traditional almost accidental way of progress, who prefer instead to place confidence in the omniscience of a dictator. I do not believe that any one nurtured in the American culture-complex *can* have such sublime trust in another; I regard Totalitarianism as the political quintessence of personal despair.

cant proportion of people who belonged in neither category. The presentation would have to follow rather different lines of development than had been planned, *if* this series of lectures was to be of value to many of those who made up the audience. The change was foreseen to entail more than five hours for achieving any approximation to the initial purpose. The principal consideration encountered in my prospective revery seeming to be the very question of the scope of the psychiatric field—discussed at the start of the first lecture—to the broader definition of which I hold, my 'decision' was in favor of maximum usefulness to the audience as found rather than as anticipated.[67] The presentation of the first session was within the time as planned; each subsequent lecture—as the audience continued to be most encouragingly numerous—was more extended. The one which would require more than two hours, however, occasioned me some thought. I considered first the physical discomfort that each auditor might experience. How hard were the seats? Having never sat on one of them, I could only surmise that they might be unusually comfortable, in keeping with many other details of the auditorium. There then came the question of the durability of the auditors' attention. What motivation brought them? Noting that the occasion was an evening in a holiday week-end, I could assume that those who attended had a sufficiency of interest; could their attention-span extend over two hours? I had on one occasion approached a test of that very point, with a purely psychiatric audience. A 110-minute talk had succeeded. Psychiatrists were certainly no more apt to be interested in my views as to the relationship of clinical practice to psychiatric research; than the members of this audience, in my outlining explanatory

[67] It was also realized that the lectures as delivered would not approximate to written language; that the transcript would need revision before publication, in the course of which, adjustment for an even more varied audience would be desirable. I regret now that my judgment in this particular was not adhered to more rigidly, for the first two of these lectures are much too close to the transcript; the others have been entirely rewritten.

psychiatric conceptions. I foresaw then that a considerable part of the audience would stay to the end; I did not foresee how great a part would remain—after the opportunity for escape which I provided by way of a recess.

This inadequacy of foresight is a good example of the variations in constructive revery. My attitude towards interpersonal relations is rather pessimistic; a measure of personal success is, therefore, more frequent than is its anticipation. The attitude was fixed in the early years, not so much by a series of failures as by the continuing danger to my security which a failure due to over-optimism would have entailed.

Foresight is the product of constructive revery which often proceeds with great speed, so that one discards several possible courses of action as improbable of success, in a moment. The tracing through in this swift prevision of alternative courses of action of a way that will probably work results in an awareness of decision to follow that course.

The utility of the foresight must depend on the adequacy of one's insight into oneself and into the situation. To the extent that one's personal formulation includes complex abstractions, rationalizations—will-power, for example—foresight is misleading and one's 'decisions' are apt to get one into false positions and states of insecurity with others. To the extent that one is preoccupied with those power operations which are so striking in the substitutive states, one's foresight is useless, for insight in any given interpersonal situation is vestigial. One foresees trains of events in which all the people concerned are parataxic illusions, including the mighty magician, oneself. To the extent that powerful systems of motives exist in dissociation, foresight must be defective. In situations, multiply integrated by recognized and by dissociated impulses, there has to be a specific defect of insight, a so-called *scotoma* for the factors representative of the dissociated motives, although, as already indicated, prospective revery may still be efficient.

The effective, but unnoted revery processes that accom-

pany many instances of inadequate foresight may be represented in awareness by a whole series of symptoms: dread,
unreasonable doubt and 'indecision,' anxious 'uncertainty,'
anxious 'certainty,' and perplexity. One may experience an
apprehensive state on plunging into an action that will miscarry in the service of a powerful dissociated impulse; the
'decision' on which this action is based usually having been an
emotional 'determination,' or else a blind impulse rising out
of a painful state of 'blankness' of mind. When the self has not
been quite so effective, the patient may express his discomfort
by some such remark as "I am going to do so and so, but I dread
it—or dread the consequences." The next step in the series is
the one at which there is a 'decision,' but, no sooner is it
reached, with all the trappings of foresight in the sense of clear
probability of success, than there appear serious doubts as to the
items in the chain of prospective revery. Again, the patient,
seemingly clear on what to do, cannot begin. This may be because other revery processes reflect unfortunate possibilities—
or sometimes present alternative, equally probable but significantly different courses of action. The patient may be uncertain, entertaining several courses of action with no index of
relative probability of success, and with or without anxiety
dependent on the degree of involvement of the self system
and on the risk of becoming aware of something. Finally, there
may be an equivalent in the field of foresight to the state of
conflict. In fact, perplexity as to action often ushers in frank
conflict. It implies an approximate balance of opposing motivation.

Clear as to the dynamic rôle of the self system, as to the
power operations and the rationalizations by which insecurity
is minimized, and as to the true rôle of constructive revery
and foresight in determining action in a given situation, the
psychiatrist is well equipped to project therapeutic action. He
is clear as to the futility, often actual harmfulness, of requiring the patient to 'exercise self-control.' He knows that the

'controlled' adjustment of behavior to interpersonal demands can only arise from insight, from an expanded self which will include currently dissociated impulses, and information about situations towards which the patient must now be manifesting scotomata. He knows that 'self-control' is but one of a large number of alleged acts and abilities which a person cannot perform or manifest—except in the private theatre of his reveries—be he ever so firmly convinced of their possibility and desirability.

Just what can the psychiatrist reasonably expect the patient to do? In my opinion there are three groups of performances that are within human ability, although most people have to learn to do them well. The first is the *noticing of changes in one's body*—voice changes, molar movements, and increases and decreases of tension. Alertness in this field is necessary if the patient is to discover the unrecognized components of behavior, including the wholly unnoticed actions in the service of dissociated impulses. This is much more useful than is the learning of alertness for minor degrees of anxiety, because many patients experience but little anxiety. They are prompt and skillful in avoiding disturbing factors. They none the less undergo marked shifts in bodily tension, these being either themselves avoidance processes or occurring in lieu of anxiety at the start of the avoidance process. If these patients are not specifically interested in noting changes in somatic tension and movements, there will be very slow growth of insight. We hope that the patient will presently become alert not only to increases of tension—generically insecurity—but to its diminutions. These latter may mark the achievement of a new insight; but much more often indicate the miscarriage of a difficult constructive effort, of the occasion of which, otherwise, the patient may have no warning whatever.

The second collaborative effort for which the psychiatrist may reasonably ask is the *noticing of marginal thoughts*. This is an inadequate verbal reference to something in which everyone has some little experience. As, for example, I am now 'listening to myself talk,' somewhat the following is in progress. I am forming sentences, always at least a clause ahead of my speech. This is dominated by reference to an illusory auditor whom I shall call I_1—he is a rather unfriendly critic not very quick to understand—a particular aspect of my self. Mere talking organism and critic I_1 see to matters of formulation, vocabulary, grammar, rhetoric, and elocution. I am also hearing what is said, as it is spoken. This is dominated by reference to an illusory auditor whom I shall call I_2, a rather intelligent creature quick to see errors and incompleteness of exposition and some of the possibilities of misunderstanding. Insofar as it is true, it is my good fortune that I_2 really dominates the situation; requires reformulation and more lucid repetition, illustration, and the like. I say this because I_1 is, as it were, that which is going on in the center of awareness, while I_2 is only marginal, the fringe of awareness. If I were not rather secure in my ability to function with I_1, if I were "nervous" about my 'speech' or my speaking, most of the I_2 phenomena would receive no attention. I might now and then get a disagreeable surprise at the unconvincing sound of something that I had thought was quite clear; this awareness of an I_2 process would, however, have to be suppressed lest I be made too insecure to continue. Or, without becoming clearly aware of the 'weak' statements, I might then 'hem and haw,' or lose my place, and my viscera suffer increase of tension, if in fact some of my skeletal muscles did not tremble.

While my marginal processes of consensual validation aid in delivery of the lecture, in an insecure speaker they may seem to be a serious handicap. It must be obvious that this effect does not inhere in the consensual validation but in the insecurity and in the confusing efforts to suppress the I_2 processes. Let me now give another example of the same general situation. Let us suppose that the speaker is entirely oblivious to everything but the reading and uttering of a prepared speech, or the delivery of a memorized oration. Be he ever so unintelligible or utterly fatuous to his real audience, little will seem to have occurred in him except fatigue from the effort. His self system has obviated any feelings of insecurity by the simple expedient of complete preoccupation with the focal activity. Everything related to I_2 is transmuted into visceral tensions, outside of awareness. I believe these examples may have made clear the utility of the marginal processes. They may also have suggested the circumstances under which these marginal processes are in large part suppressed, and those under which there seem to be no marginal processes but only changes in bodily tension.

In practice, the patient often becomes intent on telling something to the psychiatrist. Either the account proceeds with difficulty, due to disturbing marginal processes, or it goes on with increasing smoothness, due to the security that comes from their complete exclusion. In either case, not the accounts but the marginal processes are the more useful for the growth of insight. This follows from the nature of the self system. To the extent that there is no disturbance of the self, to that extent nothing new is being learned by the patient about his living. We strive to teach the patient that the marginal processes, the interrupting thoughts, as it were, are very much the thing to be noticed.

The third possibility of collaboration is the *prompt statement of all that comes to mind*. The patient must learn to trust the situation to the extent of expressing the thoughts that it provokes. This is often a very difficult achievement, until insight into at least one of the parataxic processes has been achieved. After that, there are many recurrences of difficulty, but they are not very serious. Before this first great milestone of progress, however, the patient's 'mind' seems to be terribly troublesome. Waves of obscenities may flow in. Distressing recollections of most regrettable past performances may occur. Offensive thoughts about the psychiatrist may obsess the patient. False reports may press for utterance. Almost anything that is difficult to say, or any ideas that seem impossible to express, may be expected. It is for this reason that patients seek relief from the turmoil in a flow of autistic revery, a circumstantial account of some insignificant current event, or an extravagant report of the marvelous good results that have already, entirely mysteriously, been achieved by exposure to the psychiatrist.

The particular difficulties that stand in the way of achieving any and all of these three forms of collaboration are determined by the developmental patterning of the patient. The non-integrative or psychopathic person seldom seeks to enter a therapeutic relationship, and can scarcely achieve a beginning of any collaborative effort. The self-absorbed patient quickly makes an indoor sport of changes of tension, of marginal thoughts, and of astonishing communications. The pressure towards mental health is not lacking, but its manifestations have to be sought among the lush dramatics of hysteriod phenomena. One of these patients would go from my office to the home of another patient, long acquainted with her, and gush forth lurid accounts of the past, recollection of which had been provoked in our rather useless interview, concluding with the statement that I would give anything if she would only tell me about it. These patients make gratifying subjects for any spectacular form of treatment, although the effect on their difficulties in living seems usually to be a change of form rather than remedy. They 'just love' interpretations and can assimilate any number of them to the structure of their particular syndrome of mental disorder.

The therapy of mental disorders affecting incorrigible people is rough going. It is feasible only if one always knows what one is doing. The effort required in extreme instances, however, is not ordinarily available.[68]

The patient of negativistic developmental pattern presents no insuperable difficulties in the learning of collaboration. The

[68] See, for example, Aichhorn, August. *Wayward Youth;* New York, Viking, 1935 (xiii and 236 pp.).

more troublesome aspect of treating their mental disorders appears in connection with the use of interpretations. The negativistic patient resists all interpretations and often shows great ingenuity in delaying the occurrence of insight. This difficulty is mostly an initial handicap, however, and once past the first milestone of insight into a parataxic process, the resistance to interpretations passes gradually into a careful validating process that is useful.

At this point, I may well discuss the question of these initial insights which I regard as of fundamental significance in changing an allegedly therapeutic situation from a highly tentative and risky integration into a firm and reliable collaboration. I shall illustrate such an event by referring to a patient who consulted me because, she said, she had to divorce her husband. As people who are decided on securing a divorce have more need for an attorney than a psychiatrist, I inquired as to her expectation from consulting me. I found that she was well-acquainted with psychiatry, that, in fact, she had been under treatment for some time when she was in the throes of indecision about marrying this man. I then sought to discover the necessities calling for a divorce, and, to my growing astonishment, learned more and more of the husband's perfections. The only formula of the need for a divorce seemed to be a feeling that he interfered with the patient's self-realization. Wherein this interference was manifest, I could not elicit. This seemed to present a psychiatric problem, and I undertook to aid in discovering the facts underlying the situation.

In some three hundred interviews, I learned a great deal, but I could never be certain of the precise relationship of the information to what would have been observed by an ideally objective participant in the patient's career. In other words, no certainty had been achieved. A great deal was consistent and possible; it could all be complex misinterpretation and falsification. As an example, very early in our work I was told that the patient was puzzled because she had always heard that mental disorders arose from an unhappy childhood, whereas hers had been extraordinarily free from unpleasant incidents. There was much documenting of this early happiness, and the ultimate revelation that the patient's real childhood had been swamped in amnesia. As it finally came forth, it was appalling. The 'childhood' of which she had ready and elaborate recall was a serial story with which she had compensated herself in a desolately unsatisfactory home.

About the three hundredth hour, the patient came in with me from the waiting room in a peculiar state of agitation. She said that she was overwhelmed to discover that I looked quite different than she had hitherto seen me. She had known me as a fat old man with white hair. Disregarding the other characteristics, I can scarcely have had white hair. This is both an extreme and deceptively simple illustration of a parataxic distortion of the psychiatrist in the treatment situation. Gross illusions of physical attributes are not very common, and, needless to say, the fat old white-haired man was derived from a figure in the patient's past, and had been manifesting this other person's significant attributes, despite my efforts to avoid misinterpretations and to detect parataxic concomitants—at which I had been remarkably unsuccessful. When our grandfatherly figure had been located in his place in the patient's career; and when we had seen something of his rôle in the patient's development, as indicated in the now-accessible discrepancies between my performances and her misconceptions about them; the therapeutic situation then lost its tentative quality and became productive of durable results.

Until a patient has seen clearly and unmistakably a concrete example of the way in which unresolved situations from the distant past color the perception of present situations and over-complicate action in them, there can be no material reorganization of personality, no therapeutically satisfactory expansion of the self, no significant insight into the complexities of one's performances or into the unexpected and often disconcerting behavior of others concerned. Up to this point, there is nothing significantly unique in the treatment situation; afterwards, however, the integration with the psychiatrist becomes a situation of unprecedented freedom from restraints on the manifestation of constructive impulses. This is the indirect result of the changes in the self system. The patient has finally learnt that more security may ensue from *abandoning* a complex security-seeking process than was ever achieved *by it*. This information is in itself an addition to security and a warrant for confronting other anxiety-provoking situations to discover the factors in them which are being experienced as a threat. The psychiatrist's reiterated statement as to the way by which one gains mental health now takes on something of the meaning which he has striven to communicate. The patient is beginning to understand what is sought, and its virtue. Up to now, the patient has been literally in Groddeck's words "lived by unknown and uncontrollable forces," however elaborately this fact was concealed from awareness.

Experience has taught me that it is useful to have clear and succinct statements with which to reply to the more general questions that are always, sooner or later, and again and again, asked by the patient. One may add new details to support the central formula, but it is unwise to vary from the central thought. This comes about because of the shifting relationship of perception to the underlying reality that is being perceived, due to parataxic concomitants representing activity of the self system. At best, we are none too certainly prompt in seizing even the more accessible meaning of a remark. When the remark pertains to some aspect of our living, our relations with others, even if there were nothing to conflict with any of its implications, the very act of perceiving it would have to include much related experience in the past, about which some contradictions and some definite misinformation may well be accessible to awareness. In the early phases of a treatment situation, many factors in the self conflict with the implications of any correct statement about the processes that are manifest in the mental disorder. Still more factors, practically the whole self system, conflict with *some* implications of a statement as to how the treatment situation is to do good.

One achieves mental health to the extent that one becomes aware of one's interpersonal relations; this is the general statement that is always expressed to the patient. Every one of my patients with whom I have had more than a consultative relationship has received this reply to many different questions, asked throughout the greater part of the work. This is the essential element in replying to the questions, "What ails me?," "How can I get better?," "What good will the treatment accomplish?," "Why can't I overcome this or that habit?," "What shall I do about my hatefulness—my hostility—my ugly disposition—my dependency—my domineering—my sensitivity—my suspiciousness—my uncertainty?" It is part of the framework that supports all explanations of what is going on, what might be going on, and what will presently be going on. It is one of the factual bases for interpreting unfortunate developments, unfavorable changes that are discouraging the patient. It is *the* necessary formula to which everything must be assimilable, if it is therapy.

This statement of the nature of curative change is for a long time a source of insecurity, and thus of anxiety or uncomfortable tension. It is prehended as an attack on the very core of the patient's personality. It denies the ultimate usefulness of the suppressive, the repressive, and the dissociating functions of the self system. For a long time, therefore, it is not understood in recognizable form. If the patient could seize even the most superficial of its implications, he would take it to mean that one could not make any progress without abandoning the hope of feeling secure in dealing with others. Even if one could exercise choice, one could not accept such a prospect. It would have to appear as the relinquishment of what little capability and comfort one had been able to maintain; as a grim preliminary to an incomprehensible next state. This might seem ever so desirable to the psychiatrist, but he is still a stranger of indefinite attitude to the patient.

Patients ask questions for various reasons; that is, as modes of behavior to resolve various aspects of the therapeutic situation. The physician is guided in his response by two considerations: the long-range probabilities about the situation, and the immediate phase of the treatment. The goal of the treatment, including the ultimate complete resolution of the patient-physician relationship, dictates the gradual evolution of valid insight. This calls out the succinct statements above mentioned. The momentary present state of what may be an extremely complex parataxic situation, on the other hand, can call for a great variety of actions. In general, if anything is to be said in reply to a question, both of these considerations should be subserved by it. In no case may the long-term aspect be ignored; if one relinquishes this orientation neither the physician nor the patient can long know what is going on.

I can now outline the more typical peculiarities that one encounters in treating the ambition-ridden sort of patient. I have spoken of patients' learning the three forms of collaboration. In the second lecture, I reserved the possibility of collaboration to persons who had entered or passed through preadolescence. Both of these views are relevant. The processes of psychiatric cure include the maturation of personality; that is, the evolution of capacity for adult interpersonal relations. Where the barriers to this achievement are practically insurmountable, or where other factors preclude the necessary procedures, the goal of cure is not to be sought, but only that of amelioration. I shall have more to offer in this connection, presently.

The ambition-ridden person comes to the psychiatrist to get what he can in the way of aid in his career. He may be willing to pay for this. He may be most determined in his efforts to achieve it. But he lives in a world of competitive violence and necessary compromise, and he will have none of the psychiatrist's skepticism about the finality of this formula. He cannot escape the competitive attitude, even in this regard, and all too frequently by dint of competing with the physician at every step, reduces the potentially therapeutic situation to a struggle about who is doctor and who is patient. If the psychiatrist remains detached in his attitude towards the incessant demands for recognition, the patient's insecurity is apt to disrupt the situation. The problem is chiefly one of following a course between a fraudulent acceptance of the juvenile motivation as satisfactory—in which case, the situation will proceed into a parataxic representation of an extremely important early situation *but* the psychiatrist will be too involved to assist in its clarification—and an emphatic insistence that even the patient's most satisfactory interpersonal relations are inadequate. Given the necessary interest, and tact and patience, one may come gradually to progress with one of these patients to a more mature relationship, whereupon the before-mentioned first milestone of progress can be reached, and the goal of cure posited. The long preliminaries are often interrupted before this achievement, often, I surmise, for the convenience of the physician.

Treatment situations integrated with patients of asocial development are chiefly characterized by the subtlety of distortion in the communicative processes. The structure of the self system of an asocial person is in one sense extraordinarily simple. Each tendency in this relatively simple organization extends, however, through innumerable nuances of experience back to childhood discouragement and to the sequential development of *detachment* from what I shall call representative participation with others. By this I mean that these patients even as children came to realize that their prehended reality was quite different from the illusions of them that the parents persistently entertained. The self of the asocial person is in this sense extraordinarily complex, for it is evolved on a duplex pattern of what *is* and what is expected. It is apt to be quite successful in avoiding insecurity, for the motivation manifested in any integration can shift from that relevant to the integration as perceived by the patient to that relevant to the prehended illusions of the others concerned. While we all show some ability in this regard, for more or less parallel reasons, the asocial person manifests it as a major characteristic, and often with relatively little parataxic distortion.

This does not mean that the asocial person always gracefully falls in with the other person's parataxes. He may have disintegrated most of his past interpersonal relations with anger and contemptuous disappointment. He may have left them with an increasing burden of inferiority as to his unsuitability to be a friend. He may come to the physician because he is intolerably lonely in an apparently close relationship which has endured for years. However all this may be, he will—if at least preadolescent—come fairly soon to learn the first two of my forms of collaboration, and will seem for the most part to have caught on to the third. Therapeutic processes will proceed rather smoothly for some time, but obscure difficulties will be encountered. Moreover, the patient will quite certainly become involved in powerfully-motivated integrations with one after another person outside of the treatment situation. Much that would be relevant in the treatment situation will then be discharged in these accessory situations.

In brief, these patients for a long time cannot entertain a durable conviction that the physician is what he purports to be. He cannot be so interested in the patient; he will 'let the patient down,' come to dislike or despise him. The patient protects himself with a parallel appraisal of the physician: he is not much good, he is of little importance to the patient, he is actually a rather shabby person who does psychiatry because he can't do anything else, the whole thing is probably a fraud, it is best to have somebody else to fall back on, and to help one keep one's skeptical perspective in the stress of the treat-

ment situation. And none of this somewhat changing but essentially invariant content gets itself expressed by other than
the most subtle indications. When it has finally come to its
first clear expression, the treatment situation improves, but continues to be handicapped by the patient's feeling of remoteness and unlovability, convictions that will persist far past the
first milestone as major problems of the treatment.

The inadequate person as a patient presents the great risk
of developing a new phase of the self system in subordination
to the physician. This device is a great handicap to treatment,
for it cushions any attempts to reach the underlying frustration and humiliation, the dissociation of tendencies related to
which is the principal factor in the maladjustment. These patients are for some time a boon to any domineering physician.
They come usually to be rather like the albatross around the
neck of the Ancient Mariner.

Of the treatment problems connected with handling patients
of the homosexual developmental type, few require any special consideration. These people may be sufficiently evolved
towards adulthood to enter readily into the therapeutic collaboration, in which case the physician's major problem is that
of keeping the long-term goal always in sight. This goal must
be the dissolving of the patient's barrier to full intimacy with
persons of the other sex. The prevalent error is an effort to treat
"homosexuality" as a problem in itself. This sometimes at least
reflects the special interest of the therapist; it is always interesting, even if deeply disturbing, to the patient. As the homosexuality is an adaptive attitude in partial remedy of the real
disorder, its successful 'treatment' in advance of remedy of
the real problem could only precipitate a more grave maladjustment.

The special problems of treating the chronically adolescent
are not very different from those just mentioned, and the greatest risk is of the same character; namely, the treating of an adjustive device as if it were the disorder, instead of attacking the

underlying barrier to full interpersonal intimacy. Here, too, there is more than a possibility of impairing what mental health the patient brought to the treatment. With this, I shall leave the topic of special problems associated with the developmental syndromes and proceed to the question of general risks entailed in psychiatric treatment.

We have, thus far, discussed intensive and prolonged psychiatric treatment, the sort most often engaged in by physicians trained in the psychoanalytic technique. This constitutes but a small part of the work done by psychiatrists in an effort to benefit patients. I have presented it in some detail because it is the most revealing form of psychiatric treatment, both as to the actual possibilities of beneficial intervention, and as to the fortunate and unfortunate events that make up the cure, amelioration, or aggravation of mental disorder. There is a good deal of misinformation current in non-analytic psychiatric circles in this connection, and, as I see it, very little reliable information in the hands of the laity. This is in both cases the more regrettable because it shields the worst in alleged psychoanalytic practice from the valid criticism which it so richly deserves.[69] It also interferes with that reasonable con-

[69] It is perhaps even more regrettable because of its effects on the training of candidates to become psychoanalytic psychiatrists. The prerequisite psychiatric training is imperative. Undergoing a personal analysis is obviously necessary. Subsequent work under supervision is unquestionably wise. Didactic training in theory and seminar study of practical problems is excellent. But every step in education is in large measure a matter of interpersonal relations: the training psychiatrists and what the candidates learn from them; the 'training' analyst and what he cures, ameliorates, aggravates, and systematizes—which is what the candidate learns from him; and the supervising analysts and their particular interests and competence to remedy and refine what comes to them; all these and the lecturers and seminary leaders are people, in some parts people whose interpersonal relations are in measure decidedly immature and maladjusted. This could not but be the case, considering the recency of Freud's discoveries and their limited favorable reception. Were it not for a particular aspect of the situation, this need not distress us, as progressive improvement would occur automatically. The necessary remoteness of much of the practical performances from any competent criticism *is* troublesome. The possibility—all too often demonstrated fact—of continuing extraordinary influence over the performances of one's trainee, itself an evidence either of incompetent

sideration of probabilities to the advancement of which Dr. White devoted so much of his energy.

One hears again and again of the evils done by psychoanalysis and of the dangers attendant upon its use in this or that condition, notably in the case of those apt to undergo a schizophrenic episode. In psychoanalytic circles, one hears of subpsychotic, frankly dangerously disturbed periods in the course of the presumably adequate treatment of some patients. Some psychoanalysts seem to take this as a matter of necessary course. Plausible formulae are available to rationalize it, nay, even to rationalize the occasional suicide of a training or supervising psychoanalyst. A certain distrust of psychoanalytic practitioners, if not of psychoanalysis itself, comes thus to be quite understandable.

In psychiatric consulting practice one participates in many different kinds of interpersonal relations, to the end of recommending some course of action that will benefit the patient concerned. Among these situations is that of the young medical man, perhaps already somewhat trained in psychiatry, who seeks aid in furtherance of his training. He asks, for example, if psychoanalytic training, or a personal analysis at least, is an indispensable part of the technical equipment that he will need in order to be competent in practice. It would be easy to reply in the affirmative to this question. I cannot but recall, however, the case of a young man of extraordinary gifts to whom I gave an affirmative answer, some twenty years ago. I did not then know that this was but the beginning of discharge of my responsibility. He asked me whom I would recommend as a training analyst. We discussed several. He subsequently acted on some other advice and went to work with a psychoanalyst not of my personal acquaintance. After about eight-

therapy or of grossly unhygienic design, or both, coupled with manifestation of the prevalent ambition-ridden type of development in the person of the training analyst; this situation calls for more interest in psychoanalytic training institutions and the training of particular analysts than the general psychiatrist or the interested layman is now competent to show.

een months had passed, we met again, following the interruption of his analysis. He showed evidences of a transient paranoid state and a rather violent antagonism to psychoanalysis, root and branch. His career, so far as I can judge, has realized but a small part of his original promise. This story has been repeated, in my experience, on several occasions—with adoption of "psychoanalysis" as an important part of the paranoid systematization, which was *not* transient.

I learned finally that the necessity of psychoanalytic training for full psychiatric competence is not a technical but an intensely personal matter. The consultant on this problem is concerned with making a survey of the candidate's interpersonal relations, their successes and failures, and with formulating the probable outcome of treatment of the presenting disorders in terms of practically available facilities *and* personnel. He has discharged his responsibility to the candidate when he shall have communicated the following: an appraisal of the major assets and liabilities of the candidate's personality; an outline of the steps that seem necessary and feasible for achieving success in some field—one hopes, in psychiatry; and an outline of the factors that limit the candidate's probable achievements. The necessary and feasible steps include an assessment of many factors including available personnel known to be competent to deal with the person before one.

This optimum performance with patients is not always desirable. One encounters some situations in these consultations that forbid the frank expression of certain conclusions as to the mental disorder present. Quite aside from rationalizing his adequate performances, the psychiatrist realizes that it is futile, foolhardy, or actually viciously irresponsible to undermine any patient's security when one can offer nothing that will promptly be constructive.[70] Not psychoanalysis alone but

[70] In some instances, where I have found a complex of factors which seemed to me to preclude a successful career in psychiatry, among them some grievous disorder of personality, I have disadvised the pursuit of the career on the basis of my impression of its unsuitability to the person—but only *after* I had un-

modern psychiatry as a whole provides destructively motivated people with peculiarly effective tools for doing harm.

There is no valid question of danger in psychoanalytic treatment by a practitioner competent to handle the patient concerned. There are some patients who come to the consultant for the handling of whom no psychoanalytic psychiatrist of his acquaintance is certainly competent, and there are many patients for whom psychoanalytic treatment is wholly out of the question, by reason of economic, geographic, and other facts. As one whose practice has been chiefly among persons suffering schizophrenic and substitutive states, I have been able to observe the results of adequate psychoanalytic treatment in a variety of potentially and incipiently schizophrenic states. While treatment has not always been fully successful, I know that there is no danger of aggravating the mental disorder, and no necessity for phases of the work in which the patient is seriously disturbed. I have as a practitioner and as a supervising instructor followed rather minutely the processes making up the successful treatment, the cure, of potentially and of incipiently schizophrenic patients. The course of the work has been clear, often predictable as to developments days to weeks in the future. So much for what can be done; how often it works out this way is another matter.

It would be absurd indeed to recommend intensive treatment for all schizophrenic patients, or, for that matter, for all persons showing any pattern of mental disorder. A consideration of the collaborative performances on which cure depends should make this evident, without further discussion. The consultant sees many patients in the case of whom any direct interpersonal treatment is out of the question. These include some

---

covered some interest in an alternative course, *and* some of the experience that had eventuated in the 'choice' of psychiatry. By virtue of questioning the validity of the 'choice,' and recommending reconsideration, I have spared us both embarrassment about the actual personal problems. The tendency towards mental health does the rest, with no danger of serious disturbance to the candidate.

patients whose presenting condition is in all likelihood better than their probable future course. They include also some patients who are potentially of excellent outlook, but whose care entails their removal from mutually disturbing contact with any ordinary environment. These two groups, and those who fall between them, are in general the patients who require institutional care. I shall come to consider this, shortly. Besides all these, the consultant sees a number of people for whom, for a variety of reasons, he cannot recommend intensive treatment, but who would profit from further therapeutic contact with a psychiatrist.

Intensive psychiatric treatment, including psychoanalysis, proceeds by reintegrating dissociated motivational systems, and dissipating the continuing parataxic influences of unresolved historically past situations through which the patient has lived. This is a long-term procedure, often requiring many hundred hours of work for its adequate achievement. It is obviously of but very limited application to the great numbers of people who realize that something is the matter with their lives, that in some obscure way they defeat themselves in dealing with other people, that their children are not responding satisfactorily to the parental influence; in short, that they are unsatisfied and insecure. For most of these patients, the psychiatrist has to compromise with the ideal of cure and proceed along the line of amelioration.[71]

The office and the dispensary practice of ameliorative psychiatry is in some ways the most demanding form of treatment. The consultant sees the patient a few times, during which

[71] The notion of cure is, of course, a relative one. Very few patients who are rid of all marked handicaps in living will continue in intensive treatment to uncover trifling difficulties. Those who seem to be doing this are more probably moving towards the revelation of a serious difficulty that has not been noticed by the psychiatrist—if they are not in fact entangled with the psychiatrist in some mutually satisfactory, if unrecognized, durable relationship. This latter can scarcely be regarded as a successful outcome of treatment, as it represents a great shift in the rôle of the physician, and one contrary to the social sanctions which establish his relationship to his patient.

his activity must be therapeutic, but with as its main objective a wise recommendation as to the future, to be carried out elsewhere after his investigation is completed. The psychiatrist engaged in intensive treatment has to spend a great deal of time with each of his patients, has relatively little to say most of this time, and expects a good many erroneous statements, imperfect interpretations, and inadequate situations to work themselves out to no one's disadvantage. The average institutional psychiatrist works chiefly through mediate channels and in a field so complex that the outcome is not clearly within the scope of his psychiatric responsibility. The psychiatrist who receives a patient for non-intensive treatment has none of these advantages and is often vividly aware of the disastrous effects on his reputation of a suicide or anything else that might interest the sensational press. Under the circumstances, it is not strange that some of these practitioners do little more than play safe. For reasons that by now may be fairly evident, it is some of these 'cautious' practitioners—and the cruel-destructive ones—who have most of the misfortunes in their practice.

The responsible treatment of patients by way of occasional conferences is not often a brilliant success. I have for some years occupied myself in trying to determine if this must be the case. The history of many a patient shows a great and favorable change that allegedly followed a particular personal association, perhaps a brief contact. Some of these instances leave no doubt as to their authenticity. Moreover, ironically enough, marked improvements are sometimes obtained in the first few psychiatric interviews, only to fade out in those that follow. Part of the favorable change is to be credited to the mere act of finally seeking help, after months or years of struggling with the conviction that one ought to be man enough to handle one's own personal problems. The relief of asking help and finding that the psychiatrist does not regard one as a weakling is strongly reassuring. In this is included a large part of the trouble. The occasional psychiatric treatment is often addressed to improving the functional efficiency of the self, and not to the solution of the complications arising from the activity of the self. There is all too much of the attitude of which Frederick H. Allen gives a humorous summary: the patient is told to 'buck up' and if he doesn't buck up, one commits him to a mental hospital.

Efforts addressed solely to bolstering the self system are not ordinarily conducive of benefit to the patient. If the strivings towards mental health could manifest themselves, psychiatric aid would scarcely be needed. All that can obstruct them is the self, and increasing its efficiency is, therefore, tantamount to continuing the mental disorder. There are crisis situations to which these considerations are not cogent. I can illustrate this by referring to the case of a clergyman who sought treatment for a gastro-intestinal malady in a general hospital. A few nights after admission, awakening terrified, in a twilight state, he was so disturbed that he was transferred immediately to a mental hospital. The next morning, he was quite himself—nothing was the matter with him, there was no reason for his being in a mental hospital, he had no worries or problems. That night, too, he awakened in terror, hid under the bed, and was frantically combative. The next morning, he was in fairly good condition, but obviously unnerved. The third evening, he was anxious and unwilling to go to bed. He was given a powerful hypnotic, slept well, and was again quite himself. The next night, he was again disturbed, and shortly thereafter was definitely in a schizophrenic state. The use of the hypnotic was simply a support to the self. It interfered with the activity of the dissociated components and by protecting sleep reduced the fatigue which enfeebled the self function. It deferred the psychosis, a day or so. Such brief postponement of personal disaster may provide opportunity for truly remedial work—in this case, beyond my ability. The ephemeral calm that can thus be achieved sometimes enables a patient to regain perspective and to reach a wise decision about treatment, or in regard to

some major change in his life situation that will be greatly
beneficial in reducing conflict, anxiety, or tension. I know of
few other indications for this sort of maneuver.

Direct enfeeblement of the self system is sometimes indicated, but, too, is apt to be devoid of lasting benefit. There are
various ways of accomplishing this maneuver, of which one of
the easiest is—as in the example of the clergyman—by chemical
means. From the early days of the Egyptian culture, the use of
beverages containing ethyl alcohol has persisted in the Western world. The pharmacodynamics of alcohol is most strikingly
a relaxing of the inhibiting and dissociating power of the self.[72]
Consideration of its remarkable power in this direction led me,
some years ago, to use intoxication with alcohol as a means of
obliterating conflict in schizophrenics whose exhaustion from
chronic excitement or tension was dangerous to their survival.
The gentleman of the imaginary stallion mentioned in the
fourth lecture was the first patient so treated, and with complete success. A number of other patients in gravely disquieting condition were carried into freely communicative states
by the same technique, with subsequent recovery or social
restoration.

Under full doses of alcohol, the signs and symptoms of strong
self function disappear. A patient, for example, in terror from
the projection of cravings for perverse satisfactions—*craving*
is the term by which we refer to the extremely unpleasant state
which results when there is desire for the satisfaction of some
zone of interaction so strong that it cannot be excluded from
awareness, and at the same time so symbolized that it cannot be
tolerated by the self; in other words, an abhorrent *yearning*—
may be extremely excited, combative, and directly dangerous
to himself and others. When thus intoxicated, his fear of people
around him disappears, and with it, the excitement. After a

[72] One of the colleagues achieved a bon mot of the first water: the super-
ego is the alcohol-soluble part of the personality.

More seriously, the findings about to be reported are well authenticated by
repetition by other observers.

week or so of this alcoholically hazy existence—of which he retains memory and easy recall—*in a well managed environment* where nothing that will be regretted can occur, the patient has lost the necessity for terror and excitement. This is not solely due to the enfeeblement of the self function, but the weakening of the self system is prerequisite for the change.

The enfeeblement of the self by interpersonal processes is also possible. One works towards this in occasional treatment by calling in question some of the formulated inhibitory attitudes and normative prescriptions that the patient can express. In the intensive treatment, the patient works this out mostly for himself by recalling the situations from which the attitudes survive. The direct attack is not to be undertaken lightly; one must be quite clear as to both the direct and the more obscurely symbolized factors that are expressed in the accessible formula. It may, for example, be obvious that a patient is absurdly restrained about being what he calls 'forward.' We communicate this view to him with skill enough to make the point. He rapidly develops a distressing aggressiveness which makes him a nuisance to all his acquaintances. We have only succeeded in substituting a cruder for a more refined compromise; the underlying problems of the personality are not helped, in fact are aggravated.

In my consultative work with incipient schizophrenics, I seek often to enfeeble the self with respect to some restrictions of awareness. Thus a patient gradually unfolds a home situation both distressing and mystifying. Under methodic and persisting questioning, he becomes aware of a long-accumulating resentment about unreasonable restraints on his freedom that have been imposed by one of his parents—who has resisted the fact of his chronological maturity, and appropriate efforts to perfect his socialization. When this becomes clear, the mystery of his hostile acts disappears. He is more secure as a result of understanding the naturalness of a previously disconcerting series of events. He is less secure in knowing that he is hostile to the parent. It would not be wise to leave things in this state. One must go on to develop the natural inevitability of the negative feeling, and then to some interpretation of the parent's behavior that will provide the patient with a constructive technique for circumventing the situation without unnecessary exchanges of hostility.

The goal of occasional treatment being generally alleviation rather than radical cure, one sometimes has to interfere with the growth of awareness. This seeming paradox arises from several considerations. There are problems which, once clearly recognized, demand radical treatment if serious disturbance of the personality is to be avoided. I was once consulted by a patient 49 years of age who was sent to me because, in the face of a threat of chronic physical disability, he was entertaining well-formulated suicidal intentions. I learned that he suffered periods of insomnia connected with horrible dreams, that his enjoyment of social life was undergoing a marked recession, that while it had never included sexual intimacies with women, their company had until recently been delightful, but was now becoming repugnant to him. On the night before our fourth conference, he dreamt of something like a wrestling match in the course of which the two men engaged in some mutual sexual performance. The patient had reported one somewhat related boyhood experience. I provided this patient with no opportunity to concern himself with "homosexuality" as a part of the motives that expressed themselves in the horrible and disgusting dreams, and that were concerned in the change in tenor of his life.

The indications were chiefly for the remedy of his increasing loneliness, which was reducing the value of life. To this end, we made something of a detailed study of the women who had once been appreciated, and it gradually emerged that there were still a few who were attractive. From their characteristics, those of rather markedly differentiated women, it became reasonable to formulate a plan for specific avoidances instead of a blanket aversion to the sex. Some other matters were dealt with; my point is to show the way in which one of the less unfortunate compromises which one often encounters was utilized as a practical way out of a situation in which accumulating lust coupled with increasing social distance threatened to precipitate a very serious conflict.

At this point, in somewhat obscure apropos to the discussion of this patient, I shall comment on the utility of extra-verbal expression for the at least partial solution of mental disorders that for one reason or another cannot be treated intensively. Levy in his specific and general "release therapy" of problem children,[13] has worked out a technique of this kind. Moreno, in the "psychodrama" technique for older patients,[14] seems also to use this principle. The patient acts out under more or less controlled conditions a dramatization of personnel and performances connected with his conflicts. There is some encouragement of verbalization after the activity. Durably good results, however, seem to follow in some children and juveniles without their having had much to say about the meaningful play in which they were engaged.

My experience with intensive therapy in adolescents and adults leads me to think that verbalization is usually, if not always, necessary to insure permanent benefits. One of the problems of psychoanalysis is the *acting out* of troublesome motivation—in or outside of the therapy situation, and usually both —with little or no awareness of the meaning of the performances. Objectively, the activity may from the beginning be revealing, and it generally becomes progressively more obvious until the physician, at least, cannot overlook its significance. His interpretation then usually permits the suppression of the dramatization, and the production of verbalizations in its lieu. Let me repeat, in this connection, the statement that one has

---

[13] Levy, David M., 'Release Therapy' in Young Children. PSYCHIATRY (1938) 1:387–390.

[14] Moreno, J. L., Psychodramatic Treatment of Marriage Problems. *Sociometry* (1940) 3:1–23.

information only to the extent to which one has tended to communicate one's experience—through the medium of consensually valid verbal means. Theoretically, this last qualification
gives somewhat undue importance to the use of words; by and
large, it is a good principle to which to adhere in treatment
work. Most patients have for years been acting out conflicts,
substitutions, and compromises; the benefits of treatment come
in large part from their learning to notice what they are doing,
and this is greatly expedited by carefully validated verbal
statements as to what seems to be going on.

A special case of this non-verbal expressive behavior to which
people have recourse for the reduction of tension arising from
unsatisfied tendency systems, or from conflict of motives, is
made up of games and sports. It is often demonstrable that
some activity of this sort has provided a symbolic discharge of
motives that conflict with the self to a degree that makes the
recreation an important factor in preserving relative mental
health. Many a person has doubtless been able to preserve the
peace, at home or in his community, in large measure by virtue
of the symbolic satisfactions derived from hunting, trap shooting, or bowling. The rôle of card games in a prevailingly juvenile society can be far greater in importance than a relatively
non-competitive person would guess. People who have but
very limited ability for human intimacy can assuage loneliness
through these instrumentalities, without any risk of troublesome interpersonal developments. Biological and other scientific avocations, and fishing, sailing, riding, golf, and swimming are activities that are in a special class, by virtue of the
extensive contexts of integrating tendencies that may be involved. Various interpersonal stresses and dissatisfactions associated with one's necessary employment may be kept at an
insignificant level by the elevation to prime personal significance of the intricate, long-span procedures, and highly personalized subject-matter, of, say, horticulture, the breeding
of dogs or horses, or the study of ant-communities, as one's

recreational avocation. Amateur astronomy and radio communication are two examples of the 'hobbies' which are scientifically and technologically absorbing, and associated with close but mediate relation with a well-organized group of co-workers. Riding, again often an attenuated participation in a group of like-minded people, is peculiarly significant because of symbolic investitures of the uniquely gifted sub-colleague, the horse. Golf is in most significant essence a consummately skillful performance that calls for remarkable development of perseveration, as well as for tonic and motor adjustments of almost all the skeletal muscles. It shares this with the game of billiards, with additional benefits connected with outdoor life. Fishing, sailing, and swimming have as a common element this outdoor life in its peculiar aspects that inhere in association with bodies of water. Swimming is rather in a class by itself, because it directly involves sub-cultural organismic factors that make for relaxation and repose, quite exterior to its often great symbolic rôle. I am sure that many an incipient schizophrenic has been able to reintegrate an approximation to mental health, by chief virtue of spending a summer in bathing suit at the seaside, away from any people highly significant to him. Camping expeditions to forests and mountains; mountain climbing; biological, anthropological, and archeological exploration; and activities which include moving at extraordinary velocity; these are some more of the forms of recreational behavior that have an extensive context of meaning in the non-verbal preservation of relative mental health.

Long the prescription of physicians as an adjuvant to or as the only treatment offered for a disturbed state of mind, activity as such has recently been made the basis of study as to its therapeutic possibilities. This came about somewhat indirectly, by way of a particular development in the institutional field, the *occupational therapy* with which Mrs. Slagel and William Rush Dunton were effective pioneers in psychiatry, and with the demonstration of general utility of which the treatment of those disabled in the World War—as by our Federal Board for Vocational Education, Rehabilitation Division—had much to do. In part because of the clearly demonstrable value of particular arts and crafts in rehabilitating disabled soldiers, sailors, and marines, and in part because of its leader's zeal for organizing, occupational therapy rather monopolized for some years the attention that should be accorded to activity-therapies in general. I believe that the part is now beginning to find its place in the whole, a change that I regard as decidedly constructive.

I shall turn now to the patients whose difficulties are treated in major part by a change of their cultural setting; more specifically, to those who are removed from their accustomed way of life to the peculiarly characterized culture-complex of the mental hospital. The fundamental principles of institutional treatment have had a long historical exemplification in the monastic orders and other religious and special communities—including such diverse institutions as the French Foreign Legion, the Chasseurs Alpines, and the Parisian Apaches. When life in the complex pattern of the times seems impossible, one may associate oneself—or forcibly be associated—with a group the social structure of which is less variously demanding in terms of fluid conformity.

The modern *custodial* mental hospital was brought into being largely through the almost incredible energy of Miss Dorothea Lynde Dix—1802 to 1887.[75] The *therapeutic* mental hospital began with the York Retreat established—as were several others, including the Sheppard and Enoch Pratt Hospital—by members of the Society of Friends. The work of the therapeutic institution has largely overshadowed the beneficial aspects of the merely custodial, although the great majority of those who have recovered from severe mental disorders have

[75] Tiffany, Francis, *Life of Dorothea Lynde Dix;* Boston, Houghton, Mifflin, 8 ed. 1892 (xiii and 392 pp.). Miss Dix in 1852 secured the passage by Congress of her District Hospital Bill as a result of which St. Elizabeths Hospital came into being as The Government Hospital for the Insane. She was thereafter Superintendent of Women Nurses, U.S.A., in the Civil War.

thus far been instances of so-called *spontaneous recovery*—the work of factors other than deliberate therapeutic intervention by the psychiatrist—that took place in custodial institutions.

In any society that permits a person to rise or fall in status as a more or less direct result of his own efforts, the possibility of favorable or unfavorable change in one's position in the hierarchy of personal valuation is apt to be important. Everyone knows that skill in dealing with important people is one of the effective ways to get ahead in our society of mobile vertical classes. Anything that handicaps the development or manifestation of this skill is, therefore, productive of keen insecurity. Any other source of insecurity is apt to act as just such a handicap, and thus to give rise to a 'vicious circle' of aggravating factors. It thus comes about rather generally that the severity of any mental disorder is to an important degree a result of insecurity about one's status. This part of the problem would be solved by removing the patient to a society in which vertical mobility is not possible. Just this, in effect, is achieved by his admission to the custodial institution.

The mental hospital is a sub-community strikingly different from the larger social system in which it is embedded. It exists communally with the larger society, but its organization is in a most significant way classless. It is primarily a social system made up of fixed *castes*, which does not permit any vertical mobility. Moreover, it is a social organization autocratically maintained in conformity to a relatively small number of simple, explicit, rules—in great contrast to the larger society with its however feebly democratic authority, coupled with complex, mostly implicit, often contradictory, demands that are variously and often inequably enforced by public opinion, group prejudice, the church, and the police powers of the community.[76]

[76] For two cogent sociological considerations, see Rowland, Howard, Interaction Processes in the State Mental Hospital. PSYCHIATRY (1938) 1:323–327, and Friendship Patterns in the State Mental Hospital. PSYCHIATRY (1939) 2:363–373.

For a sociological discussion of our social system and its effects on problems

Admission to the mental hospital is often the only way by which one can be separated from the particular people at home, in school, or at the place of employment, with whom one is integrated in an increasingly unfortunate situation, progressively aggravated as a result of fatigue, misdirected and misunderstood efforts, and the display of conflicting motives. As Dr. White used to say, the mental hospital is the only place where one can be "crazy" comfortably. It is used to these sorts of performances and, through its classification of patients, is more or less obviously able to deal with them intelligently. It has been unfortunate for mentally disordered persons that their voluntary admission to the mental hospital was until recently illegal or otherwise impractical. The practice was that of judicial commitment, perhaps after a brief residence on authority of a medical or other formal certification that the patient was a menace to himself or others. This had come about through legislative precaution called into being as a result of several factors; the bearing of severe mental disorder on property rights and various civil and criminal 'responsibilities,' coupled with some notorious XIX Century instances of the misuse of a custodial institution; many superstitions about "the insane" including vague to vivid convictions that mental disorders are in some fashion contagious; and a hatred of practices like the *lettres de cachet.* Many of the statutory safeguards showed no consideration of the welfare of the patient; until very recently patients in the District of Columbia had to appear before a jury and by them be found to be of 'unsound mind' before they could be retained beyond a brief period in St. Elizabeths Hospital.

Hospital classification of patients is in theory the segregation of patients on the basis of similarity of signs and symptoms. Hypomanic patients who are voluble, loud, and miscellaneously overactive, for example, would all be in the same ward

---

and current practices of preventive psychiatry, see Davis, Kingsley, **Mental Hygiene and the Class Structure.** PSYCHIATRY (1938) 1:55-65.

or group of wards, unmixed with patients who showed a different clinical picture. When one of them quiets down, he would be transferred to another ward, where he would find the other patients acting very much as he does.

The patient is transferred from one ward to another on the basis of his interpersonal performances, regardless of intentions, rationalizations, excuses, pleas, protests, "pull," or other of the thousand and one factors that make for inequality of opportunity in the larger world. Rumor and verbal tradition about the various wards may complicate the effects of patient classification, particularly in the hospital with restricted facilities for patient segregation. The basis of classification may also be inadequate or absurd. If, however, circumstances permit a reasonable approximation to the theory, the practice of classification is in itself of marked therapeutic significance.

A hateful manic patient in a ward that houses several catatonic patients is about as bad an example of non-therapeutic situations as one can find. Correspondingly, the disturbed wards of smaller hospitals are apt to be anything but areas of therapeutic segregation. Admission wards have to be the clearing area, from which patients are transferred to their appropriate group. They are the point at which effort may well be concentrated to inform the patient about hospital life, and about the non-punitive basis of classificatory transfers.

Systematic educational efforts to facilitate the adjustment of the patient in the mental hospital are not yet widely practiced. It is easy to see the difficulties that stand in the way. It is also easy to overlook the uncontrolled and often unfortunate educational influences that are bound to exist where acculturation to the hospital community is left to chance. Carefully formulated factual statements couched in relatively simple language might very well be made a part of the standard practice of all the hospital personnel who deal with newly-admitted patients. The barriers to communication with most of these patients may be great. This is all the more reason for being clear on just what one wishes to communicate. No one statement will serve with every patient, but good simple statements that are understood by the hospital personnel will usefully restrict the range of their improvisations in talking to patients, or among themselves, within hearing of patients.

In theory, the mental hospital is governed in accordance with an explicit policy calculated to achieve the practical maximum benefit of recognized principles of institutional psychiatric therapy. Its peculiar social structure requires an essentially rigid, if unusually simple, discipline of all the employees, and, along much more flexible lines, of all the patients.

The regimen of the hospital is in general mildly hygienic, sometimes markedly so. The rather rigidly enforced ordering of life by the clock is in the last analysis quite simple and understandable—probably, to many patients, a welcome relief from the irregularities to which they had felt driven. The variously encouraged participation in more or less intelligently prescribed and prosecuted activity therapy is often most helpful. If there is nothing more than work on wards, grounds, and hospital farm, it is much better than nothing.

In a few words, the aspects of the mental hospital community which are directly therapeutic are both numerous and of considerable positive value. The organization of people concerned into castes of the physicians, the technicians, the nurses, the attendants, and the patients, however undemocratic it may sound, is the product of centuries of evolution, and is therapeutically sound, irrespective of its effects on some of those who are not patients.

Besides the direct effect of the hospital community, benefit to the patient is obtained from some relatively generalized therapeutic procedures. Notable among these is *hydrotherapy*, the more or less scientific utilization of part of the historic "external hydropathy," wet packs, showers and sprays, and the continuous-flow tub. There are many complicated problems associated with the use of the wet pack, either for the patient alone in a room, or for a number of patients who receive packs in the same room. Besides the heat-transfer feature, there is that of a great degree of physical restraint. The beneficial effects of the pack in some phases of mental disorder seem to be fairly established. The benefits of the 'continuous tub' are unquestionable. Hydrotherapy, generally, and the use of showers and sprays in particular, often include, besides the hydrotherapeutic factor, a social influence. Patients moving among their fellows in *socially sanctioned* nudity, or approximations thereto, are in quite a different situation from that of the patient who insists on being nude in his room, or on the ward.

Something can be said in favor of the therapeutic use of seclusion and restraint. By seclusion is meant the separation of a patient from easy access to the company of others. By restraint is meant the use of some one of sundry devices to restrict the activity of the patient—from the sheet spread across the patient and wrapped around the sides of the bed, the unauthorized use of which may be overlooked by inexperienced physicians, to such devices as the camisole, wristlets, and anklets. As Dr. White has said, it has been fortunate for institutional psychiatry that the use of restraint was abolished; it made the psychiatrists use their minds. At the same time, if one could certainly obviate their abuse, restraint in some cases, and seclusion in many, are at times clearly indicated as positive therapeutic maneuvers. Seclusion can relieve the patient of the pressure of people and, as this effect is achieved, give him an opportunity to feel loneliness, the need for companionship.

The trouble with seclusion and restraint, as with the other instrumentalities of the hospital, is always the result of lack of intelligence, interest, and responsibility on the part of the physician who can prescribe—and, one hopes, supervise the use of —these restrictions. The psychiatrist, of all people, knows that

rules and regulations, and principles useful in reaching conclusions, are all susceptible of gross misuse for rationalizing behavior in most blatant breach of their purpose. If re-education
of those concerned is out of the question, he may well seek to
abolish any and all practices that may be channels for inhumane
indifference and cruelty.

To this briefest of glimpses into some of the useful factors in
the more mediate treatment of seriously disordered patients,
let me add a few words as to the psychiatrist's direct treatment
of patients in the mental hospital. This may be intensive or occasional, continuing or only for the duration of some phases
of the hospital residence. The hospital provides a setting for the
active treatment of some patients, in the case of whom it would
otherwise be contra-indicated because of the unpredictable or
uncontrollable risk of suicidal misadventure, breach of the
peace, or other serious concomitants. When therapy is the primary aim of the hospital, the beneficial factors inhering in the
hospital situation can sometimes be so integrated that they facilitate the work of the physician to a degree almost beyond
the possibility of any extramural setting. Unfortunately, however, the hospital setting is not generally useful for the entire
course of an intensive treatment looking towards cure. The
patient should ordinarily be paroled from the hospital some
considerable time before treatment is concluded, if maximum
benefits are to be secured—if, in fact, some disadvantageous
factors are to be avoided. We are not yet clear as to how best
to transfer a patient under intensive treatment from one psychiatrist to another, with but transient disturbance of progress.
The treatment staff of the therapeutic mental hospital should,
therefore, often carry on the treatment of patients after they
have been paroled or discharged from hospital residence. As
this is often impractical, the patients of therapeutic hospitals
are apt to be discharged at the right stage of their reorganization but thereby separated from psychiatric collaboration, or
retained in the hospital beyond the period of useful association

with the hospital community, when their reassociation with ordinary life could much more profitably be under study.

For this reason, and because there are now many instances of hospitalization of young patients in episodes that might well be quickly remedied if so drastic a change of social situation as admission to the mental hospital were not experienced, I am greatly impressed with the desirability of an innovation in the shape of special communities in which some of the great advantages of the mental hospital could be made available, without incurring the necessary exposure to factors that now make for permanent institutional adaptation of many patients. Something at least remotely like what I have in mind has already been accomplished by the Civilian Conservation Corps, the various camps of which would be a rewarding field for study. It is desirable, during the developmental stage of a therapeutic camp or community, that it be in coöperative relationship with an accessible mental hospital with good facilities for classifying patients, and a therapeutic staff.

Even this addition to the institutional facilities of psychiatry would probably have little effect on one of the most embittering experiences to which the institutional therapist is constantly exposed. I refer here to the intervention of persons by blood or otherwise related to the patient. It is only natural that relatives should demonstrate some interest, real or assumed, in what is being done for the good of the patient. No hospital administrator would object to this. It is natural but not so unobjectionable that relatives should be firm in the conviction that their visits to the patient are wholly beneficial, while they are often precisely the opposite. The problem of the suspicious relative in this rôle can often be solved by restricting visits to some one person about whom the patient's history is encouraging, and to whose visits there seems to be a minimum of bad consequences. The peculiarly disheartening performance of relatives, however, is not a complicating but the most untimely *terminating* of a patient's treatment. They often remove the patient of otherwise excellent outlook in the midst of the most profitable phase of his work—often with consequences disastrous to the patient; but never, so far as I can recall, with subsequent self-recriminations—flatly against psychiatric advice.[77]

To conclude the matter of therapeutic conceptions, let me restate the steps by which the goals of psychiatric treatment are sought. Whether the work be intensive or occasional, institutional, extramural, consultative or informal; whether the end state of the patient has come to be the achievement of an extraordinary unfolding of hitherto potential capacities for living, the cure of a serious handicap, the amelioration of a difficult situation, or failure and adaptation to an institutional life, or even a grave dilapidation; in every case the events in the therapeutic effort will have been oriented in much the same way, the foresight of the psychiatrist will have sought ways to collaborate in much the same pattern of interpersonal relations. An analysis of this pattern into ultimate terms may now be useful.

The first effective step in the solution of any problem is the synthesis of perceptions and prehensions as to the problem-situation into a perception of that in which one is involved. This usually calls for the *release of one's alertness* from inhibiting influences which are manifestations of the self dynamism. There may be dissociated tendencies that are significant in explaining the integration of the problem-situation. There may be repressed, vaguely remembered, factors. There may be suppressive effects of the magnitude of a deletion or 'clouding' of consciousness, at some crucial phase of development of the problem-situation.

The history of the patient, secured retrospectively from the

[77] It is by no means mere spleen that leads the psychiatrist to conclude, in many instances, that the treatment was interrupted because the relative saw that the patient was becoming emancipated from a subordination to the relative which had pre-existed the psychosis; the, of course, unrecognized determination being that sick or well, the patient is not going to be free of the relative.

known presenting situation, will have revealed—or at least indicated as more or less probable—the more typical manifestations of complicated interpersonal relations in terms of the explanatory conceptions discussed in the fourth lecture. The elevation into awareness of the unnoticed influences that are giving rise to the problem aspect of the situation, is facilitated by training the patient to understand the pattern of maladjustive activity in terms of the appropriate explanatory conception—not in terms of its name, or the names of alleged dynamic entities, "complexes," which the patient might be said to be suffering.

Patients usually begin this learning from rather trifling instances, rather than from insight into deeply disturbing events. It seems as if this intrusion of apparently insignificant, 'accidental' events into the fabric of daily life, and remembered dreams of rather simple context, are the two chief ways by which the striving towards mental health ordinarily circumvents the general effect of the self system.

The psychiatrist often assists in this learning by simple interpretative behavior: he says something calculated to center attention on the momentary situation, recites in essential outline the course of the significant event as he has heard it, and perhaps asks if there can be something important which was omitted from the account, or if the action could have been meant to have such and such an effect, or if some detail can be recalled that would indicate that such and such an unrecognized end was being pursued. In another sort of this apparently insignificant event, he may intervene only to ask—with stress on the importance of the matter by preferably non-verbal, perhaps intonational means—as to how the patient could have been aware of the motivation of the other person concerned, or what the evidence may be that justifies the assumption that such and such is a durable characteristic of the other person. This latter sort of event and interpretative action is often called out by patients who show prevailingly substitutive processes.

As the release of the patient's alertness proceeds, there comes a time when it is possible to *identify* one of the *parataxic concomitants* that have been permanent complicating factors in the patient's perceptions of significant other people. Here again it will usually be an at first hearing quite insignificant, mildly irrelevant, remark that communicates the distortion of the patient's formulation of the psychiatrist.

Here also interpretation usually facilitates the learning. This, again, is often merely an interrupting, seriously expressed, question as to what the patient has just said; a repetition of the patient's statement in essential outline; and an inquiry as to its implication as to the psychiatrist, or as to the basis for the expressed belief.

The first awareness of a parataxically illusory personal characterization begins the therapeutic processes connected with it. In itself, the discovery is attended by a sharp fall in the patient's feeling of security; a disturbing 'mistake' has been made, a queer and disquieting 'misapprehension' has occurred. The patient feels that the psychiatrist is annoyed or disappointed, that his appraisal of the patient must be unfavorable. It is necessary that the essentially disintegrative, distance-producing security operations that are thus called out shall be handled in some conformity with the surmised pattern of the particular parataxis. It does not help if the physician offers reassurance in terms of his more real characteristics. This would but increase the insecurity of the patient because it asserts that there was a 'mistake' or 'misapprehension,' which the physician accepts as such.

The psychiatrist, having clarified the gross outlines of the expressed parataxic distortion, remarks to some such effect as "This impression that you have had about me must have a history, must be the recollection of some such a person who was once really important to you—perhaps you can recall someone. Let us listen to whatever comes to mind." Even if, as is frequently the case in the first instance of this kind, the patient silently 'searches his memory' and recalls no one, the interpretation will have communicated security *and* useful information about the sources of parataxic distortion.

It might be thought that, once the patient *has* recalled the historic, personal source of a particular parataxic distortion, that this parataxis would disappear. Nothing so spectacular is to be expected; if it seems to have occurred, the chances are greatly in favor of quite another explanation; namely, that the patient's insecurity was not resolved, and that there has developed an even more complex parataxic situation with the physician. The remarkable thing that has certainly happened— one trusts without the just mentioned unfortunate sequel—is insight into the actual fact of illusory, parataxic, distortions as a factor that complicates the patient's interpersonal relations. This constitutes the first therapeutic milestone, to which I have already referred.

Each recurrent recognition of a particular parataxic distortion of the physician brings with it more data as to the historic, personal source. The time comes when the patient recalls vividly a series of highly significant events that occurred in interpersonal relations with this person. This recall gradually expands into a more or less comprehensive insight; first, into the 'effects' of this earlier relationship on the subsequent course of the patient's dealings with others, on the formulation of ideals of conduct and relatively fixed valuational judgments of behavior. Besides this there comes insight into the less obviously interpersonal consequences of this former relationship; into direct symbolic associations made at that time, and into much more obscure resymbolizations, substitutions, and symptomatic and related actions that had their origin in, or in subsequent relation to, the significant relationship. As these complex remainders of previously unresolved motivational "sets" expand into easily understood meaning, the patient generally experiences a great deal of unpleasant emotion—to which may be added keen regrets for disastrous effects over the years, which are now seen to have stemmed from the early experience.

Progressively, in the course of identifying all the more important parataxically surviving, unresolved situations of the patient's past, and their consequent dissolutions, there goes an *expanding of the self* to such final effect that the patient as known to himself is much the same person as the patient behaving with others. This is *psychiatric* cure. There may remain a need for a great deal of experience and education before the psychiatric cure is a *social* cure, implying a more abundant life in the community. It may be impractical to achieve this more abundant life, the collaborative participation with others, in that particular community. A change of social setting may be mandatory but impractical, in which case adequate mediate relationships and clearly understood reformulations of some of one's interpersonal goals must fill the gaps. The possibility of achieving a social cure arises solely from the fact of psychiatric cure. The probability of its achievement is a matter of circumstances, limited chiefly by factors inhering in the culture-complex and selectively reflected in all the people available for interpersonal relations. Be social cure achieved or not, however, the person who knows himself has mental health. He is content with his utilization of the opportunities that come to him. He values himself as his conduct merits. He knows and mostly obtains the satisfactions that he needs, and he is greatly secure.

Sharply to be distinguished from the conception of social cure is the so-called 'social recovery' of the institutional psychiatrist. Patients are classified for discharge from mental hospitals as recovered, social recovery, improved, or unimproved. A person is socially recovered when he is both clear as to the fact that he was so mentally disordered that institutional care was required, and free from any manifest signs or symptoms of the disorder. Investigation sometimes reveals that the patient discharged as a social recovery still suffers marked mental disorder. He has learnt, however, to treat most people as if they had nothing to do with his troubles—of which, the less he has to say, the better. Many of these patients, like many of those somewhat benefited by other forms of non-intensive therapy, continue in a favorable course and require no further attention from the psychiatrist.

A Theory of Interpersonal Relations and the Evolution of Personality

BY PATRICK MULLAHY

THE FOLLOWING is an attempt to outline the group of central ideas and insights making up Harry Stack Sullivan's theory of personality and personality development. The impression that this useful body of theory has received less attention than it merits has led to this sometimes all too schematic review of the fundamental ideas in his published statements, supplemented by personal discussion.

Because of lack of space, several ideas can scarcely be more than mentioned in a paragraph or two. There are several concepts which, for sufficient clarity, would require a paper by themselves, but it is thought best to discuss them briefly.

What is psychiatry? Is it, as one might imagine, the study of the mentally ill? And what, precisely, does mental illness mean? What are the therapeutic conceptions of modern psychiatry? According to Sullivan, the therapeutic conceptions "arise directly from the work of Freud, Meyer, and White. Were it not for Freud's formulations, we would probably still be frustrated by the obvious discontinuities in the stream of consciousness. Had it not been for Meyer's insistence that mental disorders are to be considered as dynamic patterns, as types of reaction to the demands of life, we might still be working in the laboratory on problems of neurophysiology and endocrinology. But it was White's ineffable zeal in teaching us to 'determine what the patient is trying to do,' his indomitable energy in training and in encouraging psychiatric investigators, and his vision and sagacity in the executive, administrative and promotional aspects of psychiatry in the broader sense, that gave us most of our profit from Freud and from Meyer. . . ." [1]

The next step came with the realization that psychiatry is the study of interpersonal relations. "Psychiatry . . . is the study of processes that involve or go on between people. The field of psychiatry is the field of interpersonal relations, under any and all circumstances in which these relations exist. It was seen that *a personality* can never be isolated from the complex of interpersonal relations in which the person lives and has his being." [2] The full significance of these statements can only be progressively elucidated.

As a preliminary analysis, one may divide human behavior, interpersonal relations, into two closely related kinds or categories, characterized by the pursuit of satisfactions and the pursuit of security.[3] This does not mean, of course, that human behavior occurs marked, "For the pursuit of satisfactions," or, "For the pursuit of security." These are distinctions instituted by the psychiatric investigator in the course of inquiry, which help to make human behavior more intelligible. But these distinctions also are not "mental" or subjective. The attainment of satisfactions and security are seen to be the goals, *the end-states,* of human behavior, interpersonal processes. In popular language, they explain in general terms what one is after in any situation with other persons, real or fantastic, or a blend of both. From a slightly different point of view, they are "integrating tendencies." They explain why any situation in which two or more people are involved becomes an interpersonal situation. Furthermore, it is because of these needs

[1] See p. 177.
[2] See p. 10.
[3] See p. 12.

that one cannot live and be human except in communal existence with others. For preliminary analysis, they aid in clarifying interpersonal situations, and they lead to more illuminating
and significant discoveries and interpretations.

The pursuit of satisfactions is a response to primarily biological needs. Food and drink, sleep and rest, the satisfaction of
lust are all among them. "Throughout life," be it noted, "the
pursuit of satisfactions is physiologically provoked by increased
tone in some unstriped muscles, and the securing of the satisfactions is a relaxation of this tone, with a tendency towards
the diminution of attention, alertness, and vigilance, and an approach to sleep." [4] In more popular language, the achievement
of satisfactions causes a *decrease* of tension.

The other classification, the need for, and the pursuit of, security grows out of man's cultural equipment. The "cultural"
is defined, anthropologically, as "all that which is man-made,
which survives as monument to preexistent man." [5] It is, of
course, imbedded in every person, the matrix of everything
which he thinks and does. Without it, he would not be human,
could not live. As Sullivan phrases it, "All those movements,
actions, speech, thoughts, reveries, and so on, which pertain
more to the culture which has been imbedded in a particular
individual than to the organization of his tissues and glands,
is apt to belong in this classification of the pursuit of security." [6]

How does the need for security arise? It arises from the fact
that every person, through a long history, beginning at birth,
becomes a social being. Through "empathy," a concept to be
discussed later, every infant feels some effect of the culture by
the attitudes of the significant person, mother or nurse, around
him. [7] These attitudes of the significant person, or persons, are
themselves socially conditioned. Long before the infant can

[4] See p. 88.
[5] See p. 13.
[6] See p. 13.
[7] See p. 17.

understand what is happening, he feels something of the attitudes of those who take care of him. After a while, the little one is deliberately trained and taught what is considered right and wrong. In other words, the impulses, the biological strivings, are socially conditioned, moulded according to the approved patterns of the culture. Unlike the attainment of satisfactions, the attainment of security requires the *maintenance* of some degree of muscle tonus, tension. It is said that some muscles are never completely relaxed, that most muscles are in a state of considerable tonus throughout the periods of deepest sleep. In fact changes in one's state of security are accompanied by spectacular change of tonus throughout the major muscular systems of the body. As will be seen subsequently, the attainment of satisfactions according to the socially approved patterns causes a profound feeling of well-being, of self-approval, of security. Not only does the person experience these felt needs but when, for certain reasons, they cannot be fulfilled according to the culturally approved patterns learned in early life, a feeling of intense uneasiness and discomfort, insecurity, *anxiety*, occurs.[8] This does not mean that the needs get converted into insecurity, anxiety, but that they are felt to imperil security; that is, they conflict with the necessity for achieving security.

An understanding of the power motive is fundamental, both psychologically and logically. For Sullivan, the power motive means much more than the usually restricted meaning of power in "power drive." A person is born with this power motive, or, in his cautious words, with "something" of the power motive.[9] This does *not* mean, however, that one is born with a "power drive." For Sullivan, power refers to the expansive biological striving of the infant and states characterized by the feeling of ability, applying, in a very wide sense, to all kinds of human activity. A "power drive," in the narrow sense, results from

[8] See p. 19.
[9] See p. 14.

the thwarting of the expansive biological striving, and the feeling of the lack of ability. In other words, a "power drive" is learned, resulting from the early frustration of the need to be, and to feel, capable, to have ability, to have power. A "power drive" develops as a compensation when there is a deep, gnawing, inner sense of powerlessness, because of early frustration of the expanding, developing latent potentialities of the organism. Later acculturation and experience may, and frequently does, add to the early frustration and sense of powerlessness. A person who has a feeling of ability or power does not need to gain, and will not seek, dominance or power *over* some one. A person who manifests a "power drive" does seek to dominate others. In the wide sense of the term, power is potential, and actual, accomplishment *along with* others. The accomplishment and the feeling of accomplishment are mutual. In fact, power refers to any activity where there is accomplishment, satisfaction of needs, mutual attainment of goals not distorted by unfortunate—that is, thwarting—experience. Power or ability "is ordinarily much more important in the human being than are the impulses resulting from a feeling of hunger, or thirst; and the fully developed feeling of lust comes so very late in biological maturation that it is scarcely a good source for conditioning." The power motive is more important because, in fact, it underlies them. They are expressions of biological needs. But biological needs are manifestations of the organism's efforts not merely to maintain itself in stable balance with and in its environment, but to expand, to 'reach out' to, and interact with, widening circles of the environment.

So important and fundamental is the power motive that the degree to which it is satisfied, fulfilled, and the manner in which it is satisfied and fulfilled mainly determine the growth and characteristics of personality. Stated negatively, the extent to which the power motive is frustrated, blocked, and the manner in which such frustration is accomplished, will mainly determine the development of personality. In Sullivan's words:

"The full development of personality along the lines of security is chiefly founded on the infant's discovery of his powerlessness to achieve certain desired end-states with the tools, the instrumentalities, which are at his disposal. From the disappointments in the very early stages of life outside the womb—in which all things are given—comes the beginning of this vast development of actions, thoughts, foresights, and so on, which are calculated to protect one from a feeling of insecurity and helplessness in the situation which confronts one. This accultural evolution begins thus, and when it succeeds, when one evolves successfully along this line, then one respects oneself, and as one respects oneself so one can respect others. . . . If there is a valid and real attitude toward the self, that attitude will manifest as valid and real towards others. It is not that as ye judge so shall ye be judged, *but as you judge yourself so shall you judge others. . . .*" [10]

To gain satisfactions and, particularly, security is to have power in interpersonal relations. So far as one cannot do so, that is to be power-less, helpless. As will be seen later, anxiety is an instrumentality of the self. But the self comes into being because it is necessary that one's interests be focused into certain fields that "work;" that is, attain satisfaction and security. And it is necessary that one's interests be focused into certain fields that work "in the modification of activity in the interest of power in interpersonal relations." [11]

It is perhaps advisable at this point to emphasize that the power motive, although given originally in the human organism, is not a fixed entity. It is manifested in activity, usually, although not always, in an interpersonal situation.

To be noted also is the fact that the energy of the infant, or rather its manifestations in the power motive, become quickly modified or transformed. But to modify or to transform is not to destroy. Sullivan's theories of interpersonal behavior are

[10] See p. 15.
[11] See p. 20.

therefore, rooted in biology. But, if one may use a somewhat crude metaphor, the root is not the full-grown tree. On the other hand, the tree depends on its roots for its very life. The energy of a human being, however transformed as to its expression by acculturation, is still, obviously, biological. There is continuity between the biological and the cultural. A human being is an acculturated biological organism.

However, in the course of psychiatric inquiry, one discovers that it is not a person *as an isolated and self-contained entity* that one is studying, or can study, but a situation, an interpersonal situation, composed of two or more people. The locus of the study has shifted, and with it the reference frame of the investigator, or "participant observer." Furthermore, while one may *describe* an interpersonal situation which one has studied as though one had been a detached observer, in the actual study one becomes a constituent element or part of that situation. One becomes a participant observer. And to explain what occurred in the situation, of which one is a part, one must invent a new terminology in order to convey the new reference frame of the study.

According to Sullivan, to speak about impulses, drives, striving toward goals, is to use a figure of speech necessitated by the structure of the language.[12] One never observes such impulses and drives. What one does observe is a situation "integrated" by two or more people, and manifesting certain recurring kinds of action and behavior. How is one to explain what occurs? In common everyday language, it is said that "A is striving toward so and so from B." This mode of speech seems to imply that there are certain ready-made, isolated impulses or needs in A which B can satisfy, but which existed completely independent of any influence from B. The traditional psychology postulated and termed these apparently preëxisting and independent drives as "instincts." In an almost mechanical union or accidental association, a "response" was

12 See pp. 50–51.

evoked which satisfied and fulfilled such drives. The goals of human behavior were thought to be rather rigidly fixed by the nature of such self-contained, independent, predetermined, instincts. Whatever reciprocal interplay, interaction, occurred between A and B was thought to be more mechanical than transformative. But, according to Sullivan, what one observes is action in a situation between two people. "Action in a situation between two people" can be a misleading phrase because the two people acting in a certain way together, reciprocally, make the situation. Their mode of reciprocal action, interaction, defines the situation. That is what an interpersonal situation is, a mode of interaction of two or more people. That is, he believes, what one should study. Preëxisting, fixed drives do not explain an interpersonal situation, because they are not observed. The action in an interpersonal situation *is* observed, and it is *this* that explains whatever there may be of preëxisting tendency to act. Extensive observation and study of human behavior has shown that such behavior, within certain limits, is almost infinitely varied. This is another way of saying that it is malleable, fluid, changeable to an almost incalculable degree. Furthermore, interpersonal behavior does not occur, obviously, in a mechanical, rigidly stereotyped manner. To some extent, at any rate, it is continually changing, and not haphazardly but with apparent purpose. Interpersonal acts make an intelligible pattern, a somewhat fluid, changing pattern. They are in process of becoming something. They *are* a process. They have beginning, direction, ending. Since they are reciprocal, they are transformative. The interaction brings about something different, new. Because these acts are in process of change, instead of being rigidly fixed and predetermined or haphazardly and willy-nilly occurring, they can to some extent be redirected. Goals can, therefore, be redefined, modified, changed. Within the human situation, there is a possibility of creativeness, of discovering and inventing new goals, new purposes. Human behavior is amenable to intelligence.

It is, then, a person-integrated-in-a-situation-with-another-person-or-persons, an interpersonal situation, which one studies. The interpersonal situation it is which manifests the determinate characteristics. "Many situations are integrated in which A wants deference from B, and B, mirabile dictu, wants deference from A. It looks as if there were something in A and something in B that happened to collide. But when one studies the situation in which A and B pursue, respectively, the aim of getting from the other person what he himself needs, we find that it is not as simple as it looks. The *situation* is still the valid object of study, or rather that which we can observe; namely, the action which indicates the situation and the character of its integration." [13] In other words, it is inaccurate, unscientific to speak of a person-in-isolation-manifesting-this-or-that-tendency-or-drive. What one observes is a situation, "integrated" by two or more people. The situation is an interaction, an integration, or rather an integrated interaction of two or more people. Because all but one of the people may be "illusory" personifications, or inhabitants of dreamland or the imagination, the problem is more complicated. A loving person is one who, generally, when circumstances permit, integrates situations having the traits categorized as love. A hateful person is one who, when the opportunity offers, integrates situations having the traits categorized as hate or hateful. To have an impulse or drive is to have or manifest a tendency to action in some kind of interpersonal situation. Impulses and drives cohere in "dynamisms," relatively enduring configurations of energy, which manifest themselves in numerous ways in human situations. The traits which characterize interpersonal situations in which one is integrated describe what one is. Because any person integrates interpersonal situations having many different traits, to determine whether a person may, in everyday language, be called loving or hateful, "neurotic," "psychotic," or "normal" is not an easy problem. The problem

[13] See p. 5.

is attacked more directly in his discussion of *self-dynamisms* and *dissociation*. Generally speaking, personality is, with a qualification to be noted later, a function of the kinds of interpersonal situations a person integrates with others, whether real persons or fantastic personifications.

The quotation about observing the action which indicates the situation and the character of its integration might easily be misleading. If it is taken to mean that all one has to do is *merely* to observe, in a passive manner, an interpersonal situation in order to find out what occurs, then it is misleading. Interpersonal processes, like all events, do not occur with their meaning written all over them. A situation in order to be understood has to be interpreted.[14] Because much of human behavior occurs according to stereotyped patterns, and because one has, more or less unconsciously, socially predetermined, ready-made standards and criteria for interpreting and judging such behavior, one is inclined to assume that all one does is *look at* such behavior, and that its meaning is quite independent of an observer. Actually, if, *per impossibile*, one had no standards, no theories, to judge what happens, human behavior, or any configuration of events, would be an unintelligible, chaotic jumble. Every observer brings a vast and complex set of rules and standards, socially inherited, to understand events. Therefore, while it is true one never observes goals or tendencies, or impulses, in a situation, one must postulate them. A person is born with a substratum of biological needs and potentialities. Human behavior, one must assume, is purposive.[15] The participant observer has certain theories and insights about human behavior, which he has learned from experience, whether direct or mediated through the experience of others. Those in-

---

[14] Introspection is notoriously inadequate for understanding what one is about; nevertheless a skillful participant observer probably finds it indispensable in presenting clues and hints as to human behavior.

[15] To avoid confusion, one must make a distinction between logical and psychiatric interpretation, but it does not seem necessary to go into that phase of the subject here.

sights guide him in interpreting and understanding any given situation. At the same time he is trying out these insights, testing them, as to their explanatory value in illuminating and clarifying interpersonal situations. Mistakes as to what is significant and relevant are made, but a skillful observer learns to correct or at least take account of them. Psychiatric observation is progressive. It is also self-corrective, because the investigator learns that some "insights" are irrelevant, and have to be discarded for others which are more illuminating and which organize the data more satisfactorily. What is more illuminating for explaining and solving interpersonal problems is also progressively determined more precisely and accurately.

It is hoped that enough has been said to indicate that what is observed is not given ready at hand. The observer must interpret what he observes. His interpretations will be guided by his knowledge and skill. But his knowledge and skill will depend partly on his own automatic and spontaneous elaboration of his own experience and partly on subsequent elaboration from colleagues in the same and related fields. Finally, his own alertness on the occasion as to what rôle he is playing in the situation fixes the limits as to what he observes. And his alertness in the therapeutic situation, in which he participates—that is, integrates with the patient—will be determined by his own self-system.

However, according to Sullivan, one can do too much interpreting. He says: "The supply of interpretations, like that of advice, greatly exceeds the need for them. Every patient has enough of his own misinterpretations and may well be spared the uncritical autistic reveries of his physician. At the same time, some interpretations are indispensable, if therapeutic results are to be achieved in a reasonable length of time. The first test for any interpretation should be as to its adequacy: does it cover the data to which it is applied? The second test should be as to its exclusiveness: are there other equally plausible hypotheses that cover the data? If so, the proposed interpretation justifies no presumption of its validity and, in general, it should not be offered." [16]

Interpersonal situations are self-resolving processes. Otherwise, what is manifestly impossible would occur, a person would become transfixed in a situation. A change which is satisfaction-giving or tributary to security occurs. Since interpersonal situations are a system or configuration of processes, they are fluid, dynamic—they move on, so to speak. By appropriate action some "dynamic component" in each person is discharged or resolved. However as they pass into the history of the persons involved, they do not vanish without a trace. Their effects, to however small a degree, remain as a memory, whether conscious or not, and a potentiality for similar situations in the future. [17]

In passing it seems desirable to mention what will be discussed more fully in the exposition of the *self-system, selective inattention,* and *dissociation.* There may be, and frequently are, two or three kinds of dynamic component or impulse discharged in an interpersonal situation. One is the kind which occurs within the awareness of the person or persons; another occurs outside of awareness, unwittingly, "dissociated" or "selectively inattended." [18]

Before one can begin to understand Sullivan's theories of interpersonal relations, there are two or three concepts about the "epoch" of infancy which have to be grasped. These are *empathy*, the *parataxic,* and the *autistic,* which is a sub-species of the parataxic.

According to Ducasse, "empathy" is a word coined by Titchener to translate the German *einfühlung.* [19] For Sullivan, empathy refers to "the peculiar emotional linkage that subtends the relationship of the infant with the other significant

[16] See p. 187.
[17] See p. 51.
[18] See p. 52.
[19] Ducasse, Curt John, The Philosophy of Art; New York, Lincoln Mac-Veagh, Dial Press, 1929; (v and 314 pp.)—in particular p. 151.

people—the mother or the nurse." [20] It exists long before there is any understanding by the infant of emotional expression. Empathy is said to be an "emotional contagion or communion" between the infant and the significant adult. Sullivan assumes its greatest importance is perhaps from the age of six to twenty-seven months.[21] Because the attitudes and behavior of the mother or nurse are socially conditioned, the concept of empathy is very important for understanding acculturation. However, although the fact itself may be well-established, it is not explained. Two examples of this emotional contagion or communion are given.[22] One is of a mother who hates the pregnancy and looks with disfavor upon or deplores her offspring. When this happens there are great feeding difficulties. The other is of a mother who, although deeply attached to the infant, suffers a fright or gets worried about something around nursing time. On this occasion also there are feeding difficulties or the infant has indigestion. Whether or not this is a *post hoc ergo propter hoc* will have to be established by further study of infants. He seems to imply, however, that it is closely connected with, or related to, biological states. He says: "It is biological for the infant when nourished to show certain expressive movements which we call the satisfaction-response, and it is probably biological for the parent concerned to be delighted to see these things. Due to the empathic linkage, this, the reaction of the parent to the satisfaction-response of the infant, communicates good feeling to the infant and thus he learns that this response has power." [23] And this, he adds, may be considered the primitive root of human generosity, the satisfaction in giving satisfaction and pleasure. When *anxiety* and the *self-dynamism* or *self-system* are discussed it will be seen that empathy is a very important concept for understanding the theory of the self.

[20] See p. 17.
[21] See p. 17.
[22] See p. 16.
[23] See p. 17.

The concepts of the *prototaxic*, the *parataxic*, and the *autistic* are extraordinarily difficult to grasp and to formulate.[24] They are symbol activities. But as Sullivan uses the term, anything which stands for something else, or is a sign of something else, is a symbol. For example, in prototaxic symbol activities, a concept which will be discussed more fully at a more convenient place in the exposition, the mother's nipple represents, *in a vague way*, the Good Mother, as opposed to another representation, or "proto-concept" of the Bad Mother.[25] Prototaxic symbolization lacks formal distinctions. It lacks distinctions of time and space, of before and after, of here and there. Here a qualification is necessary. To say that the prototaxic lacks the distinction of before and after means that *no connection* is established. The infant vaguely feels or "prehends" earlier and later states without realizing any serial connection. Furthermore, prototaxic symbolization occurs without reference to an ego, to "I" or "me," because the infant has no, or only a rudimentary, self. As will be seen later, the prototaxic is chiefly related to the basis of memory, and can be described as instantaneous records of total situations.

Parataxic symbolization succeeds the first, the prototaxic. As the infant develops, he gradually learns to make some discrimination between himself and the rest of the world. He no longer reaches out from his nurse's arms to touch the full moon. Gradually he learns to shrink to life size. And he gradually learns to make elementary distinctions. His symbol activity now makes distinctions of a rudimentary sort.

"We learn in infancy," Sullivan says, "that objects which our distance receptors, our eyes and ears, for example, encounter, are of a quite different order of relationship from things which our tactile or our gustatory receptors encounter. That which one has in one's mouth so that one can taste it, while it

---

[24] The term "prototaxic" does not appear in Sullivan's published lectures. The concept of the parataxic as previously formulated is much narrower in range than the formulation conveyed orally to the writer.

[25] See pp. 78–79.

may be regurgitated to the distress of everyone is still in a very different relationship than is the full moon which one encounters through one's eye but can in no sense manage." [26]

With the development of the parataxic mode of symbol activity, the original undifferentiated wholeness, oneness, of experience is broken. But the "parts," the diverse aspects, the various kinds of experience are not related or connected in any logical fashion. Various experiences just happen together, or not, as the case may be. They are concomitant. The young one cannot yet relate his experiences to one another or make any logical distinctions among them. Expressed in another way, experiences which are related to one another are felt only as being concomitant. The young one can neither connect nor contrast his experiences. Of course, he feels no need of rigid distinctions. Later on he will learn them from the significant others in his environment. What is experienced is implicitly assumed, and certainly without reflection, to be the "natural" way of such occurrences, without question or comparison. As in the prototaxic, since no connections or relations are established, there is no movement of "thought." The symbolical activity is not a step-by-step process. Inferences cannot be made. Experience is undergone as momentary, unconnected organismic states.[27] The parataxic is that which is recurrent in the prototaxic.

Eyes and ears become increasingly important. Parataxic symbols are evoked mainly through visual and auditory channels.

As has already been mentioned, the autistic is a subspecies of the parataxic. The autistic is a verbal manifestation of the parataxic. It is explained thus: "The ability to make articulate noises and the ability to pick phonemal stations in vocal sound—that is, the peculiar ones of a continuum of sounds which are used in the forming of words, which varies, incidentally, from language to language—the ability, as I say, to learn phonemes, to

[26] See p. 34.
[27] Dreams are typical examples of parataxic thinking.

connect them into syllables and words, is inborn. That is given in the human organism. The original usage of these phonemal stations, syllables, words, however, is magical, as witness the 'ma' and as witness, for example, any of you who have a child who has been promised on a certain birthday a pony. As you listen to the child talk about the pony you realize perhaps sadly that twenty-five years from now when he talks about ponies, pony will not have a thousandth of the richness of personal meaning that pony has for him now. The word of the child is autistic, it has a highly individual meaning. And the process of learning language habits consists to a great extent, once one has got a vocabulary, in getting a meaning to each particular term which is useful in communication. None of us succeeds completely in this; some of us do not succeed noticeably." [28]

Read superficially, the passage seems inconsistent. He began by saying that the autistic belonged to the infant and ended by talking about the child. But this is how he distinguishes between what he calls the epoch of infancy and the epoch of childhood. When the infant learns the rudiments of language, he passes into the epoch of childhood. [29]

The symbol activity is arbitrary, highly personal, unchecked, untested, and necessarily so because of the child's limited equipment and experience with the symbol activity and experience of others. The capacity for verbal communication is only beginning to manifest itself and its tools are scarcely formed or realized. In Sullivan's language, consensual validation is lacking. In popular language, the imagination of the child runs riot, unchecked and undisciplined by "reality."

Another example will perhaps disclose the meaning and significance of the autistic more fully. Take the illustration of a child who has been presented with a picture book containing printed matter. There is, for example, a picture of a cat, below which there is written what the child later learns as c-a-t.

[28] See pp. 18–19.
[29] See p. 18.

The animal who runs around the house also is referred to by the same name as the colored or black and white pattern in the book. Sullivan goes on to discuss the significance of this:

"I am sure no child who can learn has not noticed an enormous discrepancy between this immobile representation in the book which, perhaps, resembles one of the momentary states that kitty has been in on some occasion. I am certain that every child knows that there is something very strange in this printed representation being so closely connected with the same word that seems to cover adequately the troublesome, amusing, and very active pet. Yet, because of unnumbered, sometimes subtle, sometimes crude experiences with the carrier of culture, the parent, the child finally comes to accept as valid and useful a reference to the picture as 'kitty' and to the creature as 'kitty.'

"The child thus learns some of the more complicated implications of a symbol in contradistinction to the actuality to which the symbol refers, which is its referent; in other words, the distinction between the symbol and that which is symbolized. This occurs, however, before verbal formulation is possible.

"From the picture book and the spoken word in this culture one progresses to the printed word and finally discovers that the combination of signs, c-a-t, includes 'kitty' in some miraculous fashion, and that it always works. There is nothing like consistent experience to impress one with the validity of an idea. So one comes to a point where printed words, with or without consensually valid meaning, come to be very important in one's growth or acquaintance with the world.

"There was first the visually and otherwise impressive pet, which was called 'kitty' (an associated vocalization); then came the picture of the kitten; now comes the generic c-a-t which includes kitty, picture of kitten, a kitten doll, and alley cats seen from the windows. And all this is learnt so easily that —since no one troubles to point it out—there is no lucid understanding of the sundry types of reality and reference that are being experienced. Familiarity breeds indifference, in this case. The possibilities for confusion in handling the various kinds of symbols, naturally, remain quite considerable." [30]

Consensually validated symbols carry a meaning which has been acquired from group activities, interpersonal activities, social experience.[31] They represent some degree of differentiation which can be consensually validated, and agreed upon by one's compeers. Autistic activity may use the socially inherited symbols, language, but it gives to them a unique and personal meaning. The meaning is determined by the personal experience of the child, *not* by the society which created them. The spontaneous feeling and imagination of the child invests the symbols, whether words or pictures, with a content that is determined by his own needs and experience, *not* by the requirements of the significant adults. But on the other hand, it is to meet with, and conform to, the requirements of the significant adults, for the purpose of gaining satisfactions and maintaining security, that the self is evolved.

Gradually, of course, the child learns something of the shared meaning of language. He must. But the autistic meaning is not thereby destroyed. Words, language, thus come to have a double meaning. In fact most people manifest a confused blend of both. This helps considerably for one to maintain a wide margin of misinformation and illusion. Autistic symbols, and, more generally, parataxic symbols are, among other things, peculiarly adopted for maintaining a type of activity later discussed under 'multiple me-you patterns." But, on the other hand, they are also well adapted for another type of activity, the creative.

Empathy, parataxic and autistic activity, and anxiety, a term whose meaning will become clear later, are fundamental to the origin and development of the self-dynamism. *Dynamism*

[30] See p. 35.

[31] Consensually validated symbol activity has more recently been called "syntaxic" thinking by Sullivan. It involves an appeal to principles which are accepted as true by the hearer.

has been defined as *"a relatively enduring configuration of energy which manifests itself in characterizable processes in interpersonal relations.* It is to be preferred to 'mental mechanism,' 'psychic system,' 'conative tendency,' and the like, because it implies only *relatively enduring capacity to bring about change,* and not some fanciful substantial engines, regional organizations, or peculiar more or less physiological apparatus about which our present knowledge is nil." [32] The self-dynamism is a process or a configuration—that is, a structure—of processes. *Self-dynamism, self-system,* and *self* are employed to express the same meaning. So the self is not a fixed entity, but a configuration of interpersonal processes. It seems well to emphasize that the self is always related to interpersonal relations.

Restraints on the child's freedom, necessary for his socialization, bring about the evolution of the self-dynamism. In this evolution there are also developed other, and no less important aspects of the personality, those which occur outside clear awareness, the *dissociated* and the *selectively inattended.* The *personality* includes all of them.

As previously noted, the infant—like certain animals—has a peculiar sensitivity to something which occurs in his immediate environment. This was called empathy. He could somehow feel the warm approval and delight of the mother in his expressive, expansive movements, called the satisfaction-response. Of course, this does not mean that he understood what happened, in the usual sense. He felt it. One might say that he felt the warm approval of the mother by means of the empathic linkage, but this does not add very much because no one seems to know anything much about this mode of communication. Nevertheless the good feeling, the warm, approving attitude of the mother was so communicated that his sense of well-being, his euphoria, was increased. At another

[32] Sullivan, Harry Stack, Psychiatry: Introduction to the Study of Interpersonal Relations. PSYCHIATRY (1938) 1:121–134; p. 123, footnote 3.

time, on the occasion of his crying, or not going to sleep, when the mother is perhaps irritated or tired, she manifests annoyance, displeasure, perhaps strong disapproval or anger. Again the mother's attitude is communicated. This time, of course, it is not warm approval. It is perhaps strong disapproval. And the infant feels the disapproval. Now his sense of well-being markedly decreases. The disapproval assures discomfort. The infant feels discomfort. To speak generally, expressions of approval from the mother or nurse increase the infant's state of well-being; expressions of disapproval, of dissatisfaction with the infant's performance, decrease his sense of well-being, arousing discomfort.[33] An important item to note here is that this occurs long before he can understand the meaning of what happens.

As the infant grows older, the mother begins deliberate training. For example, she trains him in the "proper" toilet habits, those considered proper by the culture she lives in. Not only that, but the time she begins to do so will probably be determined by what her culture considers the right time to begin training the young. Now training involves disapproval of some acts of the infant, and approval of others. Certain performances of the infant bring disapproval; others, approval. This is another way of saying certain performances result in a decrease of his good feeling, state of well-being; others, an increase. Gradually, the young one "catches on." He learns why, at first probably in a dim way, his sense of well-being, can decrease or increase. Sooner or later he learns that certain performances bring discomfort; other, a comforting state of well-being, good feeling. One might say that here he first dimly learns the relationship of cause and effect, although, no doubt, he is not yet much given to logical analysis. Of course, when the mother's, or the nurse's, attitudes are inconsistent, he has a bigger problem. And, it seems safe to say, no one's attitudes are always consistent. No one's behavior is rigidly

[33] See pp. 19–20.

consistent. In other words, the infant early learns, or at least feels, some of the inconsistencies of the significant people in his environment; that is, he early learns, or feels, some of the inconsistencies of the culture in which he will grow. It is an easy inference that the fewer inconsistencies, the more rapid will be his acculturation.

The first step presumably was somehow to note the referential relation of his acts, his behavior, to increase or diminution of his sense of well-being. As the infant becomes more educable, he is subjected to more numerous and more varied instances of approval and disapproval. Sooner or later, the young one perceives the disapproval or approval of the mother or nurse, while he previously only felt it. As his observation improves, his grasp on the patterns of action approved and disapproved becomes more refined. Gradually he has learned that when this kind of discomfort is present and something is done which brings approval and approbation, the discomfort is softened, assuaged, or banished.

The child learns to focus his attention not only on behavior which brings approval and approbation, but also on that which brings disapproval, so as to be better able to avoid it. He must, in order to achieve good feeling and avoid discomfort. Thus he learns to be alert to signs of approval and disapproval. His attention becomes concentrated on noticing signs of approval and disapproval. And out of this alertness to approval and disapproval, the self is first evolved. Thus, Sullivan says: "The self-dynamism is built up out of this experience of approbation and disapproval, of reward and punishment. The peculiarity of the self-dynamism is that as it grows it functions, in accordance with its state of development, right from the start. As it develops, it becomes more and more related to a microscope in its function. Since the approbation of the important person is very valuable, since disapprobation denies satisfaction and gives anxiety, the self becomes extremely important. It permits a minute focus on those performances of the child which are the cause of approbation and disapprobation, but, very much like a microscope, it interferes with noticing the rest of the world. When you are staring through your microscope, you don't see much except what comes through that channel. So with the self-dynamism. It has a tendency to focus attention on performances with the significant other person which get approbation or disfavor. And that peculiarity, closely connected with anxiety, persists thenceforth through life. It comes about that the self, that to which we refer when we say 'I' is the only thing which has alertness, which notices what goes on, and, needless to say, notices what goes on in its own field. The rest of the personality gets along outside awareness. Its impulses, its performances are not noted." [34]

What is *anxiety?* In popular usage, it has various and obscure meanings. Anxiety has its origin in the discomfort felt by the infant at the empathized disapproval of the adult.[35] Stated in another way, the loss of euphoria—which is synonymous with a feeling of intense discomfort, due to the empathized disapproval—is, at a later stage, with the appearance of the self, called anxiety. Perhaps needless to say, when considerable hostility is felt, the infant undergoes acute suffering, without, of course, understanding what is happening to him. This capacity, under appropriate circumstances, to experience what is later called anxiety, endures without diminution throughout life. But as one grows older, one learns, if only in a dim way, how to avoid at least most situations which arouse anxiety. The avoidance of anxiety may, and usually does, occur outside clear awareness. Those who acquire facility in dealing with people learn that most situations are not threatening, or at least not to the extent which would evoke a degree of anxiety comparable to the discomfort felt in early life. In most people, to greater or lesser degree, knowledge triumphs over anxiety. But the capacity for experiencing a discomfort as intense as the original

[34] See pp. 20–21.
[35] See pp. 19–20.

remains. With the growth of the self, understanding also grows. There is some understanding of the relation of one's behavior to the feeling of acute discomfort, anxiety. At least some of the anxiety-provoking factors in the environment can be discriminated. The feeling of discomfort is now localized as in oneself. Nor is the whole environment threatening. There is refinement of meaning. The discomfort is no longer cosmic. A discrimination of oneself and the outside world has occurred, and with it, some discrimination about anxiety. Anxiety is an universal experience, although, of course, varying from person to person both as to intensity and the precise conditions for its occurrence.

The self limits and restricts awareness, and does it by means of anxiety.[36] There are two ways of interpreting anxiety. When something happens which is not welcome to the self, is not in harmony with the earlier experiences of approval and disapproval, anxiety occurs. The appearance of anxiety completely distracts attention so that one does not notice what occurs. Stated in another way, anxiety is the person's inner experience of the self-dynamism functioning so as to restrict or confuse one's awareness and prevent him from noticing and clearly understanding something which occurs. Usually the mere threat of anxiety, the mere possibility, the mere warning sign, of an occurrence not congenial to the self, is sufficient to bring about behavior calculated to avoid the experience, or prevent awareness of its significance. Anxiety restricts not only one's acts, but also one's conscious thoughts in the same way. One does not think, at least not clearly, of matters uncongenial to the self. And if a person is given to fantasy, it is certain that the fantasy will not be interpreted in a manner uncongenial to the self.

The learning of language greatly facilitates and enhances the development of the self. For the infant, the mode of communication from the outer world was empathy. The child at first learns to use words, in a highly autistic way, of course, but they enable him gradually better to "catch on" to what occurs in his immediate environment. He has not yet lost the power of empathy,[37] but language is a better instrument for conveying what is expected of him, what is approved and disapproved. Thus language goes far to complete what empathy began, the person's acculturation.[38]

It is inherent in the nature of the self to facilitate and restrict its further growth in such a way as to maintain the direction and characteristics given to it in infancy and childhood. Experiences of approbation and disapprobation occur long before one can think, long before one has acquired the use of language and all that it implies for the purposes of socialization. To be unable to think, that is, logically or syntaxically, is to be unable to discriminate the meaning of what occurs. The earliest attitudes, therefore, which one learns, and also the most pervasive and "deep-seated," are acquired literally, unthinkingly. Besides the infant's biological helplessness, he is also spiritually or psychologically helpless. The young one must, therefore, accept the attitudes and codes of behavior of the significant others, not only because he depends on them for life itself but because he has no, or only incipient, ability to think, and no, or only rudimentary, social experience. The attitudes and codes of the significant others, therefore, are accepted, necessarily without criticism or discrimination. The question of their validity cannot readily occur to him. This is another way of saying they have for him a character of inevitability, unquestionability. He has not yet acquired the ability and experience to question and compare. What happens, therefore, is neither

[37] See p. 17: "We do not know much about the fate of empathy in the developmental history of people in general. There are indications that it endures throughout life, at least in some people. There are few unmistakable instances of its function in most of us, however, in our later years. . . ."

[38] The visual and auditory channels are also of considerable importance but as yet only obscurely understood. Facial expression, tone of voice, gestures are sometimes more effective than what is said.

right nor wrong, fitting nor unfitting; it just *is*. It happens.[39]

So it happens that the "facilitations and deprivations by the parents and significant others are the source of the material which is built into the self, because through the control of personal awareness the self itself from the beginning facilitates and restricts its further growth." The facilitations and deprivations in infancy and childhood are, usually, sufficiently consistent to give the self-dynamism a start in a certain direction. Although the parents or significant others are by no means always perfectly consistent in their behavior, their approval of some acts, and disapproval of others will tend to remain during a given period of development fairly constant. It is, therefore, the parents and significant others, brothers or sisters or nurse, who determine the nature of the self-dynamism. This is so because it is self-perpetuating, "tends very strongly to maintain the direction and characteristics given to it in infancy and childhood." [40]

In order to explain *dissociation*, it is necessary first to introduce the concept of *selective inattention*.[41] Selective inattention is a process whereby certain experiences and actions are not clearly noted or appraised, if they are noted at all. The person pays no attention to their character or significance. His attention has to be recalled before he is able to pay heed to them. Sullivan claims that selective inattention is the most frequent manifestation of the restriction of awareness. It is one of the ways by which the self dynamism hinders educative experience which is not in harmony with its current organization. In other words, when certain experiences and actions are tinged with anxiety, the person does not clearly note them, or their character and significance, because to do so would be to be confronted with the possibility or necessity of change. Sometimes in the course of an interview, when the therapist

[39] In other words, he is as yet limited to parataxic experience.
[40] See p. 21.
[41] The explicit formulation of *selective inattention* is not found in Sullivan's published lectures. It was communicated orally to the writer.

directly refers to something which is selectively inattended, one of two things may happen. Either a "security operation" is provoked—that is, something is provoked which functions so as to minimize anxiety—or severe anxiety results. And in the latter case, the therapist now has the problem of conserving the doctor-patient relationship. From one point of view, the difference between selective inattention and dissociation is one of degree as "measured" by the accessibility to conscious discriminated awareness of an experience or an overt action.

Dissociated dynamisms not only exist outside awareness but ordinarily are not accessible to the self.[42] Experiences and behavior which, because of selective inattention, are not discriminated—that is, occur outside awareness—when, for example, they are indicated by a friend, can be brought into awareness, accepted by the self. This cannot happen in the case of dissociation. If the friend were to point out, or call one's attention to, dissociated behavior no such expansion of awareness can easily occur. The result of the friend's efforts is very likely to arouse anxiety, followed by anger and heated denial.

The processes by which dissociation occurs are not formulated. All that one can say is the dissociated has been rejected by the self. In other words, those dynamisms to which the self refuses awareness and recognition, except under the impact of extraordinary influences, are dissociated. Processes existing outside awareness because of selective inattention can without great difficulty be reintegrated into the self because they do not imply any immediate considerable change as to basic direction and characteristics of the self. But dissociated dynamisms, once they are recognized by the self, involve an immediate and perhaps great alteration in the basic direction and characteristics of the self. In other words, the recognition and discrimination of previously dissociated dynamisms, imply a change, fre-

[42] See p. 22. The discussion of dissociation in *The Conceptions* is likely to be misleading because there is no differentiation of processes due to selective inattention.

quently a profound change, in the sorts of interpersonal relations in which one will be integrated. The pattern of future life is altered. By the reintegration of dissociated dynamisms, there is made necessary an extensive change in personality.[43]

With one exception, the self limits and restricts awareness. The exception is that of certain gifted people who can think within the field of awareness without consciousness of self, of "I," which is ordinarily the center of what goes on. A scientist can become absorbed in what he is doing, be clearly aware of some problem or activity, yet "forget" about himself, his "ego," and all the usual apparatus of self-consciousness.[44] Most people, however, are much too busy maintaining security and warding off anxiety to become aware of anything in an unselfconscious manner. Their waking hours are completely taken with activities which are strongly colored by a need for "success."

The result is that:

"Our awareness of our performances, and our awareness of the performances of others are permanently restricted to a part of all that goes on and the structure and character of that part is determined by our early training; its limitation is maintained year after year by our experiencing anxiety whenever we tend to overstep the margin.

"Needless to say, limitations and peculiarities of the self may interfere with the pursuit of biologically necessary satisfactions. When this happens, the person is to that extent mentally ill. Similarly, they may interfere with security, and to that extent also the person is mentally ill."

The peculiarity of the self is such that it may be said to be made up of *reflected appraisals*.[45] The child appraises himself as he is appraised by the significant adults. He lacks the expe-

[43] See pp. 142–143. At this point in the reference Sullivan is discussing the schizophrenic person, but the remarks about dissociation apply in some degree to everyone.

[44] This observation is also not found in Sullivan's published papers and was communicated orally to the writer.

[45] See p. 22.

rience and equipment necessary for a careful and dispassionate evaluation of himself. He has no guide except what he has learned from the significant adults. His evaluation of himself is, therefore, based on the appraisals of the significant adults. There may be no, or very little, conflicting data about his performances which would cause him to question the appraisals of those who take care of him. And in any case, he is far too helpless to question or revolt, because he depends on them for life itself. Therefore, he is not in a position to risk his security by doubting, challenging, questioning the treatment of others, even if he could doubt or question. He tends passively to accept the judgments, first conveyed empathically, and now by words, and gestures, and deeds, as to his worth. He "naturally," inevitably, feels his worth to be what the significant adults, conditioned by their own life-experience, find it to be. If an unwanted child meets with hostility and derogation from the significant adults, he appraises, he feels, his worth to be what they find it to be. He acquires a hostile and derogatory self. And as one respects or disrespects oneself, so one respects or disrespects others. The child from then on, in this case, will tend to be hostile and derogatory toward everyone. But since unremitting hostility toward others is dangerous to his security, it may have to be disguised, perhaps masked from himself and others by a great show of friendliness.[46] However, people who are good observers, or who are themselves secure in their relations with others, will not be long deceived, because such hostility will betray itself in unwitting behavior.

It must not be understood that the self-dynamism is synonymous with momentary self-awareness, of one's awareness of "I" at any given instant. The self-dynamism is not static; it is a configuration of processes. It has background and foreground, a before and after. Nor is it discontinuous with the rest of the personality. There are marginal processes which

[46] In another instance, the hostility may be dissociated.

merge the self with the dissociated. These marginal processes are frequently manifested just before one 'drops off' to sleep, or before one becomes clearly awake. For purposes of exposition, it seemed necessary sharply to distinguish the focal awareness of the self, but actually it fades imperceptibly into those marginal processes of awareness.

Anxiety tends strongly to preclude the experience of anything which might correct or modify the direction of growth of the self, whose organization represents the stabilizing influence of past experience. The self, by means of anxiety, controls and circumscribes awareness, thus inhibiting the learning of anything radically new and different. Even when the self is a derogatory and hateful system it will inhibit and misinterpret any dissociated feeling or experience of friendliness towards others; and it will misinterpret any gestures of friendliness from others. The direction and characteristics given to the self in infancy and childhood are maintained year after year, at an extraordinary cost, so that most people in this culture, and presumably in any other, because of inadequate and unfortunate experience in early life, become "inferior caricatures of what they might have been." [47] Not only the family, but various other cultural institutions less directly, all combine, more or less unwittingly, to produce this effect.

But the controlling, limiting function of the self is not absolute. As will be seen later, certain vital needs of the organism may, if thwarted by the self, prove too powerful even for the inhibitions of the self. And all people retain some capacity for change. Children, particularly, as they grow older, sometimes retain a considerable amount of plasticity, a certain capacity for acquiring new experience, even if not in harmony with the self. School can, in the early years, furnish some corrective experience. A kind and lovable teacher may undo, somewhat, the bad effects of a destructive parent. And *vice versa*, a de-

[47] See p. 56.

structive teacher can slow, or diminish the good effects of a kind and loving parent.[48]

There is a more or less precarious equilibrium maintained between the self and dissociated processes. Under extraordinary influences, some dissociated functions can be readmitted into the self, become integrated in the self. In fact, the self of "normal" people can exist and maintain its autonomy *only* by virtue of activities in sleep and unnoticed reverie, and waking behavior. In the schizophrenic state, the self-system, although unable to prevent the eruption into awareness of dissociated tendencies, cannot absorb them, cannot integrate them, and in general disowns them. These irresistible, formerly dissociated dynamisms, maintain an autonomy independent of the self. The result is that instead of anxiety there is fear and often terror. The conflict-provoking tendencies are accorded independent personality.[49]

It must not be thought that dissociation is necessarily a mark of very serious disorder of personality. In certain circumstances, tendencies in the self, which become unacceptable, are then gradually dissociated. Processes acceptable in infancy, for example, may at a later stage, be disapproved by the significant adults and become dissociated.[50] Phrased in another way, tendencies previously congenial to the self, now arouse anxiety and are blotted out of awareness. So the significant others determine not only the kind of self, but also the dissociated.

There is another point which is highly significant in a theory of the self. It is said that a "selecting and organizing factor determines what part of these observed judgments [51] of one's personal value, what of the information that one secures

[48] See pp. 39–40.
[49] See p. 142. At this point in the reference Sullivan is discussing the schizophrenic person, but the remarks about dissociation apply in some degree to everyone.
[50] See p. 46.
[51] . . . of praise and blame from parents, teachers, friends, and other significantly related people.

through secondary channels (*e.g.*, reading), and which of the deductions and inferences that occur in one's thinking, shall be incorporated into the self." [52] From this statement it might seem that there is a factor intrinsic to the self, maintaining its autonomy despite all the vicissitudes of experience. It is clear, however, that Sullivan does not mean that, because the self is made up of reflected appraisals, and tends very strongly to maintain the direction and characteristics given to it in infancy and childhood. To say that there is a selecting and organizing factor in the self is only another way of saying that the self-dynamism by means of anxiety selects and organizes the conditions for its further growth, both as to direction and characteristics, in order to maintain the direction and characteristics given to it in infancy and childhood. However, it will be seen later that there is an intrinsic biological tendency or "factor" in the organism, which is directed toward maintaining or achieving mental health.

The structure of the self-system is such that it is capable of manifesting many different "me-you patterns" in different interpersonal situations or even in the same situation. [53] Not only does the self-system generate, in an interpersonal context, of course, these "me-you patterns," but it limits them qualitatively to what is congenial to it. [54] Stated in a different way, the self-system is *the limit*, the containing manifold, the enveloping matrix of the "me-you patterns." Furthermore, the personality, the hypothetical entity postulated in order to make *all* one's behavior intelligible, is the limit of the self-system.

If a person exhibited multiple "me-you patterns" always only in different interpersonal situations, it might seem that they must be objectively justified. For example, if a person is hostile toward *A*, affectionate toward *B*, fearful toward *C*, one might assume that the person is objectively justified because *A*

---

[52] Reference footnote 32; p. 123.

[53] For the purposes of the paper, "same situation" may be considered as one where there is no change of real persons, or of place, or interruption of time.

[54] Reference footnote 32; pp. 122–132.

may be hostile, *B*, lovable, *C*, destructive. But when the person manifests different attitudes, hostility, affection, fear, indicative of the different "me-you patterns," in the same interpersonal situation, say, with *A*, the problem gets more complicated. Where now is the locus of the objective situation? And when *A*'s reactions are not "congruent"—that is, when, for example, *A* reacts with hostility toward the affectionate person—then the problem gets even more complicated.

To account for these varying or multiple "me-you patterns," Sullivan has formulated the concept of the parataxic.[55] Suppose a patient comes to a psychiatrist, having been recommended by the family physician. The psychiatrist is otherwise unknown to the patient. Furthermore, suppose the patient believes the psychiatrist is hostile or wishes to humiliate him. The psychiatrist, who, one may assume, is a kindly and affectionate person, knows that the situation does not justify such a reaction. In other words, he knows he is not hostile to the patient, who is a stranger to him. How can the patient's reaction be explained? People do not assume without cause that the other person, or persons, integrated in a situation are hostile. However "irrational" human behavior may seem, one can discover causes for it.

The actual situation, as understood and felt by the patient, is parataxic. The patient is reliving, or is integrated in, the situation in terms of an earlier situation. Here the rôle of parataxic symbol activity is obvious. Consensually validated symbols cannot be effectively employed because they are based on, and require, carefully formulated, discriminated, and validated distinctions. Multiple "me-you patterns" can occur only when carefully formulated, discriminated, validated distinctions are *not* made. Of course the patient believes, at least on a conscious level, that he is making valid distinctions, but that is no proof of anything. Actually he is forced, unwittingly, to

---

[55] See p. 92 and reference footnote 32; p. 126, footnote. This is an earlier formulation and much narrower in range, but it is quite consistent with the recent one. The former is an instance of the latter.

employ the earlier modes of symbol activity which lack clear-cut distinctions based on carefully formulated discriminations of experience. Great masses of early experiences can therefore be carried over and relived, or revoked, without fundamental alteration and expressed in subsequent interpersonal situations by means of prototaxic and parataxic symbols. Thus "new situations" can be lived parataxically. In this case the patient has carried over into the present situation a mode of interpersonal behavior justified by, or adequate to, an earlier situation, or situations, where the significant people were hostile and did ridicule him. The patient has a hostile and derogatory self—why? Because his experience, or a great part of it, with the significant people who took care of him in early life, taught him, convinced him, that he was a person to be ridiculed, ill-treated, abused. And since he consequently dislikes, or even hates himself, even though he may partially disguise it from himself and others, he must therefore dislike, or be hostile toward others. It is therefore quite natural, inevitable, for him to expect hostility in the new situation, one which is for him closely on the model of earlier situations.

Now most people are not so unfortunate as to meet with unalloyed hostility from the significant adults who cared for them in early life. Usually children experience a mixture of attitudes, affection, indifference, as well as hostility, although one kind of experience may, and usually does, predominate. Their experiences are varied and contradictory. Hence they are raised with contradictory, or at least inconsistent, attitudes about themselves, and therefore about others. It is not surprising, therefore, that their interpersonal behavior is erratic, is inconsistent. It is not surprising, on the contrary it is inevitable, that a person's behavior may be at one time lovable, at another, hostile, and still again, indifferent toward another. By means of selective inattention, attitudes and occurrences not favorable to the prevailing "me-you pattern" are not discriminated.[56]

[56] It seems reasonable to assume that parataxic symbols are an instrumentality of selective inattention.

This accounts for the multiple "me-you patterns" in an inter-personal situation.

When one kind of experience, say love, predominates, the person has generally, when circumstances permit, a loving attitude toward himself and others. A "me-you pattern" characterized by love will predominate in his relations with others. This is another way of saying that he will tend to integrate loving interpersonal relationships. The "me-you patterns" characterized by hostility or indifference will occur less frequently because hostility or indifference is less powerfully imbedded in the self system and in the whole personality. The person is less inclined to act with hostility or indifference. His self, in order to maintain the basic direction and characteristics given to it in infancy and childhood, is, in the main, conditioned toward integrating loving relationships. When a loving person becomes integrated in hostile or derogatory relationships, the basic direction and characteristics of his self, which is a loving one, become threatened. Anxiety may intervene and disintegrate such relationships. In everyday language, a loving person does not want, as a general rule, to get involved with prevailingly hostile or prevailingly destructive people, that is, those who cannot love. The loving person, one who has respect for himself and others, one for whom the satisfaction and security of his friend, the loved one, are equally important, or nearly so, as are his own, knows that love, the genuine solicitude for the other fellow's well-being and happiness, is by far the best way, the only adequate way, to obtain, or maintain, his own satisfactions and security.

Personality is the hypothetical entity postulated "to account for the doings of people, one with another, and with more or less personified objects." [57] It "is made manifest in interpersonal situations, and not otherwise." [58] It is the most inclusive category of interpersonal behavior, including not only the self

[57] Reference footnote 32; p. 121.
[58] Reference footnote 32; p. 121.

system, with its multiple "me-you pattern," but also what exists outside awareness because of selective inattention or dissociation. As analysis will reveal, it is the reservoir of creative activity and original thought. From the personality, the self system can, under appropriate circumstances, obtain enrichment for a deeper and wider awareness. In an ideal psychiatrist the self would be coterminous with personality.[59] Needless to say there are no ideal persons because there are no ideal cultures.

It might seem that the personality compensates for the limitations of the self by accepting and maintaining dissociated tendency systems. And this is so, with a qualification. Since by definition dissociated tendencies exist outside awareness, they cannot be deliberately noted, formulated, appraised and evaluated. They are beyond the easy reach of logical thought and elaboration. It is possible for them to exist, however incompatible, inconsistent and disharmonious they may be. Since they cannot be thoughtfully, that is, logically appraised within awareness, they escape rational criticism, their status may be blind, impulsive, irrational. On the other hand some dissociated tendencies may be superior—in terms of love, freshness of feeling, freshness of insight, for example—to any tendency systems in the self. So when the self system is impoverished by toxic experience, the whole personality tends also to be impoverished. When loving tendencies have to be dissociated, the person may save, in this furtive fashion, a precious part of life experience, but such tendencies, so long as they exist in dissociation, are denied a fair chance to be deepened, expanded, fructified by conscious elaboration and experience. Such tendencies are likely to remain relatively undeveloped, immature, struggling along, so to speak, in a makeshift fashion, as best they can. When they are expressed, it is unwittingly, or in dreams, or in fantasies.

But, someone may object, what about the person who goes to bed with a mathematical problem he cannot solve and wakes

[59] See p. 184.

up in the morning with the solution? Clearly there are, or seem to be, mental processes which go on outside awareness and yet are highly fruitful. The answer is, according to Sullivan's theories, that this is *not* an example of a dissociated dynamism. Not all psychological processes going on outside awareness are dissociated dynamisms. There are two other modes of symbol activity besides the consensually or socially validated symbol activity of the self.

There are, first, "prototaxic symbols." [60] Prototaxic symbols are, as one might expect, indicative of the rudimentary state of development of the infant. All that the infant "knows" are momentary states. He has not yet developed, or learned, the forms of time and space, of before and after, of here and there. His ability to discriminate, if any, is quite rudimentary. He has no ego, because the self has not yet developed. Therefore he has no understanding of himself as a separate object from the outer world. His experiences are all of a piece, undifferentiated, undefined, not delimited; in other words, they are "cosmic." Everything belongs to the infant's own "cosmic entity." [61]

Long before the infant can utter words, or learn them, he perceives, or rather "prehends" the *mothering* one. Her nipple "provides the first of all vividly meaningful symbols—a vaguely demarcated 'complex-image' or proto-concept with very wide reference." [62] Gradually the mothering one gets distinguished as not being a part of oneself. The mothering one who contributes to the increase of euphoria, feeling of well-being, of the infant becomes characterized as the Good Mother. Since she will at times, for one reason or another, also cause a decrease of euphoria, another "complexus of impressions" becomes the Bad Mother. [63] To the infant, the two are vaguely limited but distinct people. The nipple becomes an attribute of the Good

[60] Prototaxic symbol, complex-image, and protoconcept are used synonymously.
[61] See p. 33.
[62] See p. 33.
[63] See p. 79.

Mother. It "stands for" or represents the Good Mother, in a vague way. The nipple is a pre-concept or proto-concept. Some people throughout life show evidence of this original bifurcation of interpersonal experience. Gradually, as the infant develops, this kind of symbol activity fades from waking life.

There is said to be a close resemblance between this kind of psychological activity and certain schizophrenic states where the person, for reasons too complex to be mentioned here, has regress to a very early state of development.[64] An ordinary bench can become the footstool of God. The schizophrenic is surrounded by cosmic forces.

In prototaxic symbolization, there is no movement of "thought." For the infant, experience is unconnected, discrete. The symbolization expresses momentary experiences. These momentary experiences form the basis of memory. Sullivan says that "living beings *fix*, somewhere and somehow, meaningful traces of everything they live through, not as 'perceptions' or 'states of excitation of the cortex' or the life, but rather as the pattern of how the organism-and-significant-environment existed at the moment." [65] It is on these momentary organismic states that subsequent experience is built. Subsequent experiences are "colored" by these earlier ones. In other words, subsequent experience is undergone in terms of the original felt experiences of early life. In a sense, later experiences are, on the subject side, pyramidal. So the experiences of infancy and childhood are enormously important for later experience. This does not mean that later experiences are undergone so as to repeat the earlier one. But it does mean that subsequent experiences do not make a fresh start. They are conditioned by previous experiences which perhaps, to some degree, extend to the prenatal.

The next stage of development begins with the appearance of the parataxic. Its verbal manifestation is the autistic. How-

64 See pp. 150–152.
65 See p. 105.

ever, the requirements of the developing self-system, which is another way of saying the requirements of the significant people, require that the use of words, the verbal symbol activity, be more refined and "consensually validated." Words then take on a more precise, a more scientific reference. The overt autistic behavior tends also to fade from waking life. In order to 'get on' with the significant people, in order to gain satisfactions and maintain security, the child has to conform, more or less, to *their* ideas, modes of behavior, and *their* use of language, *their* reference-frames.

But in deep sleep one can still carry on these earlier forms of symbol activity. In dreams one does not have to conform to the ideas of the significant adults. To a considerable extent, this is also true of fantasy—a kind of waking dream.

It is clear, then, that these earlier modes of mental activity persist. In a waking state, the needs of the self, the requirements of society, oblige one to be more or less "rational," to be "logical," to be consciously aware of what one is about. Meanings have to be relatively precise; that is, thought must have relatively precise reference frames. Furthermore, thinking tends to be more of a step-by-step activity. Of course, the thinking may not actually follow the rules of inference very carefully, but one must, the self must, at least make a pretense of doing this, in order to impress oneself and others for the purpose of maintaining prestige. People who do not at least make a pretense of logical thought are branded "queer" or "crazy." This means their chances of gaining satisfactions and maintaining security are endangered. And seriously to endanger these, may endanger one's very life.[66]

To be noted is the fact that the necessary refinement and precision of symbol activity carried on in healthy interpersonal relations is both a great gain and a great loss. In order to be

[66] These observations are not explicit in Sullivan's published writings. They were communicated orally to the writer.

understood with any degree of accuracy one has to use words with some referential precision. At least, words must have a shared and recognizable meaning. Science, in its more refined branches, strives for rigorous definition of terms and meanings. But, from another point of view, there is great loss. Imagination, except in rare instances, and feeling are checked. Mathematics is the outstanding example, where a special language is invented, whose symbols are devoid of all specific content and have no direct reference to anything outside the system. It is true that for a very few gifted people mathematics has a charm of its own, not to mention the great practical benefits which can be attained with its application in other fields. But traditionally people regard mathematics as dry, uninteresting, tedious, a bore. And in a modern industrial society, with the aid of the newspaper, the radio, the movies, words become hackneyed, stereotyped. Having become insipid and banal, they certainly do not stir the imagination and feelings.

The result of all this is that everyone, to some extent, and some people to a large extent, have to fall back on earlier modes of mental activity. In fact, one can distinguish three reasons for falling back to the earlier modes of symbol activity. The first is that dissociated dynamisms have to be discharged somehow, if one is to maintain a tolerable degree of mental health. They usually are discharged in sleep, in dreams, or, to a lesser extent, in undiscriminated fantasies whose meaning is not clearly understood, as well as in more overt activities. The second reason is that there is not time to do everything in a deliberately logical fashion. Nor is it necessary. If one were to think out step by step everything that one does getting up in the morning, one would never get to the office. The third reason is that these two earlier symbol processes can have a richness of emotional content which everyday experiences and activities lack. Those who can use their imagination freely know that the world of fantasy can sometimes have a richness, an intensity, a variety, and a quality which one rarely experiences, unless one is unusually fortunate, in the everyday world. Indeed, one might say that the world of art has for one of its functions, at least, to compensate for the lacks of this everyday world of humdrum activity.[67]

So the pre-conceptual, or prototaxic, mode of symbol activity characteristic of early infancy, and the parataxic and autistic characteristic of childhood, continue to be primary forms of creative thinking and spontaneous feeling. Here one is free to ignore, for the time being, in dreams and fantasy, the demands of "normal life," of "reality," the common and shared everyday world. Of course, all meaning which is to be shared by others must be expressed in symbols understood by others, and by one's own self. Feeling, also, if it is to be understood and shared by others, must employ conventional expression. But the reshaping and transformation of the earlier symbols into conventional expression comes after, just as in one's life history.[68]

In order to avoid confusion, it must be indicated that, while dissociated dynamisms are also frequently discharged in dreams and fantasy which employ the earlier modes of symbol activity, it does not follow that all mental activity, other than rational, conscious thinking, is an instance of dissociation. Just how much non-rational mental activity represents dissociated tendencies depends on the course of the self-dynamisms. A self-respecting person will probably manifest far fewer dissociated tendencies than a self-derogatory person. But it does not follow that a self-respecting person, a loving person, will manifest less of the earlier kind of thinking and feeling. The contrary may be the case.[69]

[67] It is not meant that this is, or should be, the primary function of art. Ideally, at any rate, art is an enrichment of life, not an escape from life.

[68] These observations are not explicit in Sullivan's published writings. They were communicated orally to the writer.

[69] These observations are not explicit in Sullivan's published writings. They were communicated orally to the writer.

The self dynamism "uses," or functions by means of, rational thinking but it obviously is not synonymous with rational thought.[70] The dissociated dynamism "uses" parataxic—with its sub-species, the autistic—symbol processes but is also not synonymous with them.[71] In the first case, rational thinking frequently is an instrumentality of the self. For the discharge of dissociated tendencies, the earlier modes of symbol activity are frequently employed, but they certainly did not originate for that purpose, and they exist, that is, function, independently. In other words, they have a status of their own.

One can say that the dissociated tendencies are analogous to the self, because they definitely involve the existence of others. Dissociated tendencies are discharged in actual interpersonal situations unwittingly, or in dreams or fantasies. Powerful impulses, desires, and needs are thus discharged. In an actual interpersonal situation, dissociated tendencies are "communicated" in a disguised fashion, outside the awareness of the person manifesting them. If the other person, or persons, are skillful observers, they will recognize such manifestations. In any case, they will have to take account of them.

Rational thinking can also occur as a spontaneous activity, within conscious awareness, but without reference to the self. But it occurs thus in relatively few people and under very restricted circumstances. By its very nature, rational thinking tends to be limited not only by the needs of the self, but by the constitution of things as they are, or are implicitly maintained to be by the culture one lives in. Except for a relatively few gifted people, rational thought is not the vehicle of imagination. And even in the case of great scientific discoveries, there is considerable evidence that new ideas frequently "come in a flash" and are only later elaborated according to logical procedure.[72] The earlier modes of symbol activity are not limited either by things as they are, "reality," or what one's culture

[70] It also functions in the parataxic mode.
[71] The dissociated can also use rational thought.
[72] However, one must not underestimate the importance of logical analysis.

says they are. They are free to express any fantasies, ideas, creations of the mind, subject only to the imaginative and creative power of one's mind. One can experiment with them. They give the imagination free play. And if one is sufficiently talented, one can with their aid achieve artistic creation or new scientific theories.

Sullivan has said that the "personality tends towards the state that we call mental health or interpersonal adjustive success, handicaps by way of acculturation notwithstanding. The basic direction of the organism is forward." [73] Here is ascribed an intrinsic tendency of the personality toward mental health. It implies that one is not a completely passive and helpless victim of unfortunate experience. Otherwise the prescriptive rôle of the self dynamism would entirely succeed in preventing or thwarting the effects of corrective experience, or any experience not acceptable and congenial to it; that is, in harmony with its basic direction and characteristics. Some people, at least, *do* learn better. The self-dynamism does expand somewhat, despite great resistance as manifested in anxiety. And some elements of the personality, like the need for companionship, or lust, when dissociated, are so powerful that they may force their way into awareness, even despite great suffering. Under certain circumstances dissociated elements can be re-integrated, become a part of the self.

Nevertheless, the resistance to change is very great. And for most people in this culture, and probably any other culture now existing, only a small percentage of their potentialities is ever realized. "It inheres in the nature of being human that one will relinquish, so to speak, a relative security and undergo anew a previously intolerable conflict within awareness *only* if one perceives a probability of speedy relief." [74] In the more

---

Among other things, it reveals implications in a system or concept which would otherwise be missed.

[73] See p. 97.

[74] See p. 130.

severe mental disorders, the problem of change is enormous —why? "To 'accept a dissociated tendency system into the self' is tantamount to undergoing an extensive change in personality, implying a marked change in the sorts of interpersonal situations in which one will have one's being. Not only is there this element of great change, but also there is no possibility of foresight as to the direction and extent of the change. Finally, one could not foretell that this change will be tolerable; there is every prospect of its including serious conflict, for the self dynamism includes powerful tendency systems which are responsible for the character of the present life course. The metamorphosis is scarcely an attractive prospect, even theoretically. Practically, there is no such prospect; there is only the stable course of life in contrast with terrors and anxieties, easily referrable to the unknown." [75]

If one speaks of an objective situation in interpersonal relations, what can be validly meant by such a statement? Is there such a thing; and if so, can it be understood? Are the constituents of an interpersonal situation so determinate that they can be appraised with accuracy? Or are the guiding principles sufficiently well established and reliable to make possible a reasonably correct analysis? Since the psychiatrist participates in the situation he is studying, can he at the same time remain sufficiently detached so that his own peculiarities will not seriously interfere with understanding? Can he participate in the situation and yet remain objective?

Yes, Sullivan would say, one can achieve a relative objectivity. "The psychiatrist," he states, "in developing his skill in interrogating informants, learns to integrate situations the configurations of which provoke the elaboration of information that was previously potential. He thus obtains more data from the informant than the latter has clearly perceived. The informant, so to speak, tells more than he knows. The data are

[75] See pp. 142–143.

more significant to the psychiatrist because he has more experience and more freedom in formulating interpersonal processes. He is alert to implications; his alertness is oriented to understanding interpersonal processes; and he has many fewer
specific inhibitions of alertness in the interpersonal configurations in which he participates. From the relative accessibility of
his own past, and from intimate contact with the developmental history of a number of people, he has a considerable
grasp on the actual dynamics of interpersonal relations. He
knows more about the processes that can occur in these configurations; in particular, he knows that certain alleged processes are highly improbable. Reports of these alleged events
are, therefore, most probably rationalizations, and he is able,
from experience or by inquiry, to secure clues to the unwitting motivations that underlie these conventional statements.

"Certainty about interpersonal processes is an ideal that
should seldom concern one. Information about any situation
should be considered as a formulation of probability. . . .

"When one has regard for the multiple me-you patterns
that complicate interpersonal relations, for the possible differences in individual prehension of events, and for the peculiarities of language behavior which characterize each of us . . .
the practical impossibility of one-to-one correspondence of
mental states of the observer and the observed person should
be evident. We never know all about another, we are fortunate
when we achieve an approximate consensus and can carry on
meaningful communication about relatively simple contexts
of experience. Most of us spend the greater part of our social
life in much less adequate contact with our interlocutors, with
whom we manifest considerable skill at avoiding frank misunderstanding, with whom in fact we agree and disagree quite
often with very little consensus as to subject of discussion.
The psychiatrist of all people knows the relative character of

his formulation of the other person, even if he has gained such skill that he is often quite correct." [76]

The objection is sometimes made that one cannot derive valid conclusions about "normal" people merely, or perhaps at all, from people who are mentally ill. To this Sullivan would probably reply after the following fashion:

"At this point, I wish to say that if this series of lectures is to be reasonably successful, it will finally have demonstrated that there is nothing unique in the phenomena of the gravest functional illness. The most peculiar behavior of the acutely schizophrenic patient, I hope to demonstrate, is made up of interpersonal processes with which each one of us is or historically has been familiar. Far the greater part of the performances, the interpersonal processes, of the psychiatric patient are exactly of a piece with processes which we manifest some time every twenty-four hours. . . . In most general terms, we are all much more simply human than otherwise, be we happy and successful, contented and detached, miserable and mentally disordered, or whatever." [77]

In another place he says:

" 'Mental disorder' as a term refers to interpersonal processes either inadequate to the situation in which the persons are integrated, or excessively complex because of illusory persons also integrated in the situation. It implies some—sometimes a great —ineffectiveness of the behavior by which the person is conceived to be pursuing the satisfactions that he requires. It is not, however, to be envisaged as an equivalent of *psychosis*, 'insanity,' or the like. The failure to remember the name of an acquaintance at the opportune moment is just as truly an instance of mental disorder as is a fixed delusion that one is Napoleon I." [78]

[76] Reference footnote 32; pp. 132–134.
[77] See pp. 15–16.
[78] Reference footnote 32; p. 122, footnote.

How does a patient get well? And what does "getting well" mean? Nothing miraculous is accomplished, but only an indication of the process can be given here. The patient, because of the relative freedom of the therapeutic situation, and because of skillful interpretation and guidance at opportune moments, is enabled to understand better the significance of his past and the rôle it plays in his present behavior and his outlook on life. The possibility of a different and more satisfactory mode of interpersonal relations and a new outlook on life gradually dawns upon the patient. Thus:

"Until a patient has seen clearly and unmistakably a concrete example of the way in which unresolved situations from the distant past color the perception of present situations and over-complicate action in them, there can be no material reorganization of personality, no therapeutically satisfactory expansion of the self, no significant insight into the complexities of one's performances or into the unexpected and often disconcerting behavior of others concerned. Up to this point, there is nothing significantly unique in the treatment situation; afterwards, however, the integration with the psychiatrist becomes a situation of unprecedented freedom from restraints on the manifestation of constructive impulses. This is the indirect result of the changes in the self system. The patient has finally learnt that more security may ensue from *abandoning* a complex security-seeking process than was ever achieved *by it*. This information is in itself an addition to security and a warrant for confronting other anxiety-provoking situations to discover the factors in them which are being experienced as a threat. . . ." [79]

The patient eventually grasps the significance of the statement, "One achieves mental health to the extent that one becomes aware of one's interpersonal relations. . . ." [80] He learns to understand what he is doing. "Most patients have for years been acting out conflicts, substitutions, and compromises; the

[79] See pp. 205–206.
[80] See p. 207.

benefits of treatment come in large part from their learning to notice what they are doing, and this is greatly expedited by carefully validated verbal statements as to what seems to be going on." [81] There is *"an expanding of the self* to such final effect that the patient as known to himself is much the same person as the patient behaving with others." [82] But it takes a good deal of education and experience effectively to grasp the meaning and significance of uncomplicated interpersonal relations, to realize the full benefits of a more abundant life. Increasing knowledge and insight make possible a less complicated, richer experience. New experience in turn makes possible still greater insight. This process does not stop with the end of treatment. Theoretically, at any rate, it continues throughout life.

Personality development is divided into epochs or periods of growth. These epochs are not rigidly fixed, since, he says, they vary, at least in the later stages, from culture to culture. Nevertheless, he seems to think that, although subject to variation, they are universal. One can attempt merely an outline of them here. They can be fully understood only in the light of all of Sullivan's fundamental theories of interpersonal relations. On the other hand these epochs, or rather his theories about them, are an intrinsic part of a theory of interpersonal relations. Despite some repetition it seems best to recapitulate the various epochs. One may not be able to explain interpersonal behavior solely in terms of a person's past history, but one cannot adequately explain or understand such behavior without a knowledge of the past. No one's acts are always free of parataxic elements. The several epochs are: infancy, childhood, the juvenile period, preadolescence, adolescence, and mature adulthood.

He describes the course of existence of what is later to be a human being from fecundation of the ovum as "parasitic, newborn (animal), then infantile (human)." [83] Since the new-born

[81] See p. 223.
[82] See p. 237.
[83] See p. 33.

is completely helpless, if unaided by people, he is "modified by this personal element" from the earliest stages of life outside the womb.[84] But "the long stretch of postnatal life required by the human young for the attainment of independent competence to live" is one of the factors which make civilization possible.[85] The *"mothering one"* becomes the infant's first vivid perception. Here the fact of empathy assumes primary importance. By this yet unclear mode of communication, the affection, loving care, good feeling, or their opposites, of the mothering one are perceived or felt by the infant. The nipple becomes the first vividly meaningful symbol, vaguely demarcated. Gradually by attending to outer objects which do not directly satisfy physico-chemical needs, the infant begins to mark off the limits of his own private world.

He begins to explore the possibilities and limits of his own body, and certain outer subjects. He "experiments." Summarily, infancy is "the period of maturation, of experimentation, of empathic 'observation,' and of autistic invention in the realm of power." [86]

As previously noted, the transition from infancy to childhood occurs when the rudiments of language are learned. It is during this period that the folkways of the culture begin to be deliberately taught. The development of the self-system, which, at least in a very rudimentary form, begins in infancy, proceeds rapidly with deliberate acculturation.

"Childhood includes a rapid acculturation, but not alone in the basic acquisition of language, which is itself an enormous cultural entity. By this I mean that in childhood the peculiar mindlessness of the infant which seems to be assumed by most parents passes off and they begin to regard the little one as in need of training, as being justifiably an object of education;

[84] See p. 33.
[85] See p. 33.
[86] See p. 16. *Parataxic* should probably be substituted for *autistic*, since the latter term is now confined in Sullivan's formulation mainly to verbal manifestation of the *parataxic*.

and what they train the child in consists of select excerpts from the cultural heritage, from that surviving of past people, incorporated in the personality of the parent. This includes such things as habits of cleanliness—which are of extremely good repute in the Western culture—and a great many other things. And along with all this acculturation, toilet habits, eating habits, and so on and so forth, there proceeds the learning of language as a tool for communication." [87]

During childhood, as already seen, autistic activity, the unchecked and undisciplined use of words, is pronounced. Also during this period the manifestation of anxiety, as an instrumentality of the self, begins to be discriminated.

"The era of childhood ends with the maturation of a need for compeers. The child manifests a shift from contentment in an environment of authoritarian adults and the more or less personalized pets, toys and other objects, towards an environment of persons significantly *like* him. If playmates are available, his integrations with them show new meaningfulness. If there are no playmates, the child's revery processes create imaginary playmates. In brief, the child proceeds into the *juvenile era* of personality development by virtue of a new tendency towards coöperation, to doing things in accommodation to the personality of others. Along with this budding ability to play with other children, there goes a learning of those performances which we call competition and compromise." [88]

For the young in this culture, schooling begins in the juvenile era, an experience which in itself is fraught with great consequences.

Preadolescence is said to begin between the ages of eight-and-one-half and twelve years.[89] In this period the capacity to love is developed. According to Sullivan, love exists when, and only when, the satisfactions and security of the loved one are

[87] See p. 18.
[88] See p. 38.
[89] See p. 41.

as significant to one as one's own satisfactions and security.

"This state of affectional rapport—generically love—ordinarily occurs under restricted circumstances. In the beginning many factors must be present. Some of these may be called obvious likeness, parallel impulse, parallel physical development. These make for situations in which boys feel at ease with boys rather than with girls. This feeling of species identity or identification influences the feeling involved in the preadolescent change. The appearance of the capacity to love ordinarily first involves a member of one's own sex. The boy finds a chum who is a boy, the girl finds a chum who is a girl. When this has happened, there follows in its wake a great increase in the consensual validation of symbols, of symbol operations, and of information, data about life and the world." [90]

He goes on to say that, with the appearance of love, when another, the chum, matters as much as oneself, "the great controlling power of the cultural, social, forces is finally inescapably written into the human personality."

The concluding remarks of this chapter are significant for the present state of cultural development. The author believes, "for a great majority of our people, preadolescence is the nearest that they come to untroubled human life—that from then on the stresses of life distort them to inferior caricatures of what they might have been." [91]

The stages of personality development, he says, previous to adolescence are closely, though obscurely, related to somatic maturation. "Adolescence begins with the most spectacular maturation of all, the puberty change, with its swift alteration of physiological processes to the completion of bodily development." [92] This period is characterized by maturation of "the genital lust dynamism." It is subdivided into three eras: "early adolescence, from the first evidences of puberty to the com-

[90] See p. 43.
[91] See p. 56.
[92] See p. 57.

pletion of voice change; mid-adolescence, to the patterning of genital behavior; and late adolescence, to the establishment of durable situations of intimacy such that all the major integrating tendencies are freely manifested within awareness in the series of one's interpersonal relations." [93]

Sullivan emphasizes the rôle of experience in determining sexual, or genital, behavior and the emotion of lust. "I have to add a word of caution, here," he says, "for there are those among us psychiatrists who make of sex a nuclear explanatory concept of personality, or at least of personality disorder. This is an error from insufficiency of the data. The highly civilized Chinese of the pre-Christian era were not bowled over by sex. A number of the primitive peoples who have been studied by anthropologists are found to take sex rather in their stride. Even the American Negro crashes through adolescence with relative impunity—if he is of the lower classes.

"The lurid twilight which invests sex in our culture is primarily a function of two factors. We still try to discourage pre-marital sexual performances; hold that abstinence is the moral course before marriage. And we discourage early marriage; in fact progressively widen the gap between the adolescent awakening of lust and the proper circumstances for marriage. These two factors work through many cultural conventions to make us the most sex-ridden people of whom I have any knowledge." [94]

Lust cannot easily be dissociated, or in the traditional language, be "repressed." He says:

"What happens when the sexual impulses, the impulses to genital behavior, collide with the self system . . . ? Under certain circumstances, the self is able to dissociate lust and the impulses to genital behavior. This can be achieved only by the development of new and elaborate 'apparatus' in living. . . .

[93] See pp. 57–58. Sullivan now divides the adolescent era into early and late adolescence, the former ending with the patterning of genital behavior.
[94] See pp. 58–59.

The point I wish to emphasize now is that, late as it is in maturing, the genital lust dynamism is something that can be dissociated only at grave risk to effective living, and that in most people it cannot be dissociated at all. It will again and again, at whatever great expense to security, whatever suffering from anxiety, manifest itself." [95]

What about "sublimation," or as Sullivan would phrase it, the sublimatory reformulations of interpersonal relations? Sublimation is defined thus: "a motive which is involved in painful conflict is combined with a social (culturally provided) technique of life which disguises its most conflict-provoking aspect and usually provides some representation for the opposing motive in the conflict." [96] Sublimation as he uses the term has a much wider range than the usual denotation and can refer to any tendency system or drive. A disguised and partially fulfilled satisfaction is combined with the achievement of personal security. Sublimatory reformulations sometimes work, and "work beautifully;" but they do not always work.[97]

Mature adulthood, the "fully human estate," is obviously not synonymous with chronological adulthood. The characteristics of a mature adult are only briefly mentioned. If one has had fortunate experience in living and has successfully reached and passed through adolescence, he emerges, so to speak, inevitably as a mature person. Once adolescence is "successfully negotiated, the person comes forth with self-respect adequate to almost any situation, with the respect for others that this competent self-respect entails, with the dignity that befits the high achievement of competent personality, and with the freedom of personal initiative that represents a comfortable adaptation of one's personal situation to the circumstances that characterize the social order of which one is a part." [98] In other words, adequate self-respect, respect for others, personal dignity, personal initiative adequate for one's station in life are necessary conditions for the achievement of mature personality.

Sullivan's language has been a considerable barrier to understanding. The result has been that his theory of the self, among other theories, has been misunderstood. For example, it has been thought that he believed acculturation necessarily limits the self or the personality, two concepts which in the minds of some people have been confused. What he does believe is that adequate and inconsistent acculturation limits the self and impoverishes the whole personality. The self is a product of acculturation. Without acculturation there could be no self.

The concept of psychiatric cure has also been misinterpreted. He says that along with psychiatric cure "there goes an *expanding of the self* to such final effect that the patient as known to himself is much the same person as is the patient behaving with others." It is worth noting that he does *not* say the patient as known to himself is much the same person *as he is known to others.* The practical consequences may not seem great. But there is an important theoretical difference. The patient as known to others may be, and very likely is, accompanied by parataxic distortions, because others are by no means likely to be free of limitations resulting from their own life history. If the patient knows himself as he is known to others, very likely he has an inadequate idea of himself. Ideally, the patient knows himself as he is behaving with others, free of all illusory "me-you patterns." This certainly does not mean that he will integrate situations having the same traits with everyone. A loving person, however free of self-distortion, cannot love a hateful person, because the latter is incapable of responding in a loving way. A situation having the qualities categorized as love cannot be integrated because opposites do not unite. There can only be conflict or withdrawal. In the latter case, the situation is disintegrated. If an interpersonal integration occurs and persists, it can only be on the basis of hostility, because a hateful person cannot love, but a loving person, under appropriate circumstances, can be hostile, if only for his own defence.

Individuality, as applied to a person, is a term Sullivan finds objectionable. In a somewhat obscure passage he has declared, "The unique individuality of the other fellow need never concern us as scientists." [99] Here he seems to be emphasizing the fact that a person is not an isolated entity, that personality is revealed and has its being in interpersonal relations, and is observable only in such interpersonal relations. Elsewhere this meaning is explicit.[100] He says that the personality which can be studied by scientific method cannot be observed directly, and that unique individuality would not be any concern of the psychiatrist. There seems to be some confusion on this point. In the first place, scientific method is not limited to a study of only that which can be observed directly. Furthermore, it is an open question whether any psychiatrist uses the term "individuality" when applied to a person in the same sense as when applied to an electron.[101] The criticism seems to be misdirected.[102]

It seems to be based on a confusion of two different concepts of individuality. The first is analogous to the traditional concept of "soul." Traditionally, the soul is a unique spiritual entity or substance, which can subsist independently. Some people talk about individuality as if it were literally a spiritual essence.

But there is a quite different concept of individuality. A sense of personal worth and dignity, and a recognition of solidarity or oneness with others in interpersonal relations, crea-

[99] See p. 12.
[100] Reference footnote 32; p. 121.
[101] Reference footnote 32; p. 121.
[102] Compare Welldon, Jr., J. E. C., *The Nicomachean Ethics of Aristotle;* London, Macmillan, 1930 (lxvii and 352 pp.); p. 14. "But when we speak of self-sufficiency, we do not mean that a person leads a solitary life all by himself, but that he has parents, children, wife, and friends, and fellow-citizens in general, as man is naturally a social being."

tive ability, love as self-affirmation and the affirmation of others —these express this second concept of individuality. There is nothing in the ideas which have been discussed repugnant to such a concept. Prototaxic, parataxic and in some cases rational symbol activity are all indicative of the creative potentialities of people. Self-respect, respect for others, the dignity of competent personality, freedom of personal initiative are said to be marks of adult maturity. Love is said to exist when and only when the satisfactions and security of another are equally important with one's own. So there seems to be no need to reject individuality on the ground that it implies "a self-limited unit that alternates between a state of insular detachment and varying degrees of contact with other people and with cultural entities." [103] In rejecting the notion of individuality, Sullivan exposes himself to the superficial misunderstanding that he believes personality is a passive instrument of acculturation or the equally dubious notion of cultural relativism.

The view that is argued for here is that every situation is individual, is unique. It has an immediately pervasive quality. Psychologically the situation as a qualitative whole is immediately sensed or felt. "Distinctions and relations are instituted *within* a situation; *they* are recurrent and repeatable in different situations." [104] One must, therefore, be careful to distinguish between psychological, that is *felt*, uniqueness, individuality, and the distinctions and relations instituted by discourse in investigating the situation. These distinctions and relations are necessary instruments for determining interpersonal involvements or interactions. The distinctions and relations are recurrent in studying different interpersonal situations.

When the psychiatrist is studying an interpersonal situation, he institutes distinctions and relations. Terms like *parataxic, dissociated, schizophrenic*, are terms in discourse, meanings, in order to determine or indicate how people sometimes become

[103] Reference footnote 32; p. 121.
[104] Dewey, John, *Logic, The Theory of Inquiry*; New York, Henry Holt, 1938 (v and 546 pages); p. 68.

involved with one another. These terms refer to recurring modes of interpersonal behavior. So far as these recurring modes of behavior are modeled on past experiences, are, in other words, parataxic, they prevent, or tend to prevent, radical newness in an interpersonal situation. The problem for psychiatry would seem to be *not* the supposed scientific inaccessibility of individuality, but, in dealing with people who are mentally ill, their lack of ability to experience the uniqueness of new situations. In other words, the mentally ill are not sufficiently able to feel and sense and understand the uniqueness and differences of interpersonal situations. For them the situation is, erroneously, of course, felt to be not unique but modeled on, or paradigmatic of old situations.

There would still be, of course, recurring distinctions and relations, but the problem for the psychiatrist and the patient would seem to be to learn what ones are valid and what are not valid.

If the understanding of living in order that it may be facilitated is the purpose of psychiatry, it leads one eventually to seek an understanding of the social order in which people live. The ultimate causes of mental disorder, it would seem, have to be sought in the social order itself. Expressed in another way, the study of interpersonal relations leads pretty directly to a study of the social order which is their matrix. It is now rather obvious that the inadequacies and the contradictions which the culture manifests is a fertile breeding ground for the mentally sick and the mentally handicapped. The psychiatrist, if he is to function with social effectiveness, can no longer stand aloof. He must, while maintaining his own specialty, join hands with other social scientists. This broader point of view requires a new orientation and the perfection of new techniques.[105]

NEW YORK, N. Y., May, 1945

[105] See p. 175.

Index